THE MARINE BIOLOGY OF
THE SOUTH CHINA SEA

THE MARINE BIOLOGY OF THE SOUTH CHINA SEA

Volume 1

Proceedings of the First International Conference
on the Marine Biology of Hong Kong
and the South China Sea, Hong Kong
28 October – 3 November 1990

Edited by

Brian Morton

Hong Kong University Press
香港大學出版社

Hong Kong University Press
139 Pokfulam Road, Hong Kong
© Hong Kong University Press 1993

ISBNs 962 209 354 X (Vol. 1)
962 209 355 8 (Vol. 2)
962 209 356 6 (Set of Vol. 1 & 2)

All rights reserved. No portion of this publication may be reproduced or transmitted in any form or by any means, electronic or mechanical, including photocopy, recording or any information storage or retrieval system, without prior permission in writing from the publisher, Hong Kong University Press.

Front cover: *Parasicyonis actinostoloides*,
photograph by Cheryl Osborn

Back cover: *Dendrophyllia gracilis*,
photograph by Brian Darvell

Printed in Hong Kong by Nordica Printing Company Limited

CONTENTS

Introduction		xi
Acknowledgements		xiv
List of Participants		xv
Conference Programme		xxi

Volume 1

PLENARY SESSION — 1
Plenary Paper — 1
Taxonomic sufficiency and the role of systematics in marine invertebrate studies with special reference to Hong Kong — P. Graham Oliver — 3

FISHERIES — 37
Plenary Paper — 37
Farming of marine algae in China with special reference to the northern South China Sea — C.K. Tseng — 39

Session Papers — 63
The species composition of penaeid prawns and caridean shrimps in a *gei wai* at the Mai Po Marshes Nature Reserve, Hong Kong — S.F. Leung — 65

Ecological characteristics of the fish fauna of the South China Sea — Wang Cunxin — 77

FOULING — 119
Session Papers — 119
Fouling organisms at Daya Bay nuclear power station, China — Z.G. Huang, C.X. Zheng, S. Lin, C.Y. Li, J.J. Wang and S.K. Yan — 121

Biofouling of ships in Daya Bay, China — S.K. Yan and Z.G. Huang — 131

A preliminary investigation of marine fungi in the South China Sea	L.L.P. Vrijmoed, C.S.W. Kueh, H.Q. Shen, C.H. Cai and Y.P. Zhou	137
Choanoflagellates as fouling organisms	Seamus M. Jackson and E.B. Gareth Jones	145
Biofouling of Deep Bay buoys	Z.G. Huang and S. Lin	153
An ecological study of fouling organisms in Beihai Harbour, Beibu Bay, China	J.J. Wang, Z.G. Huang, S. Lin, C.Y. Li and C.Z. Zheng	167

CONSERVATION 181
Plenary Paper 181

Research upon and conservation of corals and coral reefs in China	Zou Renlin and Wang Zhihao	183

Session Papers 191

Science and the management of mangroves in Asia and the Pacific	C.D. Field	193
Invertebrate species new to science recorded from the Mai Po Marshes, Hong Kong	S.Y. Lee	199
The conservation of Deep Bay, Hong Kong	Llewellyn Young and David S. Melville	211

POLLUTION 233
Plenary Paper 233

Biomonitoring of marine heavy metal pollution and its application in Hong Kong waters	P.S. Rainbow	235

Session Papers 251

The effects of pollutants on the filtration rate of *Perna viridis* (Bivalvia: Mytilidae)	Wang Chusheng, Zhou Xiulan and Cheng Rongzhong	253
Analysis and assessment of heavy metal pollution in Hong Kong's marine environment	Y.S. Fung	261
A gray model for predicting red tides	Wang Zhaoding, Peng Yunhui and Lin Yongshui	273

Ammonium uptake by *Ulva lactuca* (Chlorophyta: Ulvales)	Y.B. Ho	289
The occurrence of six species of red tide organisms and their relationship with environmental factors in the Pearl River estuary	Y.S. Lin and Z.D. Wang	301
Accumulation of an antifouling toxin, tributyltin, in *Argopecten irradians* (Bivalvia: Pectinidae)	Liu Jianjun	311
The effects of urban sewage on benthic community structure in Xiamen Bay, China	J.X. Jiang, J.S. Song and Z.G. Huang	321

Volume 2

ECOLOGY
Plenary Papers

		335
		335
Regional variation in the structure of tropical benthic communities: relation to regimes of nutrient input	John D. Taylor	337
Are there obligate marine scavengers?	J.C. Britton and Brian Morton	357
Crabs as predators of marine bivalve molluscs	R. Seed	393
Bivalve shells: chronometers of environmental change	C.A. Richardson	419

Session Papers

		435
Sacoglossa (Mollusca: Opisthobranchia) — specialist herbivores and partial predators: integrating ecological, physiological and morphological data	Kathe R. Jensen	437
The relationship between herbivorous molluscs and algae on moderately exposed Hong Kong shores	Gray A. Williams	459
Activity rhythms and 'homing' behaviour by two pairs of high and low-zoned intertidal limpets in Hong Kong	J.H. Liu	471
The orientation of cirripedes on their hosts from Hong Kong waters	Cai Ruxing and Huang Zongguo	493
Some aspects of the ecology of sediment fauna in Balingasay, Bolinao, Pangasinan (northern Philippines)	Helen T. Yap and Hildie Maria E. Nacorda	509

The chemical characteristics of soil and its association with standing litter biomass in a subtropical mangrove community in Hong Kong	N.F.Y. Tam, L.L.P. Vrijmoed and Y.S. Wong	521
Impact of euthrophication on marine plankton in Tolo Harbour, 1988–89	Alice L.C. Chan and C. Kim Wong	543
The physiological ecology of *Perna viridis* (Bivalvia: Mytilidae) from contrasting environments in Hong Kong	S.G. Cheung	559
Effects of reduced salinities on *Holothuria leucospilota* Brandt and *Polycheira rufescens* Brandt (Echinodermata: Holothuroidea) in Hong Kong	Rosita G. Ong Che	581
Leaf choice of sesarmine crabs, *Chiromanthes bidens* and *C. maipoensis*, in a Hong Kong mangal	S.Y. Lee	597
Enigmonia aenigmatica: an enigmatic molluscan chameleon	Shaun M. Moss	605
A comparative study of the effects of salinity upon growth and respiration in two species of mangrove	C.D. Field	615
The heart of *Hyotissa imbricata* (Bivalvia: Gryphaeidae)	Li Xiaoxu, Chen Tiejie, George A. Evseev and Yuri M. Yakovlev	621
The intertidal ecology of a rocky shore at Yangkou, Qingdao, China	Qi Zhongyan, Lin Guangyu, Yang Zongdai, Ren Xianqiu and Li Fenglan	627
Pelagic polychaetes from the South China Sea	B.L. Wu and Lu Hua	637
The distribution of intertidal fungi on *Rhizophora apiculata*	Kevin D. Hyde, A. Chalermpongse and T. Boonthavikoon	643
The effect of photoperiod and temperature on the release of monospores by *Porphyra suborbiculata* Kjellman	K.Y. Lee, H.C. Leung, I.J. Hodgkiss and K.W. Cheung	653

CONTENTS

The macrobenthic infauna of Hoi Ha Wan and Tolo Channel, Hong Kong	Andrew S.Y. Mackie, P. Graham Oliver and Paul F. Kingston	657
The Calappidae (Crustacea: Brachyura) of Chinese waters	H.L. Chen	675
Marine diatoms of the Xisha Islands, South China Sea I. *Mastogloia* the Ex. Wm. Sm. species of the group *Sulcatae*	Liu Shicheng	705
Marine diatoms of the Xisha Islands, South China Sea II. Three new species of diatoms (Bacillariophyceae)	Liu Shicheng	729

INTRODUCTION

Since 1977 and at three year intervals subsequently, the Department of Zoology of The University of Hong Kong has organized research workshops on either the Mollusca (1977, 1983, 1992) or more wide-ranging studies of the marine flora and fauna of Hong Kong and southern China (1980, 1986, 1989). The proceedings of these workshops have increased significantly the available body of research data on Hong Kong's marine life and, coincidentally, also identified trends in, for example, the impacts of coastal pollution, especially in Tolo Harbour.

In 1986, The Marine Biological Association of Hong Kong and The Guangdong Society of Oceanology and The Guangdong Society of Oceanology and Limnology jointly organized a meeting of their members in Guangzhou, China, from 18–21 December. The proceedings of that meeting were published by Ocean Press, Beijing, in 1988. Since 1980, therefore, when the first scientists from the People's Republic of China participated in a Hong Kong workshop, there has been increasing co-operation between Hong Kong and Chinese researchers and which has led ultimately to joint studies. I consider such co-operation not only valuable, but also necessary as 1997 is approached and sovereignty of Hong Kong is transferred to China on July of that year. It is also apparent that in 1997, Hong Kong's territorial waters will be no more and local scientists will be able to explore a wider area of the South China Sea and Chinese research vessels and scientists will, hopefully, be able to gain access to local waters more easily.

Sovereignty of the many island and reef groups of the South China Sea is disputed by the countries forming its border, including China, Taiwan, the Philippines and Vietnam. The natural marine resources of the South China Sea are thus also contested and marine biologists have a duty to study them and make information available which will allow for good management and, therefore, stock conservation, thereby limiting over-exploitation.

The Swire Group of Companies has funded the construction of The Swire Marine Laboratory as a facility of The University of Hong Kong. The donation of HK$12.5 million has been used to construct a modern marine laboratory which, with a residential block adjacent, will foster greater co-operation between local scientists and overseas visitors in the study of their common heritage — the South China Sea. In a very real sense, the new facility joins a chain of other marine laboratories that circumscribe the South China Sea and will, it is hoped, elevate existing levels of co-operation to a new height.

The laboratory was due for completion in November 1990 and scheduled for opening on 3 November, one week short of one year since its foundation stone was laid by Sir John Swire, Honorary President of John Swire and Sons Limited. This conference was thus organized for the preceding week and entitled The First International Conference on the Marine Biology of Hong Kong and the South China Sea. The Conference's aims were twofold; first, to celebrate the opening of The Swire Marine Laboratory and, second, to bring scientists together from Hong Kong and other countries with the aim of initiating discussion of research undertaken in the South China Sea. Representatives from South China Sea rim laboratories were joined by visitors from elsewhere, some of whom had undertaken work on Hong Kong's marine life at the earlier workshops and who, thus, had a significant interest in the region. Because of visa problems, regrettably, scientists from the Nha Trang Laboratory, Vietnam, and the Institute of Marine Biology of the USSR Academy of Sciences, Vladivostock, were unable to attend. Notwithstanding, however, 45 local participants were joined by 47 overseas scientists from ten countries.

Sponsored by The University of Hong Kong and The Marine Biological Association of Hong Kong, the Conference was held in the Hui Oi Chow Science Building of The University of Hong Kong and divided into five sessions: Ecology, Pollution, Fouling, Fisheries (including Mariculture) and Conservation. Each session was introduced by a plenary lecture and accompanied subsequently by verbal and poster presentations. The opening session was followed by a plenary lecture on the very real taxonomic problems facing workers in the area and to draw attention to the real need for the establishment and maintenance of museum reference material. Delegates were welcomed at the opening session by the Dr Lawrence H.Y. Lee, Director of the Agriculture and Fisheries Department of the Hong Kong Government, Professor C.K. Poon, Dean of the Faculty of Science and Professors D.A. Griffiths and D.K.O. Chan, Heads of the Departments of Botany and Zoology of The University of Hong Kong, respectively, and by myself as Chairman of the Conference Organizing Committee. Professor Wang Gungwu, the Vice Chancellor of The University of Hong Kong, hosted a welcoming cocktail party.

After the five day conference, delegates were invited to the opening of The Swire Marine Laboratory on 3 November 1990, officiated by Sir John Swire. The conference finally concluded with the adoption of a resolution to further strengthen bonds between marine scientists present and to effect this by reconvening a second conference on the same theme in Guangzhou in April 1993. This will be organized jointly by the South China Sea Institute of Oceanology, Academia Sinica, the Guangdong Society of Oceanology and Limnology and The Marine Biological Association of Hong Kong.

Resolution

It is hereby recorded that:

We, the undersigned, at the First International Conference on the Marine Biology of Hong Kong and the South China Sea, Hong Kong, 28 October – 3 November 1990, in recognising the need for co-operative study of all aspects of the marine science of the South China Sea with a view to the sensible, planned, utilization of its natural resources and the effective conservation and management of its coasts, seabed and waters, do hereby agree to:

1. Establish a network of South China Sea marine scientists, marine scientific societies and marine laboratories to work together, in common cause, to study, understand and discuss the natural marine resources of their common waters.

2. The established network will convene a triannual conference on the South China Sea to implement 1 above. It is proposed that The Guangdong Society of Oceanology and The Guangdong Society of Oceanology and Limnology will jointly host the next meeting at Guangzhou, China, in 1993.

3. The established network will attempt to explain to the governments and people of the South China Sea rim the need for co-operation in the sensible and planned utilization and management of their common natural resources.

Signed:

Prof. E. Gomez, Director, Marine Science Institute, University of the Philippines, The Philippines.
Prof. Z.G. Huang, Third Institute of Oceanography, state Oceanic Administration, Xiamen, China.
Prof. B. Morton, Director, The Swire Marine Laboratory, The University of Hong Kong, Hong Kong.
Dr J.B. Sigurdsson, Department of Zoology, National University of Singapore, Singapore.
Prof. C.K. Tseng, Institute of Oceanology, Academia Sinica Qingdao, China.
Prof. R.L. Zou, Vice Director, South China Sea Institute of Oceanology, Academia Sinica Guangzhou, China.

ACKNOWLEDGEMENTS

I am indebted to many persons for their support of this conference and its aims. First thanks go to the members of the Organizing Committee: Dr I.J. Hodgkiss (Department of Botany, The University of Hong Kong), Dr P.M.S. Mak (The Marine Biological Association of Hong Kong) and Ms Rebecca Fung (Secretary). I am also grateful to The University of Hong Kong and its officers, particularly the Estates Officer, Mr M. McGraw, and the Finance Officer, Mr P.B.L. Lam, for help with the conference organization and to the Vice Chancellor, Professor Wang Gungwu for hosting the welcoming reception. The Director of the Agriculture and Fisheries Department, the Council of The Marine Biological Association of Hong Kong, and the Heads of the Departments of the Botany and Zoology of The University of Hong Kong are also thanked for hosting receptions. The Centre for Media Resources and the Printing Office of The University of Hong Kong assisted in the production of the conference booklet of information and abstracts. Ms Sylvia Ng, Ms Bonnie Shum and Ms Alice Wong provided secretarial help while Mrs D.W. Kwan assisted in the provision of catering and other facilities.

I am grateful to the K.C. Wong Foundation, the British Council and the Regional Office for Science and Technology in South East Asia (ROSTSEA) of Unesco for providing funds which allowed various delegates to attend the conference. The following Hong Kong organizations and companies also supported the aims of the Conference, and their support is gratefully acknowledged.

> The Hong Kong Electric Co., Ltd.
> China Light & Power Co., Ltd.
> Bio-Rad Pacific Ltd.
> CES Consultants in Environmental Science (Asia) Ltd.
> Carl Zeiss Far East Co. Ltd.
> Shriro (HK) Ltd. (Sole Agent for Nikon Instruments)
> Schmidt & Co., (HK) Ltd.
> Medico Scientific Co. Ltd.
> Mannoko Ltd.

Finally, I am grateful to all the delegates for making the conference the success it so clearly was and as these proceedings will show. In the production of these proceedings, I have received much help from the publisher and staff of Hong Kong University Press. I am also grateful to the anonymous referees of all the papers presented, for the time and effort they spent in ensuring that those finally accepted for publication were of a high standard.

Brian Morton
29 October 1991

LIST OF PARTICIPANTS

Australia

Dr K.D. Hyde[1]	Department of Primary Industry, P.O. Box 1054, Mareeba Queensland 4880, Australia.
Ms D.S. Jones	Crustacea Department, Western Australian Museum, Perth, Western Australia 6000.

China

Prof. R.X. Cai	Department of Biology, University of Hang Zhou, China.
Prof. H. Cao	Parasitology Research Laboratory, Xiamen University, 1-203 Haibin, Xiamen 361005, China.
Prof. H.L. Chen	Institute of Oceanology, Academia Sinica, 7 Nanhai Road, Qingdao, China.
Prof. Z.G. Huang	Third Institute of Oceanography, P.O. Box 70, Xiamen, China.
Prof. J.X. Jiang	Third Institute of Oceanography, P.O. Box 70, Xiamen, China.
Prof. X.X. Li	Institute of Oceanology, Academia Sinica, 7 Nanhai Road, Qingdao, China.
Prof. G.Y. Lin	Institute of Oceanology, Academia Sinica, 7 Nanhai Road, Qingdao, China.
Prof. Y.S. Lin	South China Sea Institute of Oceanology, Academia Sinica, 164 West Xingang Road, Guangzhou, China.
Prof. J.J. Liu[2]	Institute of Oceanology, Academia Sinica, 7 Nanhai Road, Qingdao, China.
Prof. S.C. Liu	Department of Biology, Xiamen University, Xiamen, China.
Prof. C.K. Tseng	Institute of Oceanology, Academia Sinica, 7 Nanhai Road, Qingdao, China.
Prof. C.S. Wang	Third Institute of Oceanography, P.O. Box 70, Xiamen, China.
Prof. C.X. Wang	Institute of Oceanology, Academia Sinica, 7 Nanhai Road, Qingdao, China.
Prof. Z.D. Wang	South China Sea Institute of Oceanology, Academia Sinica, 164 West Xingang Road, Guangzhou, China.
Prof. B.L. Wu	First Institute of Oceanology, National Bureau of Oceanology, P.O. Box 98, Qingdao, China.
Prof. H.Z. Wu	Institute of Oceanology, Academia Sinica, 7 Nanhai Road, Qingdao, China.
Prof. S.K. Yan	Third Institute of Oceanography, P.O. Box 70, Xiamen, China.
Prof. W.X. Yan	South China Sea Institute of Oceanology, Academia Sinica, 164 West Xingang Road, Guangzhou, China.

Prof. J.M. Yang	Institute of Oceanology, Academia Sinica, 7 Nanhai Road, Qingdao, China.
Prof. R.L. Zou	South China Sea Institute of Oceanology, Academia Sinica, 164 West Xingang Road, Guangzhou, China.

Denmark

Dr K.R. Jensen	Zoological Museum, Universitetsparken 15, DK-2100, Copenhagen, Denmark.
Dr J. Knudsen	Zoological Museum, Universitetsparken 15, DK-2100, Copenhagen, Denmark.

Hong Kong

Ms C. Anderson	Department of Zoology and The Swire Marine Laboratory, The University of Hong Kong, Hong Kong.
Ms M.W. Cha	Department of Zoology and The Swire Marine Laboratory, The University of Hong Kong, Hong Kong.
Prof. D.K.O. Chan	Department of Zoology, The University of Hong Kong, Hong Kong.
Mr K.K. Chan	Department of Zoology, The University of Hong Kong, Hong Kong.
Ms A.L.C. Chan[3]	Department of Biology, The Chinese University of Hong Kong, Shatin, New Territories, Hong Kong.
Mr P.P.F. Chan	Hong Kong Institute of Fishery Ltd., 2/F, Caltex House, 258 Hennessy Road, Hong Kong.
Ms C.P.S. Cheung[4]	Department of Zoology, The University of Hong Kong, Hong Kong.
Dr R.Y.H. Cheung[5]	Environmental Protection Department, The Hong Kong Government, 11/F, Empire Centre, Tsimshatsui East, Kowloon, Hong Kong.
Dr S.G. Cheung	Department of Applied Science, City Polytechnic of Hong Kong, Tat Chee Avenue, Kowloon, Hong Kong.
Mr K.T. Chiu	Department of Zoology and The Swire Marine Laboratory, The University of Hong Kong, Hong Kong.
Ms H.M.C. Chiu	Department of Botany, The University of Hong Kong, Hong Kong.
Dr S.T. Chiu	Department of Biology, Hong Kong Baptist College, 224 Waterloo Road, Kowloon, Hong Kong
Dr K.H. Chu	Marine Science Laboratory, The Chinese University of Hong Kong, Shatin, New Territories, Hong Kong
Dr B.R. Darvell	Department of Dental Materials Science, Prince Philip Dental Hospital, The University of Hong Kong, Hong Kong.
Dr D. Dudgeon	Department of Zoology, The University of Hong Kong, Hong Kong.
Prof. C.D. Field	City Polytechnic of Hong Kong, Tat Chee Avenue, Kowloon, Hong Kong

LIST OF PARTICIPANTS

Dr Y.S. Fung	Department of Chemistry, The University of Hong Kong, Hong Kong.
Mr K.C. Ho[7]	Environmental Protection Department, The Hong Kong Government, 24 Floor, Southorn Centre, Wanchai, Hong Kong.
Dr Y.B. Ho	Department of Botany, The University of Hong Kong, Hong Kong.
Dr I.J. Hodgkiss	Department of Botany, The University of Hong Kong, Hong Kong.
Dr G. Hodgson[8]	Asia Technology Review Publishing Co. Ltd., 7/F, Centre Point, 181 Gloucestor Road, Hong Kong.
Mr C.K. Kwok	Fisheries Research Station, The Hong Kong Government, 100A Shek Pai Wan Road, Aberdeen, Hong Kong.
Mr K.Y. Lee	Department of Botany, The University of Hong Kong, Hong Kong.
Dr S.Y. Lee	Department of Zoology and The Swire Marine Laboratory, The University of Hong Kong, Hong Kong.
Dr S.F. Leung[9]	Department of Applied Biology and Chemical Technology, Hong Kong Polytechnic, Hung Hom, Kowloon, Hong Kong.
Mr A.W.Y. Leung[10]	Fisheries Research Station, The Hong Kong Government, 100A Shek Pai Wan Road, Aberdeen, Hong Kong.
Dr J.H. Liu	Department of Botany and The Swire Marine Laboratory, The University of Hong Kong, Hong Kong.
Dr P.M.S. Mak	Fisheries Research Station, Hong Kong Government, 100A Shek Pai Wan Road, Aberdeen, Hong Kong.
Mr D.S. Melville	World Wide Fund for Nature Hong Kong, 1, Tramway Path, Central, Hong Kong.
Prof. Brian Morton	Department of Zoology and The Swire Marine Laboratory, The University of Hong Kong, Hong Kong.
Prof. I.H. Ni	Department of Biology, Hong Kong University of Science and Technology 5/F, World Shipping Centre, 7 Canton Road, Tsimshatsui, Kowloon, Hong Kong
Dr R.G. Ong-Che[11]	The Swire Marine Laboratory, The University of Hong Kong, Cape d'Aguilar, Hong Kong.
Ms J. Price	Flat L6, Pendragon, 150 Wong Ma Kok Road, Stanley, Hong Kong.
Dr T. Rudd	Consultants in Environmental Sciences (Asia) Ltd., 9F Parkview Commercial Bldg., 9-11 Shelter St., Causeway Bay, Hong Kong
Ms J.H. Ruxton	World Wide Fund for Nature Hong Kong, 1, Tramway Path, Central, Hong Kong
Mr J.C.H. Sham	Fisheries Research Station, The Hong Kong Government, 100A Shek Pai Wan Road, Aberdeen, Hong Kong
Dr N.F.Y. Tam	Department of Applied Science, City Polytechnic of Hong Kong, Tat Chee Avenue, Kowloon, Hong Kong
Dr L.K.Y. Tong[12]	The Swire Marine Laboratory, The University of Hong Kong, Cape d'Aguilar, Hong Kong.
Mr E. Turner	Room 1811, Star House, 3 Salisbury Road, Tsimshatsui, Kowloon, Hong Kong

Dr L.L.P. Vrijmoed	Department of Applied Science, City Polytechnic of Hong Kong, Tat Chee Avenue, Kowloon, Hong Kong
Dr G.A. Williams	Department of Botany and The Swire Marine Laboratory, The University of Hong Kong, Hong Kong.
Mr E.C.K. Wong	Fisheries Research Station, The Hong Kong Government, 100A Shek Pai Wan Road, Aberdeen, Hong Kong
Dr P.P.S. Wong	Fisheries Research Station, The Hong Kong Government, 100A Shek Pai Wan Road, Aberdeen, Hong Kong
Dr M.W.M. Yipp	Department of Applied Biology and Chemical Technology, Hong Kong Polytechnic, Hunghom, Kowloon, Hong Kong
Mr L. Young[13]	Department of Zoology, The University of Hong Kong, Hong Kong.

India

Dr R. Kasinathan	Centre for Advanced Studies in Marine Biology, Annamalai University, Parangipettai - 608 502, Tamil Nadu, India.
Dr A. Purushothaman	Centre for Advanced Studies in Marine Biology, Annamalai University, Parangipettai - 608 502, Tamil Nadu, India.

Israel

Dr U. Marchaim	Migal-Galilee Technological Centre, Kiryat-Shmona, 10-200, Israel.

Philippines

Prof. E.D. Gomez	Marine Science Institute, University of the Philippines, Diliman, Quezon City 1101, Philippines.
Mr J.R.H. Lim	Genu Products Philippines Inc., Room 306 Philamlife Building, Osmena Boulevard, P.O. Box 568, 6000 Cebu City, Philippines.
Dr H.T. Yap	Marine Science Institute, University of the Philippines, Diliman, Quezon City 1101, Philippines.

Singapore

Dr J.B. Sigurdsson	Department of Zoology, National University of Singapore, Kent Ridge, Singapore 0511.
Mr K.S. Tan	Department of Zoology, National University of Singapore, Kent Ridge, Singapore 0511.

Taiwan

Dr T.R. Chang	Department of Fisheries, National Taiwan Ocean University, Keelung, 20224 Taiwan.
Dr B.Q. Huang	Department of Fisheries, National Taiwan Ocean University, Keelung, 20224 Taiwan.

LIST OF PARTICIPANTS

Dr B. Sun Pan	College of Fisheries Science, National Taiwan Ocean University, 2 Pei-ning Road, Keelung, 20224 Taiwan.

United Kingdom

Prof. E.G. Gareth Jones	Department of Biological Sciences, Portsmouth University Portsmouth, Hampshire PO1 2DY, UK.
Mr A.S.Y. Mackie	Department of Zoology, National Museum of Wales, Cathays Park, Cardiff CF1 3NP, Wales, UK.
Dr P.G. Oliver	Department of Zoology, National Museum of Wales, Cathays Park, Cardiff CF1 3NP, Wales, UK.
Ms E. Platts	'Belmont' New Road, Littleton, Winchester, Hampshire S022 6QR, U.K.
Dr P.S. Rainbow	School of Biological Sciences, Queen Mary and Westfield College, Mile End Road, London E1 4NS, U.K.
Dr C.A. Richardson	School of Ocean Sciences, University College of North Wales, Bangor, Gwynedd, LL59 5EY, UK.
Ms H. Ross	Royal Ulster Museum, Belfast, North Ireland, United Kingdom
Dr R. Seed	School of Ocean Science, University College of North Wales, Bangor, Gwynedd LL59 5EY, UK.
Dr J.D. Taylor	Department of Zoology, The Natural History Museum, Cromwell Road, London SW7 5BD, UK.

U.S.A.

Prof. J.C. Britton	Department of Biology, Texas Christian University, P.O. Box 32916, Fort Worth, Texas 76129, U.S.A.
Dr J.E. Lewis	Department of Botany, University of Hawaii, 3190 Maile Way, Honolulu, HI 96822, Hawaii, U.S.A.
Mr S.M. Moss[14]	Department of Zoology, University of Hawaii, 3190 Maile Way, Honolulu, HI 96822, Hawaii, U.S.A.

Present address:

[1] Dr K.D. Hyde	Department of Botany, The University of Hong Kong, Hong Kong
[2] Prof. J.J. Liu	Department of Zoology, Duke University, Durham, NC 27706, U.S.A.
[3] Ms A.L.C. Chan	The Swire Marine Laboratory, The University of Hong Kong, Cape d'Aguilar, Hong Kong.
[4] Ms C.P.S. Cheung	World Wide Fund for Nature Hong Kong, 1, Tramway Path, Central, Hong Kong.
[5] Dr R.Y.H. Cheung	Department of Applied Science, City Polytechnic of Hong Kong, Tat Chee Avenue, Kowloon, Hong Kong.
[6] Dr K.T. Chiu	Environmental Protection Department, The Hong Kong Government, 28/F, Southorn Centre, 130 Hennessy Road, Wanchai, Hong Kong.
[7] Mr K.C. Ho	School of Science and Technology, Open Learning Institute, Hong Kong.

LIST OF PARTICIPANTS

[8] Dr G. Hodgson — c/o G.P.O. Box 3534, Hong Kong.

[9] Dr S.F. Leung — Fisheries Research Station, The Hong Kong Government, 100A Shek Pai Wan Road, Aberdeen, Hong Kong.

[10] Mr A.W.Y. Leung — The Swire Marine Laboratory, The University of Hong Kong, Cape d'Aguilar, Hong Kong.

[11] Dr R.G. Ong Che — Vocational Training Council, 27 Wood Road, Wanchai, Hong Kong.

[12] Dr L.K.Y. Tong — c/o Department of Zoology, National Museum of Wales, Cathays Park, Cardiff CFI 3NP, Wales, UK.

[13] Mr L. Young — World Wide Fund for Nature Hong Kong, 1, Tramway Path, Central, Hong Kong.

[14] Mr S.M. Moss — BDDS-L3N-UNPATTI, Universitas Pattimura, Jln. Martha Alfons, Poka, Ambon, Indonesia.

CONFERENCE PROGRAMME

Monday 29 October

Opening Session   Chairman: Prof. Brian Morton
Speeches of Welcome by:
     Prof. C.K. Poon, Dean, Faculty of Science
     Prof. D.K.O. Chan, Head, Department of Zoology
     Prof. D.A. Griffiths, Head, Department of Botany
         The University of Hong Kong, Hong Kong
     Dr Lawrence H.Y. Lee, Director, Agriculture and Fisheries Department, The Hong Kong Government; President, The Marine Biological Association of Hong Kong

Plenary lecture

P. Graham Oliver — Taxonomic sufficiency and the role of systematics in marine invertebrate studies with special reference to Hong Kong

Session 2: Fisheries   Chairman: Dr K.D. Hyde

Plenary lecture

C.K. Tseng — Farming of marine algae in China with special reference to the northern South China Sea

Session lectures:

A.W.Y. Leung — Assessing and developing the deep sea prawn resources on the continental slope south of Hong Kong

E.D. Gomez, A. Juinio and N. Bermas — Some aspects of the reproduction of *Panulirus longipes longipes*

E.C.K. Wong — Treatment against ectoparasites of marine fishes

J.M. Yang — A primary fish survey of the Yellow River estuary

J.C.H. Sham — Fishing performance of the first pair of steel trawlers licensed in Hong Kong: a comparison with wooden trawlers

S.F. Leung — The species composition of penaeid prawns and caridean shrimps in a *gei wai* at the Marshes Nature Reserve, Hong Kong

Tuesday 30 October

Session 3: Fouling — Chairman: Prof. E.D. Gomez.

Plenary lecture:
E.B. Gareth Jones — Ecology of marine fungi with particular reference to adhesion

Session lectures:
Z.G. Huang, C.X. Zheng, S. Lin, C.Y. Li, J.J. Wang and S.K. Yan — Fouling organisms at Daya Bay nuclear power station, China

S.K. Yan and Z.G. Huang — Biofouling of ships in Daya Bay, China

L.L.P. Vrijmoed, C.S.W. Kueh, H.Q. Shen, C.H. Cai and Y.P. Zhou — A preliminary investigation of marine fungi in the South China Sea

Seamus M. Jackson and E.B. Gareth Jones — Choanoflagellates as fouling organisms

Session 4: Conservation — Chairman: Dr C.A. Richardson

Plenary lecture:
R.L. Zou and Z.H. Wang — Research upon and conservation of coral and coral reefs in China

Session lectures:
J.H. Ruxton — The conservation work of WWFHK
Video 1. Local publicly broadcasted video:
  'Conservation of Hong Kong corals'
Video 2. Survival Anglia Ltd.
  'Mai Po: Oasis in the Orient'

C.D. Field — Science and the management of mangroves in Asia and the Pacific

S.Y. Lee — Invertebrate species new to science recorded from the Mai Po Marshes, Hong Kong

Llewellyn Young and David S. Melville — The conservation of Deep Bay, Hong Kong

Wednesday 31 October

Session 5: Pollution — Chairman: Prof. B.L. Wu

Plenary lecture:
P.S. Rainbow — Biomonitoring of marine heavy metal pollution and its application in Hong Kong waters

Session lectures:

D.K.O. Chan and S.J. Liu — Paralytic shellfish poison (PSP) in Hong Kong shellfish: occurrence and effects on the cardio-ventilatory system of fish

C.S. Wang, X.L. Zhou and R.Z. Cheng — The effects of pollutants on the filtration rate of *Perna viridis* (Bivalvia: Mytilidae)

Y.S. Fung — Analysis and assessment of heavy metal pollution in Hong Kong's marine environment

Z.D. Wang, Y.H. Peng and Y.S. Lin — A gray model for predicting red tides

Y.B. Ho — Ammonium uptake by *Ulva lactuca* (Chlorophyta, Ulvales)

Thursday 1 November

Session 6: Ecology I Chairman: Dr J. Knudsen

Plenary lecture:
John D. Taylor — Regional variation in the structure of tropical benthic communities: relation to regimes of nutrient input

Session lectures:

J.E. Lewis — Distribution of shallow-water benthic marine algae in the northern South China Sea

Kathe R. Jensen — Sacoglossa (Mollusca: Opisthobranchia) — specialist herbivores and partial predators: integrating ecological, physiological and morphological data

M.W. Yipp and F.G. Shin — Drag force acting against locomotion in the mangrove gastropod, *Terebralia sulcata* (Born 1778)

Gray A. Williams — The relationship between herbivorous molluscs and their food supply on moderately exposed Hong Kong shores

J.H. Liu — Activity rhythms and 'homing' behaviour by two pairs of high and low-zoned intertidal limpets in Hong Kong

Session 7: Ecology II Chairman: Dr J.B. Sigurdsson

Plenary lecture:
J.C. Britton and Brian Morton — Are there obligate marine scavengers?

Session lectures:
R.X. Cai and Z.G. Huang — The orientation of cirripedes on their hosts from Hong Kong waters

Helen T. Yap and Hilde Maria E. Nacorda	Some aspects of the ecology of sediment fauna in Balingasay, Bolinao, Pangasinan (northern Philippines)
N.F.Y. Tam, Y.S. Wong and L.L.P. Vrijmoed	The chemical characteristics of soil and its association with standing litter biomass in a sub-tropical mangrove community in Hong Kong
Alice L.C. Chan and C. Kim Wong	The hydrography and marine plankton of Tolo Harbour, Hong Kong
S.G. Cheung	The physiological ecology of *Perna viridis* (Bivalvia: Mytilidae) from contrasting environments in Hong Kong
Rosita G. Ong Che	Effects of reduced salinities on *Holothuria leucospilota* Brandt and *Polycheira rufescens* Brandt (Echinodermata: Holothuroida) in Hong Kong

Friday 2 November

Session 8: Ecology III
Chairman: Prof. Yang Jiming

Plenary lecture:

R. Seed	Crabs as predators of marine bivalve molluscs

Session lectures:

J.B. Sigurdsson and K.S. Tan	Aspects of the ecology of intertidal monsoon drains in Singapore
S.Y. Lee	Leaf choice of sesarmine crabs, *Chiromanthes bidens* and *C. maipoensis*, in a Hong Kong mangal
Shaun M. Moss	*Enigmonia aenigmatica*: an enigmatic molluscan chameleon
C.D. Field	A comparative study of the effects of salinity upon growth and respiration in two species of mangrove
C. Anderson	The effects of sexual selection on the feeding ecology of *Uca arcuata*, a fiddler crab from a Hong Kong mangrove

Session 9: International
Chairman: Prof. C.D. Field

Plenary lecture:

C.A. Richardson	Bivalve shells: chronometers of environmental change

Session lectures:

I.H. Ni	Population dynamics and community ecology of fisheries resources — a quantitative case study of seal-capelin-cod interactions in the northwest Atlantic

D.S. Jones	A review of fouling barnacles in Australian waters.
K. Sathiyamurthy Purushothaman and R. Kasinathan	Distribution and composition of organic detritus in a tropical estuarine system
Y.D. Ramu, P. Shamuganandam, T. Nallathambi and S.R.J. Dious	Comparative studies on two species of *Conus* from the southeast coast of India
G. Hodgson	How to be scientifically sexy

POSTERS PRESENTED

Fisheries:

C.X. Wang	Ecological characteristics of the fish fauna of the South China Sea
H.Z. Wu and K.H. Chu	The structure of a coastal nekton community in the northern South China Sea
X.H. Zhu	Larval rearing of the shrimps *Penaeus chinensis* and *Metapenaeus ensis* on artificial diets
P.P.F. Chan	Aquaculture or prevention of water pollution in Hong Kong — which is more important?

Fouling:

Z.G. Huang and S. Lim	Biofouling of Deep Bay buoys
J.J. Wang, Z.G. Huang, S. Lin, C.Y. Li and C.Z. Zheng	An ecological study of fouling organisms in Beihai Harbour, Beibu Bay, China
W.X. Yan, Y. Dong, G.H. Liang and H.J. Wang	Marine fouling organisms in offshore waters of the South China Sea

Pollution:

L.L.P. Vrijmoed, C.S.W. Kueh, H.Q. Shen, C.H. Cai and Y.P. Zhou	Distribution of heterotrophic bacteria in the South China Sea
Y.S. Lin and Z.D. Wang	The occurrence of six species of red tide organisms and their relationship with environmental factors in the Pearl River estuary

J.J. Liu	Accumulation of the antifouling toxin TBT in *Argopecten irradians* (Bivalvia: Pectinidae)
J.X. Jiang, J.S. Song and Z.G. Huang	The effects of urban sewage on benthic community structure in Xiamen Bay, China
S.T. Chiu, C.Y. Chan, T.W. Chan, L.M. Ho, K.M. Hung, M.S. Yang and P.S. Wong	Tributyltin in mussels from Hong Kong mariculture zones
S.T. Chiu, F.P. Tam, M.S. Yang and P.S. Wong	Heavy metal contamination of Hong Kong mariculture zones.

Ecology:

H. Cao	The natural infection dynamics of *Musculista senhausia* (Bivalvia: Mytilidae) by *Prosorhynchus* sp. (Trematoda: Bucephalidae) in Xiamen, China
X.X. Li, T.J. Chen, George A. Evseev and Yuri M. Yakovlev	The heart of *Hyotissa imbricata* (Bivalvia: Gryphaeidae)
Z.Y. Qi, G.Y. Lin, Z.D. Yan, X.Q. Ren and F.L. Li	The intertidal ecology of a rocky shore at Yangkou, Qingdao, China
B.L. Wu and H. Lu	Pelagic polychaetes from the South China Sea
Kevin D. Hyde, Aniwat Chalermpongse and Thirawat Boonthavikoon	The distribution of intertidal fungi on *Rhizophora apiculata*
K.Y. Lee, H.C. Leung, I.J. Hodgkiss and K.W. Cheung	The effect of photoperiod and temperature on the release of monospores by *Porphyra suborbiculata* Kjellman
B.Q. Huang and T.R. Chang	Circadian rhythm of oxygen consumption in the three-striped tigerfish (*Therapon jarbua*)
Andrew S.Y. Mackie, P. Graham Oliver and Paul F. Kingston	The macrobenthic infauna of Hoi Ha Wan and Tolo Channel, Hong Kong
H.L. Chen	The Calappidae (Crustacea: Brachyura) of Chinese waters
J.X. Jiang, R.G. Li, S.J. Zhang and F.W. Zheng	Studies on the ecology of a rocky shore in a sub-tropical estuary: the Jiulong River, Xiamen, China

M.W. Cha	*Tapes philippinarum*: an example of shell pseudo-polymorphism
S.C. Liu	Marine diatoms of the Xisha Islands, South China Sea. I. *Mastogloia* Thw. Ex. Wm. Sm: species of the group *Sulcatae*
S.C. Liu	Marine diatoms of the Xisha Islands, South China Sea. II. Three new species of diatoms (Bacillariophyceae).

PLENARY LECTURE

The Marine Biology of the South China Sea
(ed. B. Morton). Proceedings of the First
International Conference on the Marine
Biology of Hong Kong and the South China Sea,
Hong Kong, 28 October – 3 November 1990.
Hong Kong: Hong Kong University Press, 1993.

TAXONOMIC SUFFICIENCY AND THE ROLE OF SYSTEMATICS IN MARINE INVERTEBRATE STUDIES WITH SPECIAL REFERENCE TO HONG KONG

P. Graham Oliver

Department of Zoology, National Museum of Wales, Cathays Park,
Cardiff, Wales, UK

ABSTRACT

Systematics and taxonomy are defined and shown to be integral to most other biological disciplines. The necessity and current ability to discern and identify the components of the fauna to the species level are discussed in relation to other biological disciplines.

(i) Biodiversity is reliant on systematics and is shown to be poorly estimated for the Indo-Pacific marine invertebrate fauna and for Hong Kong in particular. The problems of species recognition, geographical variation and polymorphism are discussed with relevance to the extensive Indo-Pacific faunal province. Without adequate taxonomic studies the interpretation of variation is questioned and the relationship between the Hong Kong fauna to the remainder of the Indo-Pacific remains unclear.

(ii) Ecology. It is argued that an adequate taxonomy and systematics are essential to ecological studies especially those concerned with community analysis. Such studies are doubly important as they are often used to reflect the implications of pollution or environmental change. These studies frequently employ diversity indices at the heart of which lies our ability to discern species. A stable nomenclature is thus essential, but such studies are severely hampered by an inadequate taxonomy as shown by examples from Hong Kong.

(iii) Conservation. Given the need to conserve threatened or unique marine habitats or species it is necessary to detail these accurately in order that the political decisions have a sound basis. It is essential that any species which is listed as either threatened or of local importance is not simply a widespread species known under another name.

(iv) Physiology. Anomalous results can be obtained if more than one species is used for experimental work. The great diversity of the Hong Kong fauna results in a number of groups which contain morphologically similar species but are ecologically and physiologically distinct.

(v) Exploitation. Many marine invertebrates are exploited for food and an increasing number are being investigated for pharmaceutical properties. Any future management of these resources will depend upon being able to discern which species are most valuable.

The current systematics of the Hong Kong fauna can still be regarded to be in its infancy and there is a great need to undertake not only original research but also to produce working guides to the fauna for the student, the specialist and the non-specialist. To proceed with these aims requires the re-establishment of systematics as a core element in the biological sciences. The importance to other biological disciplines must be stressed and an increase in funding and training must be sought. The acquisition of regional voucher collections and museums to hold them is advocated. Due to the historic development of systematics, future work would benefit from an increase in international cooperation, especially between developing countries and those currently holding the historic collections, literature and expertise.

INTRODUCTION

Since 1977, The University of Hong Kong has, through a number of workshops, brought many scientists together to study the marine biology of the South China Sea. These workshops have not only succeeded in integrating disciplines but have been very effective in stimulating cooperation between scientists from many countries with an interest in this region. This feature of the bringing together of efforts and thinking is entirely relevant to this lecture as it concerns the unifying disciplines of systematics and taxonomy. This lecture is not simply a review of the role of these disciplines within zoology but is also be a plea for a renewed interest in systematics and the need for a standardised taxonomy for the Indo-West Pacific. I hope to demonstrate that the achievement of the latter will depend greatly upon international co-operation. To do this the biological community must be ready to promote systematics, not only within academic circles, but also to the political and commercial sectors who are ultimately the funding sources of all our research.

Over the last decade there has been a resurgence in systematics which has been due greatly to the recognition of the enormous diversity of the tropical rain forests linked with their increasing destruction. Systematics is the only discipline that can provide data on the loss of this diversity. Faced with the enormity of this task, systematics has been revived. This revival coincided with the introduction and now widespread acceptance of cladistic analysis of phylogeny which brings a more rigorous and analytical approach to the discipline. In the vanguard of this revival have been a number of organisations formed to promote systematics and by far the most active has been the Association of Systematics Collections. Much of this paper is a condensation of many articles published in their newsletter and I would refer those interested in the promotion of systematics to this publication. Although the revival has been concentrated on the systematics of tropical terrestrial faunas, I believe that in marine areas of high diversity such as the Indo-Pacific, the need for systematic studies and a practical taxonomy are long overdue. The majority of the nations bordering the Indo-Pacific are classed as less developed countries and are generally the least able to support such studies. However the development and conservation of their natural resources is most urgent. Hong Kong is a striking example of the relationship of a community with the marine environment as it is dependant on it for commerce, as a food source, as a refuse dump and for recreation. To combine these requires a deep understanding of the marine ecosystem and I hope to show that this depends greatly on an adequate knowledge of the systematics and taxonomy of its components.

I shall concentrate upon the marine invertebrate fauna as it is most familiar to me and the least studied. I am certain, however, that the same principles apply to the vertebrate faunas, especially to the multitude of marine fish species inhabiting these waters.

SYSTEMATICS: A DEFINITION

Definitions of systematics vary widely and are often entwined with the concept of taxonomy. If we are to encourage support for the discipline then we will need a concise definition of it and its constituent parts. For this I have drawn extensively upon Whitehead (1990).

Systematics: The classification and naming of the diversity of organic forms. The understanding of the processes that produce and sustain that diversity. Inherent here are the concepts of evolution, speciation, radiation and biogeography. The result is a classification of life which shows the evolutionary relationships between organisms and reflects their genetic lineages.

Taxonomy: is that part of systematics concerned with the naming of organisms and the theory and practice of classifying these taxa within a hierarchy. In the past the majority of taxa were not strictly arranged in accordance to their phylogeny and indeed today many classifications remain on morphological similarities alone.

Nomenclature: is the application of the correct names in accordance with the international codes of nomenclature as laid down by the International Commission for Zoological Nomenclature.

The data required to establish a classification are no longer primarily those derived from comparative morphology. It is fair to say that information is drawn from almost every other discipline of biology. In Figure 1, I have attempted to illustrate the relationship of taxonomy to systematics and their reliance on other biological disciplines to provide supporting evidence for the classifications. Data from all of these disciplines can be used to strengthen the classifications.

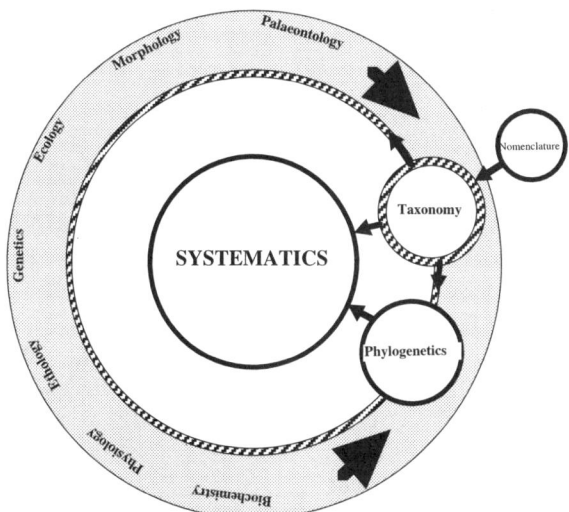

Fig. 1. A diagrammatic representation of the integrative nature of Systematics and its component parts, Taxonomy, Phylogenetics and Nomenclature.

Systematics can therefore be seen to be a unifying discipline bringing together information from all other fields of research. In return, through the resulting classifications and via taxonomy, systematics provides a common framework through which all other disciplines can communicate. Within and between disciplines, taxonomy provides a universal nomenclature which allows the comparison of results both past and present. I would now like to expand upon some of the problems arising from inadequate taxonomic data.

BIODIVERSITY AND SYSTEMATICS

Biodiversity is generally taken to be equivalent to species richness and should not be confused with ecological uses of the term diversity. Biodiversity must, however, be taken in a wider context to levels such as genetic diversity and to community diversity.

Indices of species richness rely totally on our ability to discriminate species and on our assessment of local inventories. Species discrimination currently relies heavily on morphology and even here there is frequently conflicting interpretations concerning variation. Polymorphism, ecophenotypic, and geographical variation can confuse the species taxonomy and frequently render inventories unreliable and non-comparative. With the advent of protein and later RNA and DNA analysis, new definitions of species were made possible. Because of practical restrictions we still define species primarily on morphological characters and species diversity is still the prime measure of biodiversity. Through these genetic techniques it was also realised that populations were often distinct and that this variation was essential to the ability of species to adapt to local or changing conditions. Without such variability we would not be able to carry out the intensive breeding programmes in agriculture. For the continuation of the development and exploitation of our natural resources, it has been realised that we must maintain as much of this genetic diversity as possible. Consequently, systematics at the population level is becoming more important not only in assessing genetic diversity but also the variation within species.

Inventories

Over the last decade there has been an increasing realisation that we are still a very long way from completing an inventory of species now inhabiting the earth (Wilson 1988; May 1988). At the regional level there are also enormous gaps in inventories rendering it impossible to assess the distribution of regions with high biodiversity or to judge local effects on biodiversity.

Let us take the local example of the Hong Kong marine fauna and our ability to assess possible losses of biodiversity through pollution, for example. Table 1 lists the number of new taxa and taxa new to Hong Kong described in the proceedings of the workshops held in Hong Kong since 1977.

These data clearly indicate that:

1. There are still new taxa of marine invertebrates being described and there are numerous taxonomic problems, both suggesting that in many groups there are still undescribed species. Some of these papers indicated that the Hong Kong populations

Table 1
New taxa and taxa new to Hong Kong described in the Proceedings of the Hong Kong Workshops of 1977, 1980, 1983 and 1986.

TAXA	New species	New to Hong Kong	Presence of unresolved taxonomic problems	Reference
Sponges		12	+	van Soest 1982
Sponges	7	12	+	Pulitzer-Finali 1982
Scleractinian corals		49	+	Veron 1982
Gorgonians		15	+	Zou and Scott 1982
Benthic polychaetes		38	+	Shin 1982
Coral associated polychaetes		61	+	Mak 1982
Leucosid crabs		10	+	Hill 1982
Barnacles	1	30	+	Foster 1982
Pontoniine shrimps		5		Bruce 1982
Bopyrid isopods	9	18		Markham 1982
Echinoderms		30		Clark 1982
Ascidia		25	+	Kott and Goodbody 1982
Mollusca	15		+	Christaens 1980; van Belle 1982; Jensen 1985; Lin and Qi 1985; Qi and Ma 1985

were unlike those from other parts of the Indo-Pacific, but that the significance of these variations was unclear.

2. That the local biodiversity was far from being calculated. This can be inferred from the large number of taxa being listed from Hong Kong for the first time.

The uncertainty in the identity of many of the taxa included in these proceedings further indicates that there is still enormous scope for systematic studies in the Hong Kong region and I am sure that this applies to most other regions of the Indo-Pacific. Indeed Goto (1982) and later repeated by Scudder (1986) both estimated that only 10% of the world fauna of marine invertebrates has been described.

Problems in species discrimination

The loss of biodiversity was highlighted primarily by tropical entomologists who now realise that many species of insects are becoming extinct even before they have been formally described. Terrestrial environmental destruction is widely recognised but a similar loss in the oceans is thought to be less widespread. However, if we observe the rapid encroachment of urban development and its resultant pollution here in Hong Kong, we can immediately realise that there is regional loss of biodiversity. Marine species are regarded as being less restricted in range than terrestrial species, because the majority possess a planktonic dispersal stage. It has therefore been argued that within marine systems regional losses are less important as replacement is likely from other areas within the range of each species. This is a complacent attitude as it assumes a general principle which may well be untrue. Such a conclusion does not take into account the variation shown by numerous species and nor does it consider the value of population genetics to the long term survival of species. This brings me to a discussion on the variation of species, the biogeography of the Indo-Pacific faunas and species discrimination.

The maps illustrated in Figure 2 represent four of the more typical distribution patterns shown by Indo-Pacific species. They are of species of shell belonging to the genus *Strombus* but could be from any group of marine invertebrates.

Map A is typical of a large number of species which are considered to be morphologically uniform across the whole of their distribution. With distributions such as this it is easy to understand why replacement of local extinctions is thought to be valid.

Maps B and D show discreet and continuous distributions of taxa which are recognised to be morphologically distinct but in which the taxonomic status is subspecific or varietal. Very many Indo-Pacific species show such patterns but the significance of the variation is normally not examined. In some cases, the varieties are recognised as subspecies therefore inferring some degree of biological isolation (Map B), whereas in others the variation is regarded as clinal, overlapping and therefore of varietal status only. The actual genetic variation or genetic isolation of the varieties is rarely tested and the taxonomic status is usually subjective. In some species, morphological variation is not recognised but the distribution may be markedly discontinuous (Map C). The possibility that genetic isolation may be present despite morphological similarity is rarely considered.

The use of subspecific taxa is usually without foundation and often indicates the presence of unresolved systematic problems. It may also represent poor systematic methodology, especially through lack of comparative data and the use of a restricted suite of taxonomic characters. The genetic significance of this clinal variation is generally not examined, but it is likely that populations become increasingly genetically distinct along the cline and in response to local conditions. If this is found to be widespread then local extinctions do result in the loss of genetic diversity.

Other distribution patterns show species with restricted isolated ranges and there are areas of endemicity within the Indo-Pacific, such as the upwelling region off southern Oman. These species and these areas are much more vulnerable, but the faunas remain uncatalogued and the extent of endemicity remains vague without any advances in systematic studies.

The systematic problems highlighted by these distribution patterns are mainly centred on speciation along a cline or with the role of physical isolation and dispersal capabilities.

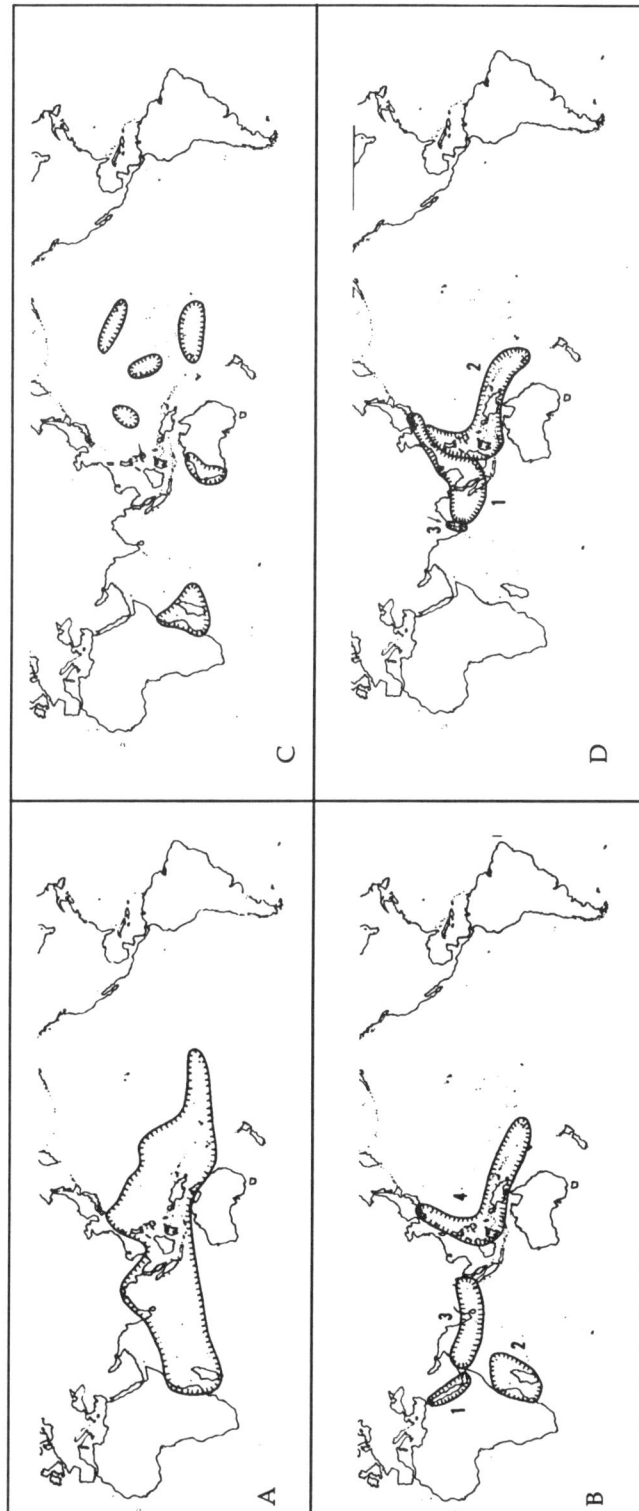

Fig. 2. Four maps showing a variety of distribution patterns commonly exhibited by Indo-Pacific marine invertebrates.

Another problem is concerned with polymorphism, to what extent it occurs or is it more often an indication of unresolved systematics. Work by Robertson (1985) on the widespread trochoid gastropod *Tricolia* represents the extreme of polymorphism and his analysis suggests that there are geographical patterns in the degree of expression of the different forms. In many cases where such patterns exist we are unaware of the role of population genetics and ecophenotypic variation. Both of these need to be a more prominent part of systematic studies and the latter is an area where integration with ecology is required.

One study which highlights all of the above problems was that on the Indo-Pacific mangrove snails belonging to the genus *Littoraria* by Reid (1986).This study is instructive as it concerns a group with a long nomenclatural history (since 1758) and is one which has fluctuated with the changing views of the biogeography of the region.

The genus *Littoraria* includes a number of highly polymorphic species which during the initial phases of description were all given species rank based on shell characters alone. As ideas of biogeography developed and polymorphism within a species was established the species rankings were dropped. A single pan-tropical species was established under the widely accepted name of *L. scabra* with subspecific names applied to the Indo-Pacific, Caribbean and West African populations. Reid re-examined this complex using a much wider range of characters including genital anatomy, habitat ecology and reproductive strategy. The conclusion of his study was the establishment of 20 species in 4 subgenera. The distribution patterns for these species is varied, some have pan-tropical ranges, e.g., *L. scabra* and *L. intermedia* from Hawaii to East Africa, whereas others are much more restricted such as *L. philippiana* to Queensland and *L. cingulata* to NW Australia. Some widespread species still showed clinal variation in shell form. Reid shows that species richness was under-estimated by the previous taxonomy, but now was also able to indicate those areas with greatest species richness for this genus. It is with this kind of detailed study, that we can assess accurately areas of high biodiversity and distinguish the variation in species composition from region to region. Unfortunately, there is very little systematic work done to this detail and many distribution patterns remain unexplained.

Cosmopolitan species, i.e., species with a global distribution pattern, are not uncommon in the Indo-Pacific in groups such as the sponges and polychaetes. If we take the sponges as an example, there is however a strong suggestion that many of the cosmopolitan distributions are the result of inadequate taxonomy. Many of the species belong to genera in which the discriminative characters are either few or difficult to interpret. This is compounded by the very few studies on sponge taxonomy and the regional isolation of these studies which made comparisons difficult. The probability that many of these so called cosmopolitan species are assemblages of undifferentiated closely related species is supported by recent biochemical studies by workers such as Bergquist *et al.* (1990) who have shown the variation in the presence of a variety of chemical compounds.

The above examples are a reflection of the inconsistency of much taxonomic work and the inability of comparative morphology alone to discriminate species in many groups of organisms. In many of these cases we do not have sufficient data to give an overall distribution pattern and we do not have ecological data to assess sympatry where the ranges overlap. The development of protein, DNA, RNA and biochemical analysis is timely as it allows us to examine the genetic relationships of populations and this can give us a much greater insight into the significance of morphological variation. These techniques must be applied to living or frozen specimens and as such are of little application to material stored in museum collections. This work is best carried out in the immediate vicinity of the study area but we can see that to approach the problems of population genetics across a large faunal province such as the Indo-Pacific poses severe logistical problems. To overcome these international cooperation would seem to be the only way forward.

The introduction of genetic characters has also had the effect of challenging the species concept as exemplified in the reviews of Masters and Spencer (1989) and Coyne *et al.* (1988). No matter what decisions we make upon the discrimination of species we cannot ignore the fact that we are dealing with variation and that much of it remains unexplained. Whichever choice we make, we should not dismiss variation as inconsequential. As I have said above, such variation may well have a functional role in the adaptability of species to local conditions and this in turn may be reflected in small but important changes in the ecology and physiology of the races of these variable species.

To conclude the question of biodiversity, I argue that we are far from having an adequate inventory of marine invertebrate species of this region. That the inventory we do have is unreliable and inconsistent, that for most groups the discrimination of species is highly subjective and the significance of population variation is generally untested. It is my belief that local losses of biodiversity are to be avoided as we are still unaware of the value of population variation to the continued existence of a species across its entire ranges and through time.

ECOLOGY

Ecology is a varied discipline with an ever increasing component towards applied studies. Whichever branch we take, the need to accurately define the component species involved is important. I also believe that the systematic relationships of taxa have an important bearing on ecological interpretation.

Systematics in community ecology

Community ecology is one of the most relevant aspects. Striking examples of this are baseline surveys carried out to assess communities either close to or being threatened by pollution or development. One of the most common methods of assessment is the effect on the community ecology of the benthos both in terms of biomass and diversity. Just as with species richness the ecological measurement of diversity relies on our ability to discriminate the component species. Our ability to contrast and compare these results between regions and within a region over time depends upon a consistent nomenclature.

I would like to use as an example of such studies those carried out here in Hong Kong on the long term variation of the benthic fauna of Tolo Channel and Mirs Bay. Urbanisation of the Tolo Harbour region has given cause for concern for the water quality and marine communities of the adjacent areas which receive considerable amounts of domestic waste. I must state at the outset that the problems I wish to highlight are functions of the available systematics and taxonomy and are not related to the ecological methodology.

From these studies a number of important indicator species have been recognised and I would like to discuss the systematics of the bivalve species cited.

Two large species of venerids are frequent in the area, namely *Paphia undulata* and *Tapes philippinarum*. Lam (1980) reviewed the taxonomy of these and related species and concluded that there were two closely related species of *Tapes* present in the region and that one was highly polymorphic. Her work on morphometrics of these allowed them to be distinguished and without it I think considerable confusion would still exist. In *Paphia* she recognised that there is still an unresolved taxonomic problem in the discrimination of *P. undulata* and *P. texturata*. Despite the revision of Fischer-Piette and Metivier (1971), she effectively concluded that on shell characters it was doubtful if the two forms were other than variants of a single species. By contrast, the current systematic position given in the Japanese literature (Kira 1962; Habe 1964, 1977), not only gives specific status to each form, but also places them in separate subgenera. If ecologists are to use indicator species, then it is essential that closely related species are not confused and that there is some degree of compatibility between regions. One may ask how this type of confusion can arise and I would suggest that this is an example of a taxonomy which has not taken into account the ecology of the species. Lam also had the advantage of working with very large samples of *Paphia* from a single area and was able to recognise the variation present. The taxonomy of Fischer-Piette and Metivier (1971) was undoubtedly based on small samples in museum collections in which the range would not be expressed. Another example of this type of problem is the taxonomy of the very common venerid *Veremolpa*. This species is usually cited as *V. micra*, a species described from Japan, but has also been named as *V. scabra*, an Indo-Pacific species. In this case, there appears to be only a single species present in Hong Kong, but in the Japanese literature there are 6 species recognised. Horikoshi and Thompson (1980) noted that in Japan, *Veremolpa* was classed as a mid bay species, but in Tolo Channel it appeared to be a bay mouth species. They then proceeded to assess the physical characters of Tolo Channel on the inferred habitat of *Veremolpa*. Given the taxonomic confusion of the species in the genus, it could be that the ecological difference between Japanese and Hong Kong could be explained if the species were different, i.e., *V. scabra* and *V. micra*.

The remaining species that I would like to consider belong to the Tellinoidea, a very important group of deposit feeding bivalves which are widely used as community indicator species. The most important of these in Tolo Channel is a species of *Theora*, a genus related to the very ecologically important genus *Abra*, which is frequently used by community ecologists in temperate regions. The situation with this species is similar to that of *Veremolpa* in that the relationship of the Hong Kong species to others in the Indo-Pacific is unclear. It has been referred to both *T. lubrica* and *T. lata*, both of which are recognised in the Japanese literature. In the temperate waters of the North Atlantic, four species of *Abra* are used to define communities as they are known to have quite specific substrate preferences. It is therefore essential that the number of species of *Theora* is correctly assessed if this genus is to be widely used as an indicator of community type. For the remaining tellinids we find that frequently no species name is applied rendering inter-regional comparisons impossible. We also find that in the tellinids: (a) the names applied do not appear in any of the regional taxonomic texts and (b) that subgeneric names are applied but the species involved bear little resemblance to the type species of these subgenera. In our example here these names have been applied by taxonomists using museum collections and the full range of literature available. Consequently, I suspect that the names are quite accurate, but I know that one species frequently cited, i.e., *Tellinides corbuloides*, is figured only in the original description which dates to 1854, and is in a rather rare book which is not available to the majority of ecologists anywhere. The inappropriate use of subgeneric names and generic names is primarily the result of poor taxonomic methodology. Despite the importance of the Tellinoidea there has never been a review, the majority of subgeneric names have been introduced as monotypic and the later assignment of species to them has been confused because the original definition of the generic names were all too frequently inadequate and non discriminatory. Application of taxonomy in this manner is not at all helpful to the ecologist and is a hindrance to the comparison of ecological studies.

I would now like to turn to the polychaetes of the same survey to illustrate another complexity of the taxonomy of many of the Indo-Pacific faunas. For this I have used the list of polychaetes (Table 2) cited by Shin (1990) in his latest review of the benthos of the Tolo Channel and Mirs Bay. Against this I have noted which species have a distribution beyond the Indo-Pacific [C] those that are not identified to species level [U] and have included notes on recent advances in the systematics of some of the species.

The general conclusion is that the cosmopolitan distribution of most of these species is now being challenged; that is to say that somewhere close to half the names are now in doubt. Also taking into account that a further ten species were not identified, we calculate that 72% of this list has inadequate taxonomic status. Furthermore, Mackie and Oliver (in press) list over 80 species of polychaete from the latest survey of only a small portion of Tolo Channel, suggesting that the present list may have used a taxonomy which could not discriminate many of the species present.

There is an increasing awareness of the frequency of sympatric sibling species. This was most graphically shown for the widespread indicator species of pollution the polychaete *Capitella capitata*. This species was recorded by Horikoshi and Thompson from Tolo Harbour. However Grassle and Grassle (1977) have shown that off New England there are six sibling sympatric species present and it is therefore very doubtful if the Hong Kong species is conspecific. This discovery renders the use of *Capitella* as an indicator somewhat redundant as the sibling species show marked differences in life history and reproduction

This inadequate taxonomy has little to do with the ecologist, but is the result of the general neglect of taxonomic studies and the continuing localisation of taxonomic texts. To some degree it is also a result of poor taxonomic methodology. The bivalve identifications were taken from texts which were either not entirely applicable to this region or from texts which were far from comprehensive. A common problem with many molluscan texts is that they do not figure all the species cited, and it is impossible for the ecologist to explore further because the availability of taxonomic literature is limited. The extent of polychaete literature is even more limited, and tends to consist either of expedition reports or regional lists. The regional lists mainly figure only new taxa, other species are rarely redescribed and not figured. In this way erroneous records and the lack of recognition of taxa are perpetuated. Many polychaete descriptions especially from the earlier periods are now insufficient to discriminate the species and very often whole suites of characters go unmentioned. For this reason, it is easy to see how many species can fit a single description and how the acceptance of cosmopolitan distributions has come about.

What can the ecologists do to ensure the compatibility and comparability of their

Table 2
List of polychaete species recorded from Tolo Channel indicating the frequency of unidentified (U) and cosmopolitan species (C) recorded. Basic list from Shin 1990.

Species	C	U	Notes
Harmothoe imbricata	C		
Sthenelais boa	C		
Sthenolepis yhelni	C		
Anaitides sp.		U	
Linopherus hirsuta			
Leocrates wesenberglundae			
Sigambra tentaculata	C		
Ophiodromus pugettensis	C		
Platynereis sp.		U	
Leonnates persica			
Aglaophamus lyrochaeta			
Nepthys sp.		U	
Glycera alba	C		
Glycinide sp.		U	
Diopatra variabilis			
Lumbrineris shiinoi			
Shistomeringos incerta			
Phylo kupfferi			
Minuspio cirrifera	C		Now 5 species in Japan, (Mackie 1984)
Paraprionospio pinnata	C		Now 4 species in Japan (Yokoyama and Tamai 1981)
Prionospio ehlersi	C		Not this species (Mackie and Hartley 1990)
Polydora sp.		U	
Magelona crenulifrons			
Poecilochaetus sp.		U	5 species now recorded from Hong Kong (Mackie 1990)
Chaetozone setosa	C		
Cirratulus sp.		U	
Cirriformis tentaculata	C		
Tharyx sp.		U	
Spiochaetopterus costarum	C		
Sternapsis scutata	C		
Pherusa sp.		U	
Mediomastus sp.		U	
Cossura coasta			
Lagis koreni	C		
Ampharete arctica	C		
Liomia medusa	C		
Terebellides stroemi	C		Now split into several species (Williams and Imajima 1985)
37 SPECIES	17	10	

studies? The maintenance of voucher specimens can help in a number of ways. They can act as a source of reference for future ecologists on which to base their species lists. They can act as a retrospective for assessing the relevance of name changes. They can act as a source of comparison of taxa between regions and of course can act as a resource for systematic work. However, if taxonomic revision results in the splitting of a former species into a number of new species then voucher material is usually insufficient to reassess past data and the only recourse would be to retain the entire samples from the ecological study. The maintenance of a voucher collection is time and space consuming enough, but to retain complete ecological samples is generally totally impractical even to the largest of museums. It does suggest however, that museums have a very important role to play and is one that needs expansion rather than contraction. To me, therefore, it is very apparent that the ecologist desperately requires the minimum of a practical taxonomy for the identification of marine invertebrates in Hong Kong. It may also be true and certainly is for the UK that ecologists also need a more detailed background in systematics. Unfortunately we have been over run by molecular biology, biochemistry and other sub-organism disciplines to such an extent that many zoology students can no longer recognise even the invertebrate phyla. I believe that ecological studies cannot be carried out without a basic understanding of systematics and with better training the ecologist may be able to take a more constructive role in the discrimination of species.

Taxonomic resolution in community analysis

Another trend currently receiving considerable backing is that a traditional taxonomy and systematics are generally irrelevant to ecological studies. The belief that one need only to recognise species but not place them in a taxonomic framework is increasing, and is driven by financial pressures from the increasing commercial component of ecological studies, especially in the area of impact surveys. The use of higher taxa only in the comparison of benthic communities and the effects on them by environmental changes are presented by Warwick (1988), Kingston and Riddle (1989), and Platt et al. (1990). The underlying principle of their hypothesis is well illustrated by this diagram taken from Kingston and Riddle (1989).

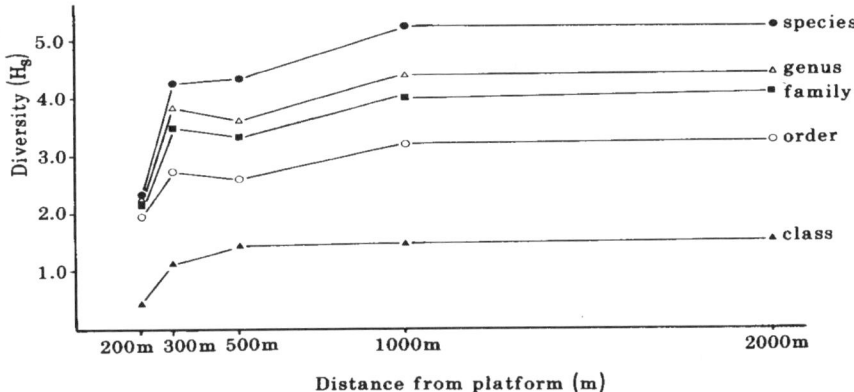

Fig. 3. Effect of taxonomic resolution on diversity indices. After Kingston and Riddle 1989.

It illustrates the diversity, as calculated by the Shannon-Weiner index, at a number of stations which are sited progressively distant from a source of pollution, in this case oil-based drilling cuttings from an oil exploration well. The effects of the pollution are normally estimated by the loss in diversity calculated from the combined abundance at the species level, in this case the top line. The large drop between the 300 and 200 m. stations is strongly indicative of disturbance. The other lines are calculated by grouping the fauna at progressively higher taxonomic levels and we can see that even at the class level the shape of the curve remains essentially similar although the magnitude of the changes becomes less. The loss of refinement with decreasing taxonomic resolution I believe is the most critical factor to be considered. First, what kind of pollution causes this type of response. In this case it is quite extreme and is visible in its effect on the sea floor by the examination of underwater photographs. I think we should retain a methodology which will indicate disturbance at the early stages of its effect not once it is so obvious as this. We should, therefore, be more interested in the flatter region of these curves. The effect of losing taxonomic resolution can be illustrated in Figure 4. Note that I have set up a cladogram with ten species belonging to four genera (G1–G4) and two families and adjacent to this columns showing relative abundance of each for 3 stations.

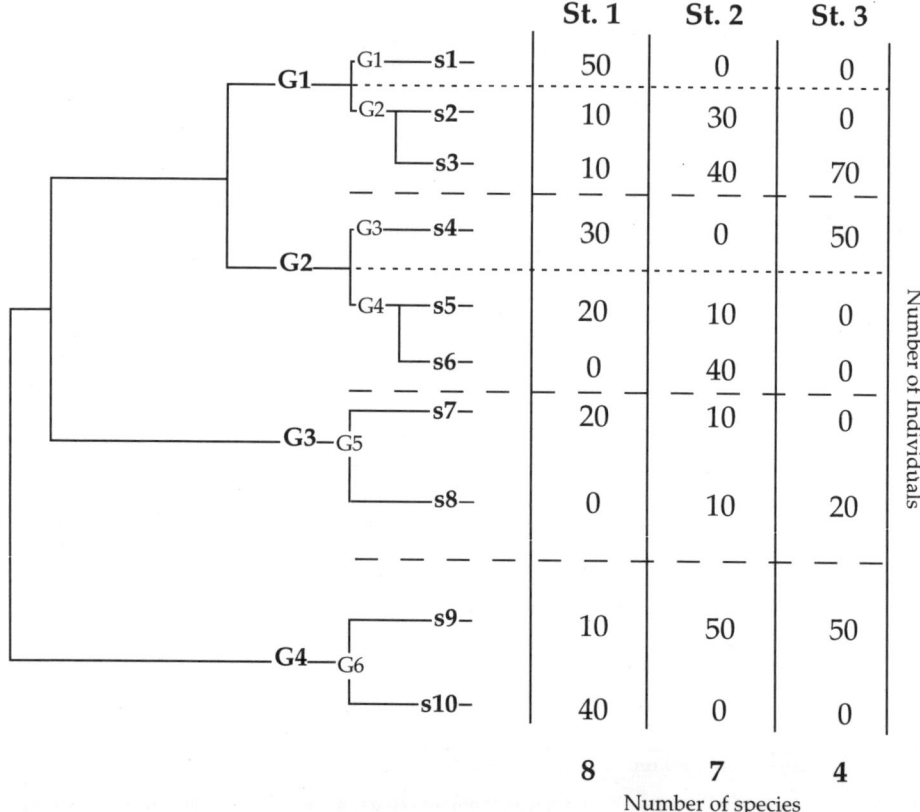

Fig. 4. Diagram of a cladogram illustrating the loss of refinement at the species level when calculating diversity indices at the generic level.

At the species level, the changes in relative abundance and diversity would be detected. But at the generic level, all three stations retain the same scores despite the alterations in species composition and relative abundance. The benthic communities of Hong Kong do contain numerous genera which are multispeciate and could therefore give the type of community used in my diagram. I realise that it is unlikely that the numbers of individuals would remain in proportion and some changes in the diversity indices are likely. Even so, they would not indicate changes in species composition and may well not show loss of biodiversity. I would, therefore I would suggest, as indeed Kingston and Riddle (1989) do, that 'Extreme caution should be exercised in the adoption of such an approach as the loss of information could be critical if subtle effects are not to be overlooked.' I would also like to point out the effect of moving the generic classification. Note that I have indicated that some of the species in a genus are more closely related than others. If we carry out an instantaneous revision and split these genera at these points (G1–G6) we now see the diversity changes begin to appear. Systematic research is therefore essential to stabilise changes in taxonomy. I would like to point out that in Platt *et al.* (1990) it was stated that taxonomic reduction of the macrobenthos in their study had little effect on the diversity indices, but that for the nematodes there was considerable loss of discrimination above the generic level. I would only like to point out that both Platt and Warwick are nematode taxonomists and it could be that their systematic expertise influenced the taxonomic resolution. This work does appear to provide some estimate of community status, but I feel is not sufficiently refined to elucidate the underlying causes, which may be varied. Species composition and diversity changes occur naturally or through the effects of man's influence. To recognise and differentiate these changes I believe requires the more refined techniques of studying the communities at the species level. It is interesting to note that the baseline studies carried out in the North Sea have not adopted the higher-taxa-based method despite its more cost effective advantages of savings in time and labour. I personally believe that this approach has arisen not through any advances in methodology, but simply because there is now a shortage of systematically trained personnel to carry out the taxonomy of these ecological studies. If the South China Sea ever does develop an extensive off-shore oil industry it will be interesting to watch how the taxonomic and ecological resources can cope with carrying out similar surveys. If we cannot supply an adequate taxonomy and staff trained in systematics, it is difficult to see how we could adequately monitor the effects of such a development in this region.

So far I have concentrated on the role of taxonomy in ecological studies but there is a role for phylogenetic systematics as well. For this I shall return to another aspect of the work by D.G. Reid (1990) on the littorinids. Reproductive and developmental types have often been interpreted in an ecological context, relating the various strategies to their possible adaptive value in relation to local ecological conditions. This is the basis of the concept of optimal strategies where adaptations are correlated with habitat. Reid argues that an interpretation involving the evolutionary approach is more rigorous and that the evolutionary history at least in this case is a better explanation of reproductive strategy than local ecological adaptation.

The field of applied ecology is expanding rapidly and has fundamental implications for our exploitation of the natural resources of our planet. Much discussion has taken place on the need to integrate all aspects of applied ecology and this diagram illustrates how one eminent ecologist (Barrett 1989) recently perceived such an interface.

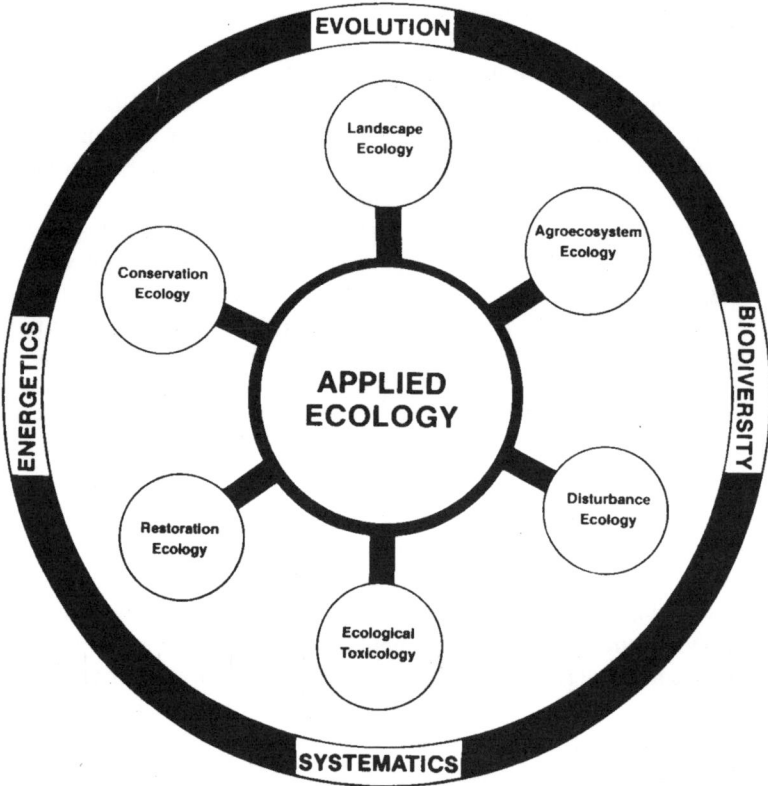

Fig. 5. Diagram illustrating the integrative nature of systematics and biodiversity to aspects of applied ecology. After Barrett 1989.

Note the fundamental integrative topics of Evolution, Biodiversity and Systematics, and note that I have already argued that the discipline of Systematics itself is intimately linked to biodiversity and evolution, through phylogenetics and encompasses taxonomy. Prof. Gary Barrett of Miami University went on to state that:
'Evolutionary biology must permeate the academic philosophy upon which applied ecology is built.'
'That biodiversity (genetic, species or ecosystem type) must be a driving force behind conservation and restoration endeavours.'
'That personnel, facilities and curricula in the area of systematics must be provided to fulfil successfully these integrative teaching, research and service objectives.'

CONSERVATION

One branch of applied ecology that is especially reliant on systematics is conservation ecology (Hoagland 1987; V.W. Reid 1990). I have already stressed the value and role of maintaining biodiversity at its natural levels. Many conservation projects are aimed at precisely this goal and reserves are frequently designated in areas of naturally high biodiversity. Intuitively, we require an adequate taxonomy if we are to describe the diversity we wish to preserve. Here in Hong Kong efforts are being made to designate a marine reserve at Hoi Ha Wan in Tolo Channel. Without the considerable efforts made by numerous specialists in recent years we would not be able to select this site as one with considerable diversity both in habitats and species. While on the subject of maintaining reserves with high biodiversity I would like to mention the role of systematics in choosing reserve sites (May 1990; Vane-Wright *et al.* in press). Phylogenetic systematics produces a classification in which the closely related and, therefore, the genetically most similar taxa appear together in the hierarchy. Such a theoretical cladogram is illustrated on the left of the diagram. To the right of the diagram the occurrence of each taxon is marked for a number of localities selected as possible reserve sites. The reserve best suited for selection to retain the maximum genetic diversity is the one which encompasses the widest range of branches of the hierarchy, and not simply the greatest number of species. If only one site can be chosen the optimum choice

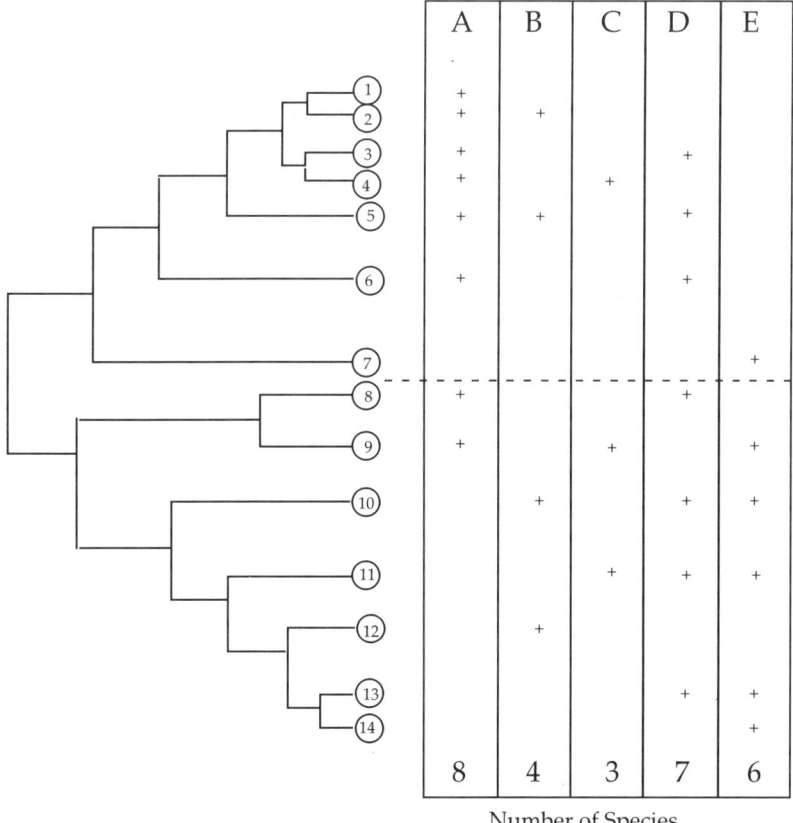

Fig.6. Diagram of a cladogram illustrating the hypothetical effect of phylogeny on the maintenance of biodiversity in a number of reserve sites.

is site D not site A, as it encompasses examples from each of the major dichotomies despite site A having more species. If two sites could be designated, then sites A and E would be chosen because they encompass the widest combined range of genetic diversity.

Conservation efforts are also made at the individual species level and we have a now widely accepted list of endangered species. Most of us can probably recognise a giant panda and I also assume most customs officers can as well, but there are increasing demands for some invertebrates to be placed on lists of protected species. In order to legislate in such cases it is essential that we either have a simple working taxonomy, or that our legislation has no loopholes caused by inaccurate systematics. Not only is the ability of the legislation at stake but also the credibility of the conservation advice. It would, for example, not be wise to claim that a rare endemic species be legislated for, only to find that it was no more than a local colour variety of a widespread common species.

PHYSIOLOGY

Studies on comparative physiology can yield erroneous results if the systematics of the species under study are not understood. In this simple case (Ross and Oliver personal observations) thermal tolerance of three populations of bivalves, within the genus *Isognomon* from Hong Kong, were investigated (Fig. 7). The traditional taxonomy of the Isognomonidae, based on shell morphology alone, has always been confused due to considerable plasticity in shell shape. The extreme interpretation of this was made by Fischer-Piette (1976) who concluded that there was a single pan tropical species. The study by Ross and Oliver attempts to elucidate the systematics of the Hong Kong species. The expected result that the littoral populations are more thermal tolerant is revealed (Fig. 7A). There does appear to be wide variation in the response or there is some erroneous data included in the experiment as revealed by the large dip in the second peak. If, however, the habitat of the littoral populations is used to divide the sample then the erroneous appearance is resolved. The data therefore suggests that three species are present and not two (Fig 7B). This conclusion can be supported by shell and anatomical differences. This example shows not only how physiology can be used in systematics but, conversely, how a poor taxonomy could confuse the physiologist.

A further example of the importance of systematics to physiology relates to work recently undertaken on the zonation of mangrove snails in relation to their stress tolerance. McMahon and Britton (1985), and Yipp (1985) both use the name *Littorina scabra*, but using Reid's (1986) taxonomy (discussed above), this species does not occur in Hong Kong. Comparison of studies is, therefore, difficult without a stable taxonomy.

EXPLOITATION

Marine invertebrates are an important component of exploitable food resources (Caddy 1989) especially among the Crustacea and Mollusca, but also holothurians, echinoids and ascidians. Many are also now proving to be an untapped reservoir of useful organic compounds which have their main relevance to the pharmaceutical industry.

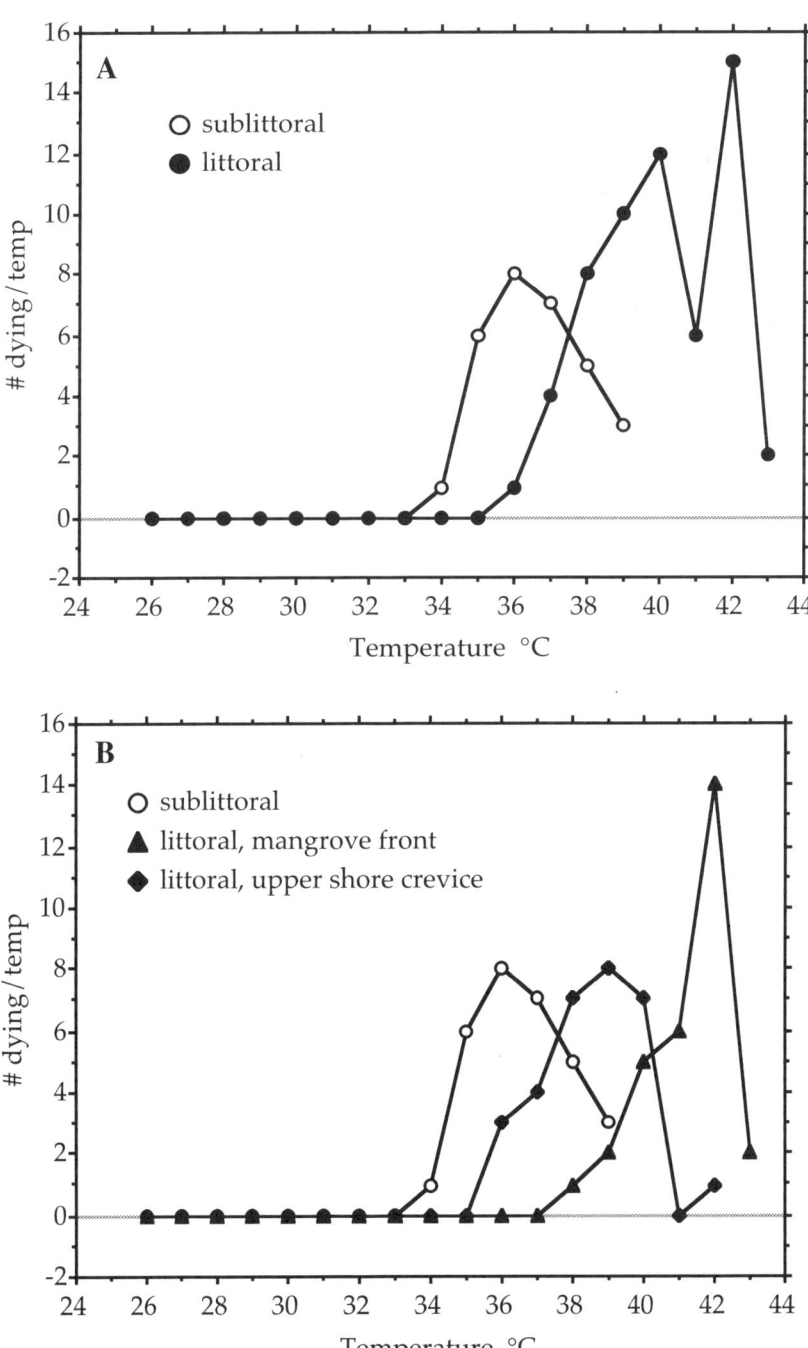

Fig. 7. Diagram illustrating the effect of species discrimination in the genus *Isognomon* on the interpretation of a physiological experiment.

Fishery management is necessary to maintain these resources and, at the purely practical level, we require a useable taxonomy for fishery officers to recognise the species being fished and to evaluate the numbers of each taken. Tseng and Cheng (1982) noted that there was no practical guide to the twelve species of shrimp commonly landed in Hong Kong.

Of the bivalves frequently collected for food around Hong Kong and elsewhere in the Indo-West Pacific there are no such guides for the clams (Veneridae, mainly *Tapes* and *Circe*), scallops (Pectinoidea, notably *Pecten* and *Spondylus*) or blood cockles (Arcoidea, notably *Anadara*)

Of these, *Tapes philippinarum* is now an important species. As Lam (1980) showed, however, there is considerable polymorphism in this species and even within Hong Kong there was confusion with *Tapes variegatus*. Many similar forms occur throughout the Indo-Pacific and without a sound taxonomic base it is difficult to assess the potential number of species or the species content of unexploited stocks. Caddy (1989a) made special reference to the increasing awareness that the fisheries term of 'stock units' had to be more closely defined in terms of genetically isolated populations. This he deemed was especially necessary for the management of essentially sedentary invertebrates such as clams and whelks. Given the range of many Indo-Pacific species and the variation shown by many it is evident that the recognition of species, subspecies, local races and genetically separate populations are very relevant to fisheries management. Even within apparently the same stock, some genetic and morphological separation of populations can be apparent. American lobsters were found to be divisible into local genetically separate populations which rarely interbred (Cobb and Caddy 1989). It was generally found that there were inshore and offshore populations and that these could be distinguished by a multivariate analysis of 16 morphological characters. Given the increasing trend towards overexploitation and resultant loss of local stocks it is clear that we are losing genetic diversity. Munro (1989) in a review of the giant clam fishery noted that many stocks of *Tridacna gigas* and *Tridacna derasa* had already become extinct and that if their remaining genetic diversity was not conserved immediately, that all such resources would be lost.

I have already discussed the importance of systematics to distributional ecology, reproductive strategy and physiology and these apply very importantly to economic species. In the North East Atlantic and especially in the North Sea there is currently great concern about the status of fish stocks and the effects of pollution. Under investigation is the incidence and distribution of gut and gill parasites, including their use to differentiate populations of certain widespread species. The systematics of helminths, cestodes and nematodes of fish of the Hong Kong region is very fragmentary and would be of great benefit to fisheries biology.

TAXONOMIC INSUFFICIENCY: HISTORICAL PROGRESSION

I have hopefully persuaded you all that systematics and taxonomy are an essential and integrative discipline but just how have we arrived at such an unsatisfactory state of affairs with the Indo-Pacific fauna.

The fauna of the Indo-Pacific has been described progressively since the middle of the 18th century. Illustrations and descriptions of species first appeared in these early iconographies many of which are pre-Linnaean (pre 1758). Later, once the Linnaean system of nomenclature had been adopted there was a rapid growth in the study of natural history which coincided with the imperial expansion of European countries. Exploring expeditions brought back to Europe vast arrays of 'wondrous' creatures from the Indies and these were eagerly described and placed in the cabinets of private individuals and later in museums. I believe that partly due to nationalistic rivalry and to the difficulty of travel in the late 18th and 19th centuries that there appeared what I would like to call 'national taxonomies'. A cursory examination of the early literature on the Mollusca clearly shows that the French worked on the base set by Lamarck and Deshayes, the English on Sowerby and Reeve, and the Germans on Kobelt, Dunker and Pfeiffer. In the late 19th and early 20th centuries the Americans joined in with the work of Gould, Pilsbry and Dall. During this first phase there was very little biological basis to the discrimination of taxa resulting in a tendency to describe all morphological varieties as species. Theories of biogeography and dispersal were not developed and there was a resulting tendency to consider geographical separation as an excuse for naming new species. This drive to describe new taxa was also probably driven by the sheer enthusiasm inspired by the exotic material but may also have been partly enhanced by a pride of possession syndrome which is still prevalent among collectors of natural history objects. It should be remembered that many of the early taxonomists were not biologists by training but were enthusiastic amateurs. I must also add that in the mollusca there was also a monetary value in describing new species as these were sought after by private collectors, a practice which has not yet died out. The combined result was that there appeared an excess in names and a lack of comparison between descriptions.

However, in some taxa the problem of discriminating small differences in microscopic characters was hampered by poor optical equipment. In soft-bodied groups fixation and storage, if not carried out properly, led to loss of characters and reduced the shelf life of the material. Many of the early collections lack adequate data especially concerning details of location and ecological data. In morphologically similar species such data are frequently the initial key to their recognition. Consequently, the combination of these factors led to poor descriptions, poor discrimination of species and to a deficiency in nomenclature for these types of animals. The factors leading to this taxonomic insufficiency are summarized in Figure 8.

TAXONOMIC REVISION: A LOST CAUSE?

The concepts of producing revised taxonomies either as systematic monographs or regional faunas is a 20th century development and is primarily post 1950. It can be argued that it has only seen any great advance since the realisation that biodiversity is both important and threatened and since systematics was revitalised with the introduction of cladistic analysis in the mid sixties. In Europe, I would say that we have now a two-tier taxonomy. The traditional practical taxonomy which is geared to providing descriptions and inventories of species and the new phylogenetic taxonomy which is just beginning to provide insight and give some evolutionary basis to the traditional taxonomy. The former is only now reaching any sort of definitive level with the production of texts which at last allow biologists in other disciplines to adequately identify the organisms which they are studying. Examples of these are the Linnaean Society syn-

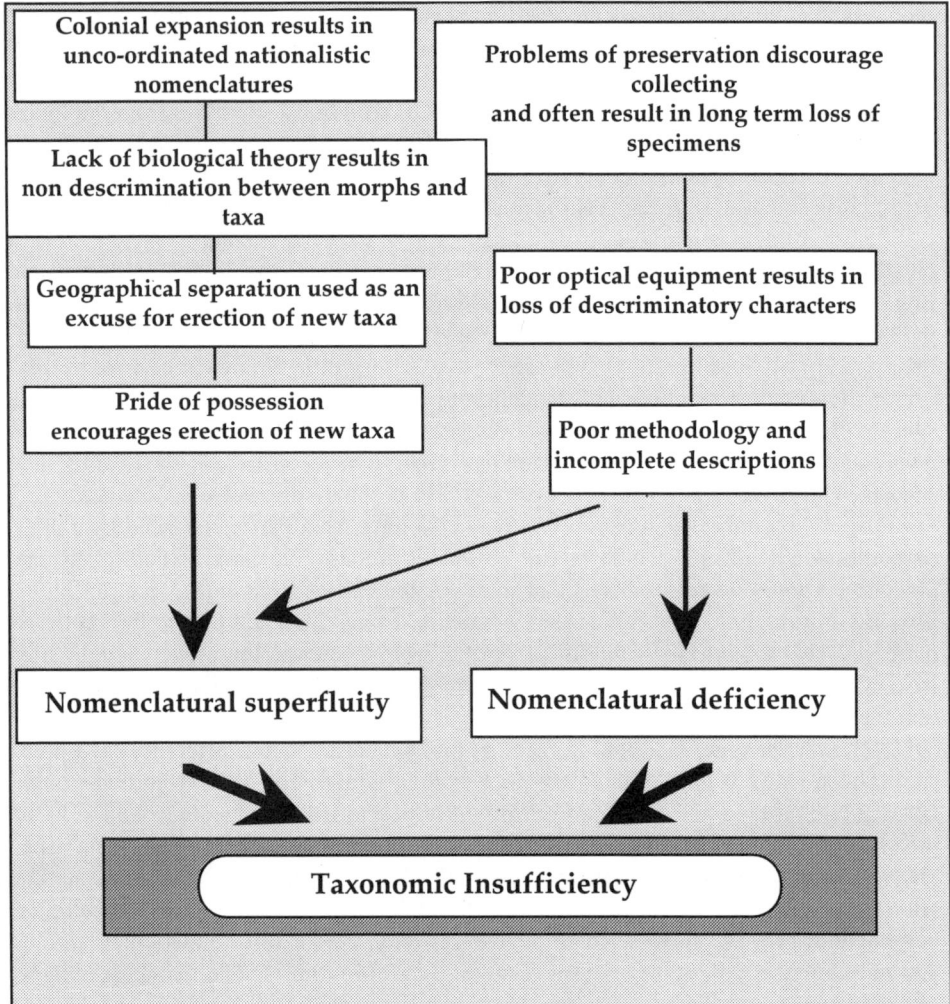

Fig. 8. Diagram illustrating the factors resulting in taxonomic insufficiency of the Indo-Pacific marine invertebrate fauna.

opses of the British fauna, but even these are not complete, the notable exception being those volumes destined for most of the polychaete families. Similar treatises exist or are in preparation, namely: the Scandinavian fauna under the MIOS project; the French fauna is mostly described in Faune de France, a rather dated but important series; the German fauna in *Der Tierwelt Deutschland* and there is in preparation *Fauna Iberica*, an inventory of the Iberian Peninsula by a Spanish team based in Madrid. Such texts are available to very few of the Indo-Pacific groups as a whole and in a regional context they are also very sparse. To date, we have very few systematic monographs and the regional faunas remain primarily on regional taxonomies and are not comparable between regions. There are however beginning to appear some well worked regional taxonomies such as for Japan and Australia but these are far from comprehensive and only partly applicable to the Indo-Pacific as a whole. Phylogenetic systematic studies are even more scarce but this is not surprising given the recent and often reluctant acceptance of cladistics.

Why there are not more basic taxonomic texts available and why systematics is still very far from producing comprehensive classifications is a complex problem.

(i) The reasons for this are, I believe, due greatly to the complexity and enormity of the task of reviewing the confusion created in the past. One must have access to a vast literature, some of which is now very rare and hard to come by. Also needed is access to the European and American collections, which are the primary storehouse of the historical data and the bulk of type material.

(ii) Historical material is generally unable to provide the range of taxonomic characters and biological data now needed to carry out adequate systematic studies, so one must also have access to new material and data from the total geographical range of the group under review. The Indo-Pacific being a very large geographical region, results in the need to consider extensive geographical variation which poses severe logistical problems.

(iii) There is the problem of language which prevents much of the literature from reaching beyond national boundaries. In this respect the early Japanese and now Chinese and Russian literature remains underused because of the lack of translations and I am sure that this is a two way process.

(iv) The training of taxonomists and systematists has declined over the period when the resurgence and integrative nature of the discipline has occurred.

(v) The funding of systematics has declined especially with relevance to the number of posts available.

The severity of the latter problems was highlighted at the 4th International Congress of Systematics and Evolutionary Biology (Hoagland 1990). Speakers from the USA, Britain and the USSR all told of declining funding and lack of positions for systematists. Delegates from less developed countries related similar trends but most of these faced with rampant development and uncontrolled pollution highlighted the urgency to assess the effects on biodiversity.

The factors leading to the current lack of taxonomic revisions are summarized in Figure 9.

TAXONOMIC SUFFICIENCY: A WAY FORWARD?

I believe that it is essential to produce workable practical taxonomies for the Indo-Pacific and that in the initial stages that this would be more practical to be done on a regional basis. Once regional faunas have been compiled, integration of these could be carried out at a later date. These regional faunas would at least allow some degree of taxonomic sufficiency within the region and would allow consistency in the determination and naming of species. To avoid a repetition of confusion between these regional taxonomies the descriptions and figures must be of a high standard and should be backed up by voucher specimens of all species cited. It will not be good enough to figure only a few species and the descriptions must allow comparison. Consequently, if different names are used it must be possible to identify those groups of species which are being confused and where detailed revisionary work is required. If these texts are produced

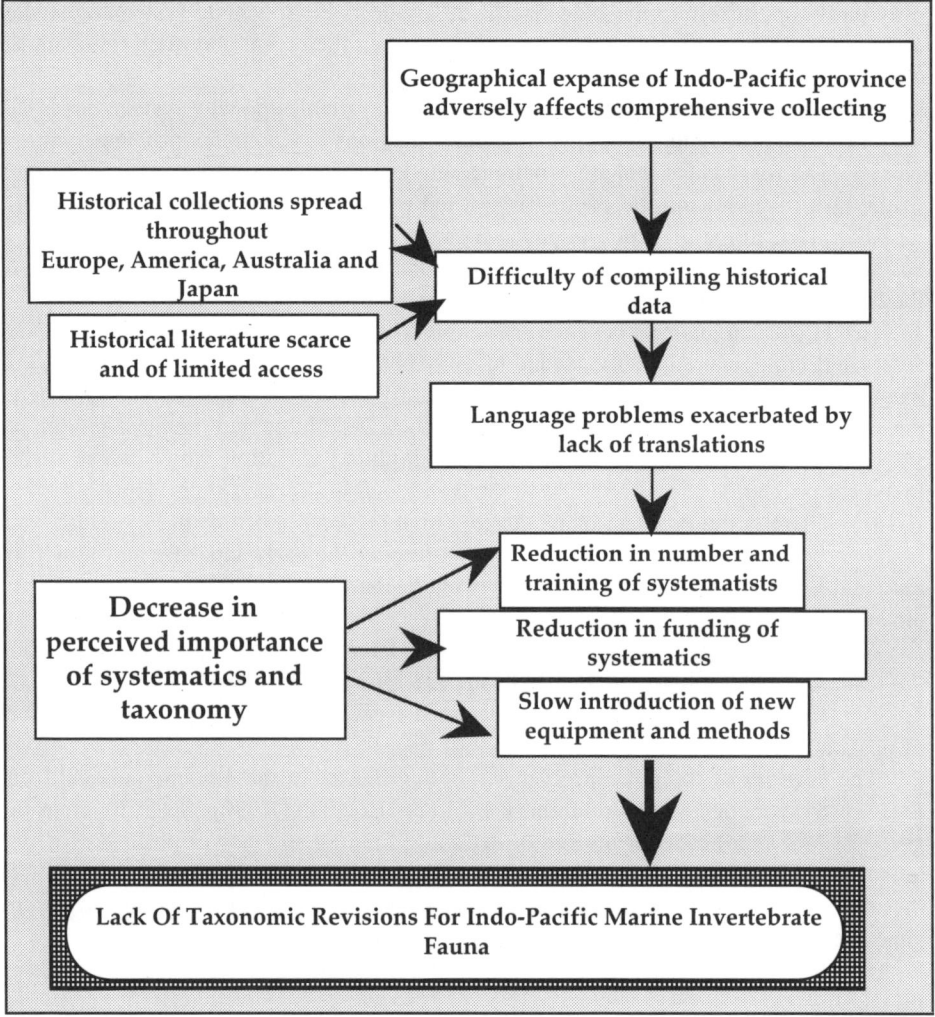

Fig. 9. Diagram illustrating the factors leading to a lack of taxonomic revisions for the Indo-Pacific marine invertebrate fauna.

to this high standard then inter-regional comparison could be done even if the nomenclature was not comparable. You may ask why I am not advocating a drive towards the production of revisions on a systematic rather than geographic basis? I believe that the latter is more pragmatic as it can be seen to have a more immediate local relevance. I suspect that it will just not be feasible to muster the amount of resources on an international scale to carry out revisions across the expanse of the Indo-Pacific province, at least not in sufficient terms to rapidly increase the taxonomic data required in the immediate future. Where this has been attempted, e.g., the monograph series *Indo-Pacific Mollusca*, it has failed through lack of government and institutional support. This series only survived by directing its work onto those groups which were collected by

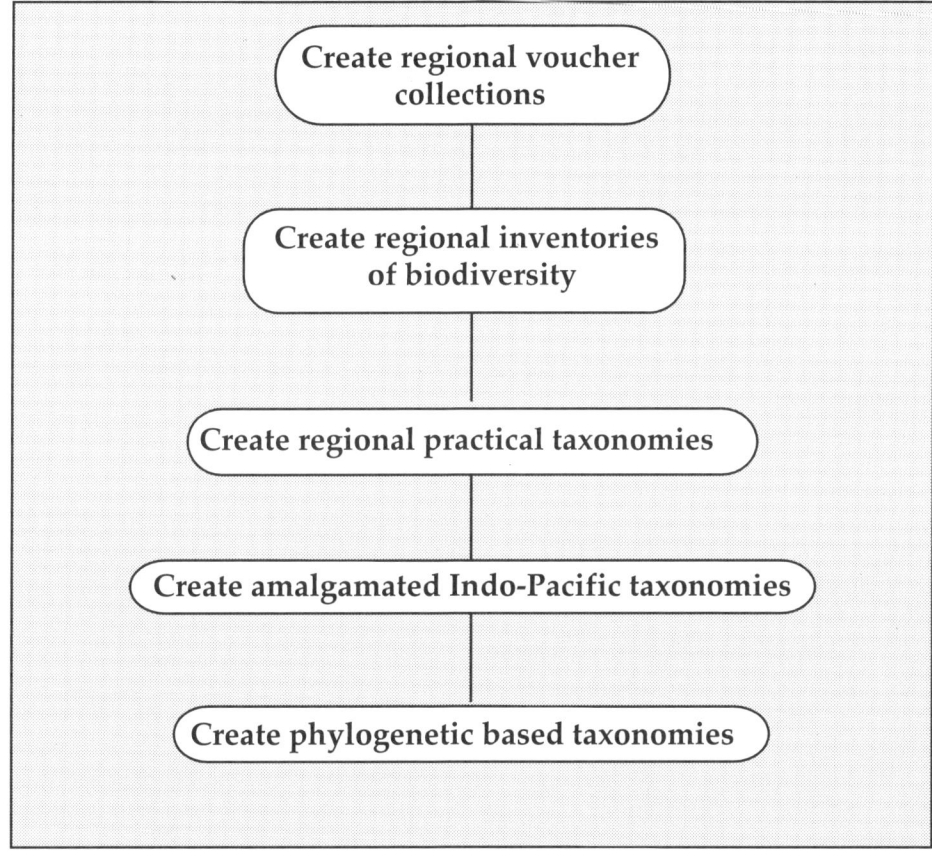

Fig. 10. Diagram illustrating a suggested sequence for the development of taxonomic studies for Indo-Pacific marine invertebrates.

amateurs and consequently became very restricted in scope. Systematic based taxonomies would require an even greater degree of intense research but have the advantage of producing data which are more relevant to the integrative approach with ecology. This progression of taxonomic development is summarized in Figure 10. Scudder (1986) recognised the logistic limitations to phylogenetic systematics and hypothesised that over the next 25 years the majority of studies would remain traditional in format and that the morphospecies concept would remain the dominant unit of classification. I however feel that with correctly directed funding we need not feel so pessimistic about the broad development of phylogenetic classifications.

How can we progress towards these ends? I would like to make the following suggestions.

(i) Creation of regional inventories of biodiversity and the maintenance on a regional base of collections representing this diversity. This would provide the basis upon which regional taxonomies could be built and would be a source of data for subsequent integration of systematics. These regional collections would also act as a source of reference for ecologists. Concerning Hong Kong in particular, the creation of a natural history museum would greatly enhance the compilation and maintenance of voucher collections for, at the moment, there is no institution geared towards collections.

(ii) The role of systematics should be promoted actively and governments and other funding agencies should be lobbied in order to stress the relevance of systematics and the urgency of the study of biodiversity especially in those areas most under threat by development, habitat destruction or over exploitation. One agency of promotion in many countries is the local natural history museum which through its education role can stress the value of biodiversity and conservation.

(iii) Development agencies and developers should be made aware that the effects of many potential projects cannot be adequately assessed because of the lack of adequate systematic data. These organisations should be encouraged to fund supporting systematic research for the environmental impact assessments that are now mandatory in many European countries.

(iv) Training of systematists is required and there should also be background training for ecologists and conservation biologists whose interest in systematics is secondary. This training should be backed up by the creation of more posts in systematics, especially in the developing countries and be concomitant with the development of systematic collections in those countries. Regional natural history museums should be encouraged to be an integral part of higher education and research and thereby provide long term posts in systematics.

(v) The introduction of new technologies should be promoted especially those employing biochemical, protein and DNA analysis. A regional centre for the long term storage of deep frozen material for such analysis would be of great value (Dessauer 1988).

It should however be realised that systematics is essentially an international discipline and that the distribution of faunas and floras do not conform with political boundaries. It must also be recognised that the majority of the historical material relating to the Indo-West Pacific is held in European, American, Australian and Japanese museums. International cooperation is therefore essential to the furtherance of integrated systematics and funds specifically aimed at fostering international links should be exploited and promoted (Knutson 1987). These could be directed more specifically at the following.

(vi) Increase access to the historical data on taxonomy for systematists in developing countries (summarized in Figure 11). This can involve the funding of visits to the relevant institution or the creation of databases of this historical data with a regional or systematic emphasis. It must, however, also be realised that the long established museums are under increasing financial and resource pressure such that their role is compromised. One recent review outlined the many areas requiring urgent attention (Nicholson 1989). Lobbying from potential users of these international collections is needed to remind the funding bodies of their broader role within the scientific community.

(vii) Foster liaison between systematists across the international spectrum. This could take the form of workshops at periodic intervals at which practical contributions could be made within specific systematic groups.

(viii) Systematists working with the historical data in European and American institutions should be encouraged to work in conjunction with and visit others directly involved in the region.

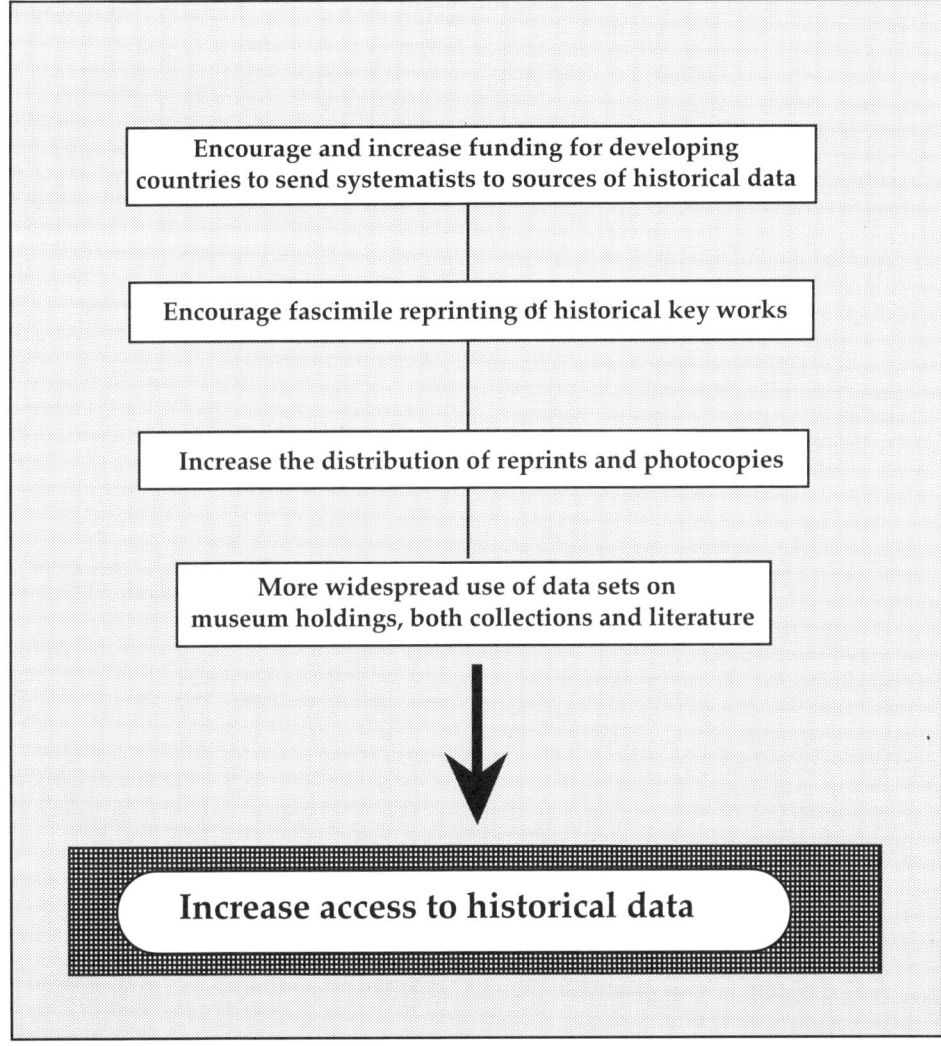

Fig. 11. Diagram illustrating the requirements for increasing access to historical data.

(ix) To allow trainee systematists in developing countries to receive teaching in institutions with historical data and relevant expertise. The need for systematics training has been highlighted in the USA (Humphrey 1989) and is equally relevant to this region.

(x) Steps should be taken to make the relevant systematic literature more widely available: (a) translation services should be expanded; (b) historic and out of print key works should be reprinted and (c) duplicate reprints and photocopies should be made more available to developing countries.

These measures are summarized in Figure 12.

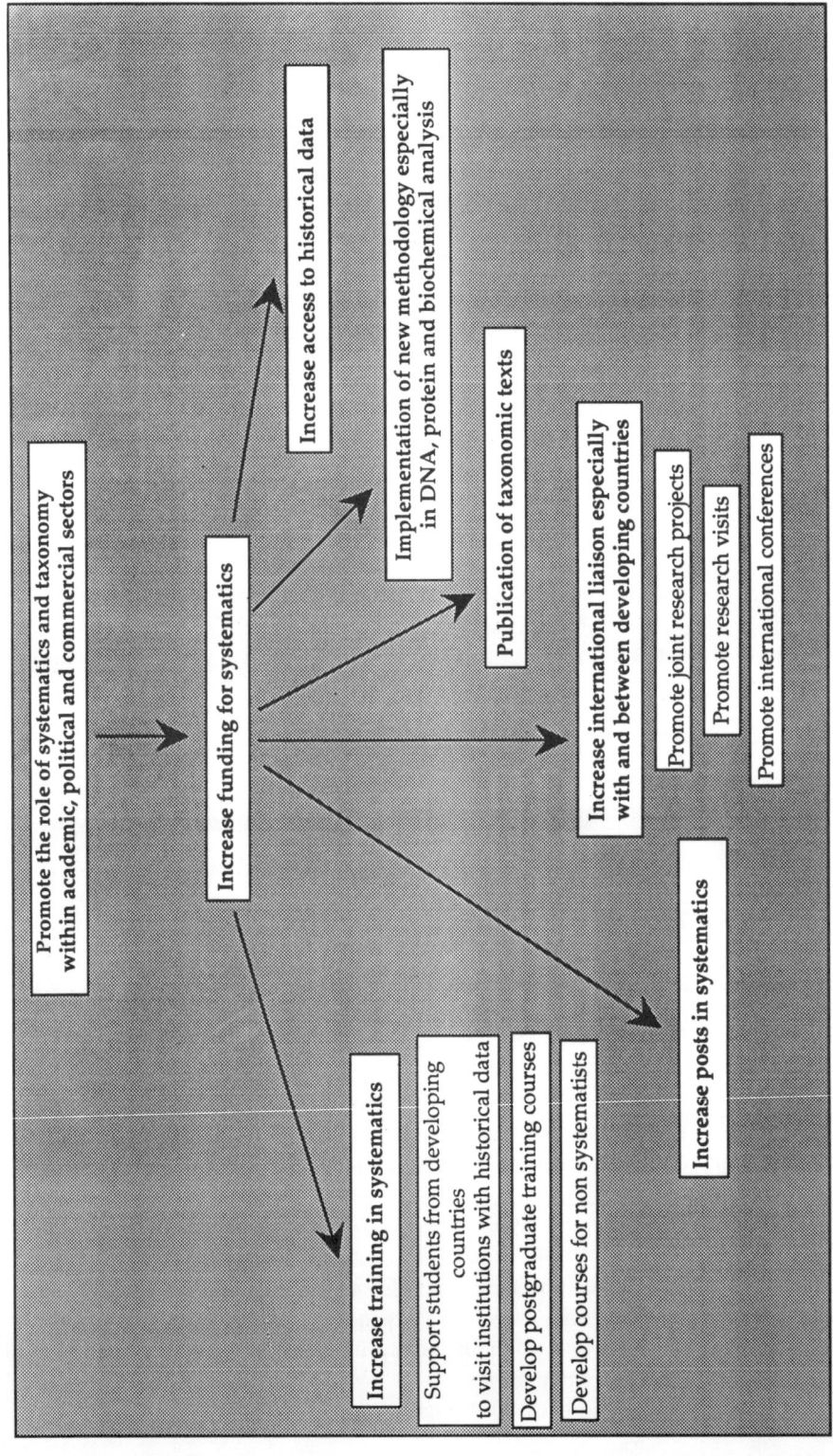

Fig. 12. Diagram illustrating a series of progressions towards taxonomic sufficiency for the Indo-Pacific marine invertebrate fauna.

CLOSING REMARKS

Throughout, I have emphasised the integrative nature of systematics, that a good taxonomy and an understanding of systematics is essential to the progress of many other disciplines especially ecology and conservation biology. Also it should have become clear that taxonomy provides the common framework through which we can compare biodiversity and ensure that we have a common nomenclature. Not only is systematics an integrative discipline within biology it is essentially international in scope. The loss of biodiversity is a global problem, organisms do not respect national boundaries and consequently systematics must be integrative across the scientific community. I therefore hope that the opening of The Swire Marine Laboratory can, just as the workshops held by The University of Hong Kong did, act as a focus for cooperative efforts in all aspects of biology. More particularly, perhaps it can also act a stimulus for a resurgence of funding for systematic research at least in the production of inventories and identification guides to the marine flora and fauna of Hong Kong.

ACKNOWLEDGEMENTS

I would like to thank the following colleagues for their helpful discussion which contributed to the contents of this paper: John Taylor, David Reid, Andy Mackie, Helena Ross and Mary Seddon. I would also like to thank all of the delegates at the conference who provided constructive criticism during and after the discussion period of the lecture.

I would like to thank Prof. Brian Morton for the invitation to give this paper and the National Museum of Wales who financially supported my attendance at the conference.

REFERENCES

Barrett, G.W. 1989. Applied Ecology: An emerging integrative paradigm for the 1990s. *ASC Newsletter* 17(3):37.

Bergquist, P.R., Cambie, R.C. and Kernan, M.R. 1990. Scalarane sesterterpenes from *Collospongia auris*, a new thorectid sponge. *Biochemical Systematics and Ecology* 18:349-57.

Bruce, A.J., 1982. The pontonine shrimp fauna of Hong Kong. In *Proceedings of the First International Marine Biological Workshop: The Marine Fauna and Flora of Hong Kong and Southern China, Hong Kong, 1980* (ed. B. Morton and C.K. Tseng), 233-84. Hong Kong: Hong Kong University Press.

Caddy, J.F.(ed.). 1989. *Marine Invertebrate Fisheries: their assessment and management*. New York: John Wiley and Sons.

Caddy, J.F. 1989. Recent developments in research and management for wild stocks of bivalves and gastropods. In *Marine Invertebrate Fisheries: their assessment and management* (ed. J.F. Caddy), 665-700. New York: John Wiley and Sons.

Christaens, J. 1980. The limpets of Hong Kong with descriptions of seven new species and subspecies. In *Proceedings of the First International Workshop on the Malacofauna of Hong Kong and Southern China, Hong Kong, 1977* (ed. B. Morton), 61-84. Hong Kong: Hong Kong University Press.

Clark. A.M. 1982. Echinoderms of Hong Kong. In *Proceedings of the First International Marine Biological Workshop: The Marine Fauna and Flora of Hong Kong and Southern China,*

Hong Kong, 1980 (ed. B. Morton and C.K. Tseng), 485-502. Hong Kong: Hong Kong University Press.

Cobb, J.S. and Caddy, J.F. 1989. The population biology of decapods. In *Marine Invertebrate Fisheries: Their assessment and management* (ed. J.F. Caddy), 327-374. New York: John Wiley and Sons.

Coyne, J.A., Orr, H.A. and Futuyma, D.J. 1988. Do we need a new species concept? *Systematic Zoology* 37:190-200.

Dessauer, H.C. 1988. A national program to develop, maintain and utilize frozen tissue collections for scientific research. *ASC Newsletter* 16(2):3/9-10.

Erséus, C. 1990. Marine Oligochaeta of Hong Kong. In *Proceedings of the Second International Marine Biological Workshop: The Marine Fauna and Flora of Hong Kong and Southern China, Hong Kong, 1986* (ed. B. Morton), 259-336. Hong Kong: Hong Kong University Press.

Fischer-Piette, E. 1976. Révision des Aviculidées. 1. *Crenatula, Pedalion, Foramelina. Journal de Conchyliologie* 113:3-42.

Fischer-Piette, E. and Mêtivier, B. 1971. Révision des Tapetinae (Mollusques:Bivalves). *Mémoires du Muséum National D'Histoire Naturelle Série A, Zoologie* Tome LXXI.

Foster, B.A. 1982. Shallow water barnacles of Hong Kong. In *Proceedings of the First International Marine Biological Workshop: The Marine Fauna and Flora of Hong Kong and Southern China, Hong Kong, 1980* (ed. B. Morton and C.K. Tseng), 207-32. Hong Kong: Hong Kong University Press.

Gibson, R. 1990. The macrobenthic nemertean fauna of Hong Kong. In *Proceedings of the Second International Marine Biological Workshop: The Marine Fauna and Flora of Hong Kong and Southern China, Hong Kong, 1986* (ed. B. Morton), 33-212. Hong Kong: Hong Kong University Press.

Goto, H.E. 1982. *Animal Taxonomy.* London: Edward Arnold.

Grassle, J. 1979. Polychaete sibling species. In *Aquatic Oligochaete Biology* (ed. R.O. Brinkhurst and D.G. Cook), 25-32. New York: Plenum Press.

Habe, T. 1964. *Shells of the Western Pacific in Colour, Vol II.* Osaka: Hoikushu.

Habe, T. 1977. *Systematics of Mollusca of Japan: Bivalvia and Scaphopoda.* Tokyo: Hokuryukan.

Hill, D.S. 1982. The Leucosiidae (Crustacea:Decapoda) of Hong Kong. In *Proceedings of the First International Marine Biological Workshop: The Marine Fauna and Flora of Hong Kong and Southern China, Hong Kong, 1980* (ed. B. Morton and C.K. Tseng), 195-206. Hong Kong: Hong Kong University Press.

Hirayama, A. 1990. Marine gammaridean Amphipoda from Hong Kong I and II. In *Proceedings of the Second International Marine Biological Workshop: The Marine Fauna and Flora of Hong Kong and Southern China, Hong Kong, 1986* (ed. B. Morton), 449-502. Hong Kong: Hong Kong University Press.

Hoagland, K.E. 1987. ASC, Systematics and Conservation Biology. *ASC Newsletter* 15(4):37.

Hoagland, K.E. 1990. ASC Workshop on systematics resources, training and jobs held at ICSEB IV. *ASC Newsletter* 19(4):53-6.

Horikoshi, M. and Thompson, G.B. 1980. Distribution of subtidal mollusca collected by trawling in Tolo Channel, Hong Kong, with special reference to habitat segregation in two venerid bivalves. In *Proceedings of the First International Workshop on the Malacofauna of Hong Kong and Southern China, Hong Kong, 1977* (ed. B. Morton), 149-62. Hong Hong: Hong Kong University Press.

Humphrey, P.S. 1989. An agenda for graduate education in systematic biology. *ASC Newsletter* 17(5):61-62/64.

Hutchings, P.A. 1990. Terebellidae (Polychaeta) from the Hong Kong region. In *Proceedings of the Second International Marine Biological Workshop: The Marine Fauna and Flora of Hong Kong and Southern China, Hong Kong, 1986* (ed. B. Morton), 377-412. Hong Kong: Hong Kong University Press.

Imajima, M. and Williams, S.J. 1985. Trichobranchidae (Polychaeta) chiefly from the Sagami and Suruga Bays, collected by R/V Tansei-Maru. *Bulletin of the National Science Museum, Tokyo*, Series A, Zoology 11:7-18.

Jensen, K.R. 1985. Annotated checklist of Hong Kong Ascoglossa (Mollusca: Opisthobranchia), with descriptions of four new species. In *Proceedings of the Second International Workshop on the Malacofauna of Hong Kong and Southern China, Hong Kong, 1983* (ed. B. Morton and D. Dudgeon), 77-108. Hong Kong: Hong Kong University Press.

Jensen, K.R. 1990. Three new species of Ascoglossa (Mollusca, Opisthobranchia) from Hong Kong, and a description of the internal anatomy of *Costasiella pallida* Jensen, 1985. In *Proceedings of the Second International Marine Biological Workshop: The Marine Fauna and Flora of Hong Kong and Southern China, Hong Kong, 1986* (ed. B. Morton), 419-32. Hong Kong: Hong Kong University Press.

Kingston, P.F. and Riddle, M. 1989. Cost effectiveness of benthic faunal monitoring. *Marine Pollution Bulletin* 20:490-6.

Kira, T. 1962. *Shells of the Western Pacific in Colour, Vol. I.* Osaka: Hoikushu.

Knutson, L. 1987. Strengthening support for systematics collections and research in developing countries. *ASC Newsletter* 15(4):38-9.

Kott, P. and Goodbody, I. 1982. The ascidians of Hong Kong. In *Proceedings of the First International Marine Biological Workshop: The Marine Fauna and Flora of Hong Kong and Southern China, Hong Kong, 1980* (ed. B. Morton and C.K. Tseng), 503-53. Hong Kong: Hong Kong University Press.

Lam, V.W.W. 1980. Shell form and diagnostic differences in the structure of the siphons and ciliary currents of the ctenidia in coastal species of the Tapetinae (Bivalvia:Veneracea) in Hong Kong. In *Proceedings of the First International Workshop on the Malacofauna of Hong Kong and Southern China, Hong Kong, 1977* (ed. B. Morton), 11-32. Hong Kong: Hong Kong University Press.

Lin, G.Y. 1990. Two new Opisthobranchia from Hong Kong. In *Proceedings of the Second International Marine Biological Workshop: The Marine Fauna and Flora of Hong Kong and Southern China, Hong Kong, 1986* (ed. B. Morton), 433-6. Hong Kong: Hong Kong University Press.

Lin, G.Y. and Qi, Z.Y. 1985. A preliminary survey of the Cephalaspidea (Opisthobranchia) of Hong Kong and adjacent waters. In *Proceedings of the Second International Workshop on the Malacofauna of Hong Kong and Southern China, Hong Kong, 1983* (ed. B. Morton and D. Dudgeon), 109-24. Hong Kong: Hong Kong University Press.

Mackie, A.S.Y. 1984. On the identity and zoogeography of *Prionospio cirrifera* Wirén 1883 and *P. multibranchiata* Berkeley, 1927 (Polychaeta:Spionidae). In *Proceedings of the First International Polychaete Conference, Sydney* (ed. P. Hutchings), 35-47, Linnean Society of New South Wales.

Mackie, A.S.Y. 1990. The Poecilochaetidae and Trochochaetidae (Annelida: Polychaeta) of Hong Kong. In *Proceedings of the Second International Marine Biological Workshop: The Marine Fauna and Flora of Hong Kong and Southern China, Hong Kong, 1986* (ed. B. Morton), 337-65. Hong Kong: Hong Kong University Press.

Mackie, A.S.Y. and Hartley, J.P. 1990. *Prionospio saccifera* sp. nov. (Polychaeta: Spionidae) from Hong Kong and the Red Sea with a redescription of *Prionospio ehlersi* Fauvel, 1928. In *Proceedings of the Second International Marine Biological Workshop: The Marine Fauna and Flora of Hong Kong and Southern China, Hong Kong, 1986* (ed. B. Morton), 363-76. Hong Kong: Hong Kong University Press.

Mak, P.M.S. 1982. The coral associated polychaetes of Hong Kong, with special reference to the serpulids. In *Proceedings of the First International Marine Biological Workshop: The Marine Fauna and Flora of Hong Kong and Southern China, Hong Kong, 1980* (ed. B. Morton and C.K. Tseng), 595-618. Hong Kong: Hong Kong University Press.

Markham, J.C. 1982. Bopyrid isopods parasitic on decapod crustaceans in Hong Kong and Southern China. In *Proceedings of the First International Marine Biological Workshop: The Marine Fauna and Flora of Hong Kong and Southern China, Hong Kong, 1980* (ed. B. Morton and C.K. Tseng), 325-92. Hong Kong: Hong Kong University Press.

Masters, J.C. and Spencer, H.G. 1989. Why we need a new genetic species concept. *Systematic Zoology* 38:270-9.

May, R.M. 1988. How many species are there on earth? *Science* 241 (4872):1441-9

May, R.M. 1990. Taxonomy as destiny. *Nature* 347:129-30.

McMahon, R.F. and Britton, J.C. 1985. The relationship between vertical distribution, thermal tolerance, evaporative water loss rate and behaviour on emergence in six species of mangrove gastropods from Hong Kong. In *Proceedings of the Second International Workshop on the Malacofauna of Hong Kong and Southern China, 1983* (ed. B. Morton and D. Dudgeon), 563-82. Hong Kong: Hong Kong University Press.

Munro, J.L. 1989. Fisheries for giant clams (Tridacnidae:Bivalvia) and prospects for stock enhancement. In *Marine Invertebrate Fisheries:Their assessment and management* (ed. J.F. Caddy), 541-58. New York: John Wiley and Sons.

Nicholson, T.S. 1989. An outline of problems and needs in systematic collections in the next two decades. *ASC Newsletter* 17(1):6-7.

Oliver, P.G. 1990. A new species of *Noetiella* (Bivalvia: Arcacea) from Hong Kong. In *Proceedings of the Second International Marine Biological Workshop: The Marine Fauna and Flora of Hong Kong and Southern China, Hong Kong, 1986* (ed. B. Morton), 413-8. Hong Kong: Hong Kong University Press.

Platt, H.M., Warwick, R.M., Clarke, K.R., Agard, J. and Gobin, J. 1990. Benthic communities and disturbance in a subtropical marine environment. *Progress in Underwater Marine Science* 15:43-54

Pulitzer-Finali, G. 1982. Some shallow water sponges from Hong Kong. In *Proceedings of the First International Marine Biological Workshop: The Marine Fauna and Flora of Hong Kong and Southern China, Hong Kong, 1980* (ed. B. Morton and C.K. Tseng), 97-110. Hong Kong: Hong Kong University Press.

Qi, Z.Y. and Ma, X.T. 1985. A new species of Ovulidae from Hong Kong. In *Proceedings of the Second International Workshop on the Malacofauna of Hong Kong and Southern China, 1983* (ed. B. Morton and D. Dudgeon), 125-6. Hong Kong: Hong Kong University Press.

Reid, D.G. 1986. *The Littorinid Molluscs of Mangrove Forests in the* Indo-Pacific *Region: The Genus Littoraria.* London: British Museum (Natural History).

Reid, D.G. 1990. A cladistic phylogeny of the genus *Littorina* (Gastropoda): implications for evolution of reproductive strategies and for classification. *Hydrobiologia* 193:1-19.

Reid, W.V. 1990. Systematics: A central element of a strategy for conserving biodiversity. *ASC Newsletter* 19(4):61.

Robertson, R. 1985. Archaegastropod biology and the systematics of the genus *Tricolia* (Trochacea: Tricolidae) in the Indo-West-Pacific. *Monographs of Marine Mollusca* No. 3:1-103.

Scudder, G.G.E. 1987. The next 25 years: invertebrate systematics. *Canadian Journal of Zoology* 65:786-93.

Shin, P.K.S. 1982. Some polychaetous annelids from Hong Kong waters. In *Proceedings of the First International Marine Biological Workshop: The Marine Fauna and Flora of Hong Kong and Southern China, Hong Kong, 1980* (ed. B. Morton and C.K. Tseng), 161-72. Hong Kong: Hong Kong University Press.

Shin, P.K.S. 1982. The macrobenthic infauna of Tolo Harbour and Tolo Channel, Hong Kong. In *Proceedings of the First International Marine Biological Workshop: The Marine Fauna and Flora of Hong Kong and Southern China, Hong Kong, 1980* (ed. B. Morton and C.K. Tseng), 721-32. Hong Kong: Hong Kong University Press.

Shin, P.K.S. 1985. A trawl survey of the subtidal Mollusca of Tolo Harbour and Mirs Bay, Hong Kong. In *Proceedings of the Second International Workshop on the Malacofauna of Hong Kong and Southern China, Hong Kong,1983* (ed. B. Morton and D. Dudgeon), 439-48. Hong Kong: Hong Kong University Press.

Shin, P.K.S. 1990. Benthic invertebrate communities in Tolo Harbour and Mirs Bay: A review. In *Proceedings of the Second International Marine Biological Workshop: The Marine Fauna and Flora of Hong Kong and Southern China, Hong Kong, 1986* (ed. B. Morton), 883-98. Hong Kong: Hong Kong University Press.

Tang, C. 1990. Philothalmid larval trematodes from Hong Kong and the coast of South China. In *Proceedings of the Second International Marine Biological Workshop: The Marine Fauna and Flora of Hong Kong and Southern China, Hong Kong, 1986* (ed. B. Morton), 213-32. Hong Kong: Hong Kong University Press.

Tseng, W.Y. and Cheng, W.W. 1982. The economic shrimps of Hong Kong. In *Proceedings of the First International Marine Biological Workshop: The Marine Fauna and Flora of Hong Kong and Southern China, Hong Kong, 1980* (ed. B. Morton and C.K. Tseng), 285-314. Hong Kong: Hong Kong University Press.

Vane-Wright, R.I., Humphries, C.J. and Williams, P.H. in press. What to protect? Systematics and the agony of choice. *Biological Conservation.*

van Belle, R.A. 1982. Supplementary notes on Hong Kong chitons (Mollusca:Polyplacophora). In *Proceedings of the First International Marine Biological Workshop: The Marine Fauna and Flora of Hong Kong and Southern China, Hong Kong, 1980* (ed. B. Morton and C.K. Tseng), 468-84. Hong Kong: Hong Kong University Press.

van Soest, R.W.M. 1982. A small collection of sponges (Porifera) from Hong Kong. In *Proceedings of the First International Marine Biological Workshop: The Marine Fauna and Flora of Hong Kong and Southern China, Hong Kong, 1980* (ed. B. Morton and C.K. Tseng), 85-96. Hong Kong: Hong Kong University Press.

Veron, J.E.N. 1982. Hematypic Scleractinia of Hong Kong — an annotated list of species. In *Proceedings of the First International Marine Biological Workshop: The Marine Fauna and Flora of Hong Kong and Southern China, Hong Kong, 1980* (ed. B. Morton and C.K. Tseng), 111-26. Hong Kong: Hong Kong University Press.

Warwick, R.M. 1988. The level of taxonomic discrimination required to detect pollution effects on marine benthic communities. *Marine Pollution Bulletin* 19:259-68.

Whitehead, P. 1990. Systematics: an endangered species. *Systematic Zoology* 39:179-84.

Wilson, E.O. (ed.) 1988. *Biodiversity*. New York: John Wiley and Sons.

Yipp, M.W. 1985. Tidal rhythms of *Littorina melanostoma* and *L. scabra* in a Hong Kong mangal. In *Proceedings of the Second International Workshop on the Malacofauna of Hong Kong and Southern China, Hong Kong,1983* (ed. B. Morton and D. Dudgeon), 613-22. Hong Kong: Hong Kong University Press.

Yokoyama, H. and Tamai, K. 1981. Four forms of the genus *Paraprionospio* (Polychaeta: Spionidae) from Japan. *Publications of the Seto Marine Biological Laboratory* 26 (4/6):303-17.

Zou, R.L. and Scott, P.J.B. 1982. The Gorgonacea of Hong Kong. In *Proceedings of the First International Marine Biological Workshop: The Marine Fauna and Flora of Hong Kong and Southern China, Hong Kong, 1980* (ed. B. Morton and C.K. Tseng), 135-60. Hong Kong: Hong Kong University Press.

FISHERIES
PLENARY PAPER

The Marine Biology of the South China Sea
(ed. B. Morton). Proceedings of the First
International Conference on the Marine
Biology of Hong Kong and the South China Sea,
Hong Kong, 28 October – 3 November 1990.
Hong Kong: Hong Kong University Press, 1993.

FARMING OF MARINE ALGAE IN CHINA WITH SPECIAL REFERENCE TO THE NORTHERN SOUTH CHINA SEA

C.K. Tseng

Institute of Oceanology, Academia Sinica, Qingdao 266071, China

ABSTRACT

Aquaculture of marine algae commenced in China more than 300 years ago in Jinmen (Quemoy) County, near Xiamen (Amoy), Fujian Province. The seaweed involved was the glueweed, *Gloiopeltis furcata*, and the method involved rock-cleaning. This was followed by the mariculture of the purple laver, *Porphyra haitanensis*, by a similar method about 200 years ago in Pingtan County, also Fujian Province. Modern mariculture of seaweed started in 1952 when the raft cultivation of kelp was initiated in Qingdao for commercial production of the *haidai*, *Laminaria japonica*. This was followed in 1957 by the net-raft commercial cultivation of *Porphyra tenera* at Dalian and of *Porphyra haitanensis* in 1964 in Fujian. Raft cultivation was also effected for *Undaria pinnatifida*, *Gracilaria* spp. and *Kappaphycus alvarezii*. In recent years the agarophyte, *Gelidium amansii*, has also been cultivated on floating rafts. Commercial cultivation of *Eucheuma gelatinae* was initiated in 1960 and the method of cultivation was revised in 1974 by tying the alga with rubber rings to coral chips. It is thus a modified method of rock cultivation. Pond cultivation of *Gracilaria tenuistipitata* var. *liui* was effected in Hainan. For microalgae, pond cultivation is practised. At present, species of *Dunaliella* and *Spirulina* are the only two marine microalgae under large-scale cultivation, the former for beta-carotene, the latter for the entire plant. The microalgae *Isochrysis*, *Phaeodactylum* and *Tetraselmis* are also cultivated. At present, the following 17 taxa in thirteen genera of marine algae are under cultavation in China: 12 taxa of seaweeds, i.e., *Laminaria japonica*, *Undaria pinnaatifida*, *Macrocystis pyrifera*, *Porphyra yezoensis*, *P. haitanensis*, *Gelidium amansii*, *Gracilaria tinuistipitata*, *G. tenuistipitata* var. *liui*, *G. lemaneiformes*, *G. asiatica*, *Eucheuma gelaatinae*, *Kappaphycus alvaarezii*, and five taxa of microalgae, i.e., *Dunaliella salina*, *Isochrysis galbana*, *Phaeodactylum tricornutum*, *Spirulina platensis* and *Tetraselmis subcordiformis*. In the South China Sea, commercial and trial cultivation of eight species including one variety has been effected. The future of marine algae cultivation in the South China Sea region is discussed.

INTRODUCTION

In 1988, China produced 216,415 tons of *Laminaria*, 15,576 tons of *Porphyra* and 12,712 tons of other seaweeds, including *Undaria*, *Gelidium*, *Gracilaria*, and *Eucheuma*, totalling 244,703 tons dry weight (Liang 1990). Richards-Rayadurai (1990), who quoted FAO figures, put world seaweed production at 4 million tons wet weight, of which 1,298,490 tons of brown seaweeds and 155,790 tons of red seaweed came from China. These accounted for 39.6% of the world production and more than the combined production of Japan at 19.3% and South Korea at 11.6%. While China produces only 300 tons of agar and 100 tons of carragenan it produces about 8000 tons of alginate per annum, and is thus next to the US in quantity of phycocolloid production. It may be said that seaweeds and seaweed products are playing an important role in Chinese fisheries.

BEFORE NEW CHINA

Farming of land plants has a history of tens of thousands of years, whereas farming of commercial marine algae or marine phycoculture (Tseng 1981) has a short history of perhaps three or four hundred years. Marine algal farming probably started in the Orient, especially in China and Japan where seaweeds have long been appreciated as food.

In China, the first seaweed cultivated was undoubtedly the glueweed, *Gloiopeltis furcata* (Tseng 1933), which grows abundantly in Jinmen County near Xiamen. Glueweed has been appreciated by the Chinese people both as food and for sizing silk since the Song dynasty about 1000 years ago. At least three or four hundred years ago, the people of Jinmen County cultivated the glueweed by a simple 'rock cleaning' method. This was effected by scraping weeds from littoral rocks at certain times of the year, generally in late autumn, to provide places for the glueweed 'seeds' to settle. Although the people had never seen the 'seeds' they were keen observers and by means of trial and error finally mastered the art of production of glueweed by this simple method of enhancing production. Jinmen County was able to produce about half of China's total production of glueweed.

Later, about two hundred years ago, the people of Pingtan County, on Haitan Island, in eastern Fujian Province, applied a similar method for cultivating the highly desired purple laver (*Porphyra* spp.) (Tseng and Chang 1956). It is suspected that they had learned the rock-cleaning method of cultivation from the people of Jinmen. As in the case of the glueweed, they knew nothing about the *Porphyra* 'seeds' but learned by trial and error that the 'seeds' of *Porphyra* emerged from the sea a few days before White Dew, the 15th Chinese Solar Term occurring on about 15 September, before which the rocks had to be cleaned to receive the 'seeds'. This kind of enhancing production of the purple laver, like that of the glueweed, was very effective and made Pingtan County the production center for purple laver in China. This method differs from that of modern phycoculture, however, in that people had to depend upon nature for the 'seeds', which they had never seen.

In 1927, the Japanese kelp, *Laminaria japonica*, was introduced accidentally from Japan to China and cultivated by traditional Japanese methods on stones and rocks in the sublittorol region. Fertile kelps were placed close to the stones and rocks so that the shed zoospores would adhere to the rocks. In the 1940s, *Undaria pinnatifida* was introduced to Qingdao and a similar method of cultivation was employed. This was the condition of china's seaweed farming in old China.

AFTER THE ESTABLISHMENT OF THE PEOPLE'S REPUBLIC OF CHINA

Farming of seaweeds in New China has undergone a rapid change and, beginning in 1952 by employing a new device, the floating raft method, kelp cultivation was placed on a solid scientific basis, especially with the innovation of the summer sporelings low temperature cultivation method, new fertilizer application methods, southward transplantation etc. Success in the kelp cultivation industry was followed by that in the purple laver cultivation industry. Today, besides *Laminaria* and *Porphyra*, *Undaria*, *Macrocystis*, *Gracilaria*, *Eucheuma* and *Kappaphycus* have also been cultivated on the basis of their respective biological characteristics. The three microalgae, *Isochrysis*, *Phaeodactylum* and *Tetraselmis*, have also been cultivated for feeds for marine animals similarly under cultivation. With the help of biotechnology, experimental tissue culture of *Gelidium* and *Porphyra* has yielded good results. In recent years, large scale cultivation of the microalgae *Dunaliella* and *Spirulina* has been quite successful and this industry is beginning to take shape. Thus, to date, the thirteen economically important marine algae: *Laminaria*, *Undaria*, *Macrocystis*, *Porphyra*, *Gelidium*, *Gracilaria*, *Eucheuma*, *Kappaphycus*, *Dunaliella*, *Isochrysis*, *Phaeodactylum*, *Spirulina* and *Tetraselmis* are under cultivation. It will not be too long before seaweeds such as *Gloiopeltis* will join the list of economically successful phycoculture species.

The scientific basis for commercial cultivation of marine algae

The substratum

For unicellular and filamentous algae which grow floating in water, the substratum is water. Ponds and tanks are specially built to limit these algae within enclosures. They may be of different areas but, generally, 20 to 50 and 100 m^2 are more convenient.

For multicellular benthic algae, the seaweeds, the situation is more complicated. They have rhizoids which, unlike roots, are not the only organs for the absorption of water and nutrients, since this function is shared by all parts of the seaweeds immersed in the aquatic medium. The substratum serves merely to provide a suitable attachment site. Yet substrate selection is important in other ways, such as convenience, availability, durability and economics. There are two general kinds of substrate, the natural and the artificial, the former including rocks and stones, and the latter rafts made up of ropes of natural or synthetic fibres. In both cases, however, the spore-liberating fronds must be brought close enough to the substratum so that the spores liberated may have the best chance to adhere to it (Tseng 1981).

Chinese mariculturists for some years used ropes made of either hemp or palm fibres for artificial substrates. These had to be soaked in water for quite some time in order to leach out undesirable substances in the natural fibres. In the course of development of the seaweed industry, it was noted that natural fibres had a number of defects, and so in the early 1960s synthetic fibres were introduced. At present, most of the ropes used in the seaweed industry are made of synthetic fibres.

Temperature

Temperature is one of the most important factors controlling the activities of marine algae. Every species (or phase in the life history of the species) has its maximal, optimal, and minimal temperature for growth and development. Differences in the various phases are particularly conspicuous;in some cases the sporophyte phase has a higher and the gametophyte phase a lower optimal growth temperature whereas in other cases the reverse is true. For instance, in the case of *Porphyra yezoensis*, the optimal temperature gradually decreases from 20°C for the germination of conchospores to 18–20°C for germlings of less than 100 cells, to 14–18°C for the small leafy thalli about 1–2 cm tall. During the low temperature (lower than 5–6°C) winter season, the growth of small leafy thalli is very slow. The large leafy thalli, however, have a much lower optimal growth temperature and over-wintered thalli have an incredibly low optimal temperature of 3–5°C, according to observation made at Qingdao. It is therefore critical that the seeding of conchospores takes place not too late in the season to allow sufficient growth so as to avoid passing through the winter with small leafy thalli (IOEP 1976; IOESP 1978).

In the case of *Laminaria japonica*, four stages of growth and development have been differentiated. The first is the juvenile sporeling stage, which includes the zygote to a sporeling a few centimetres long but before the clear differentiation of the basal growth zone. The second is the young sporophyte stage, characterized by vigorous growth in frond length. The third is the robust sporophyte stage, characterized by a large increase in thickness and dry weight. The fourth is the mature sporophyte stage, characterized by the formation of sporangial sori. The four different stages of growth and development have different temperature requirements, a thorough understanding of which is indispensible to successful cultivation. In the juvenile sporeling stage, the optimal growth temperature is lower than 20°C, dropping to about 15°C. In the second young sporophyte stage, the temperature requirement tends to be lower than that in the previous stage, and for growth in frondal length, the optimal temperature is 5–10°C, at which all plants grow best regardless of size. At 1–5°C and 10–13°C all plants show good growth in length, but smaller plants less than 2.5 m long generally grow better than the larger ones. In the third robust stage, growth in length becomes less important, and gives way to increase in thickness and dry weight. There is an upward shift in the optimum temperature to between 13–20°C. In the fourth stage the sporophyte becomes mature and produces numerous sporangial sori and generally no growth occurs (Tseng 1981; Zeng 1984).

Light

Light is a basic environmental factor in the normal activities of marine algae. Each species has an optimal light intensity for its vegetative growth. Thus, for example, in the indoor cultivation of the filamentous conchocelis stage of *Porphyra yezoensis*, light intensity is controlled by a series of screens since the optimal intensity for its growth is about 3000 lux in the middle of the day from early May to early July. Beginning in early July and lasting until late August or early September, which is the critical period for conchosporangial production, the maximal light intensity is further reduced to 750 lux. Beginning in late August to early September, the light intensity is still held at 750 lux but the light period is further reduced to 8–10 hours per day by artificially darkening the culture rooms. Under such conditions conchospores appear in late September and their mass discharge generally takes place in early October (IOESP 1978).

In the same way that the sporophyte phase of *Porphyra* (the conchocelis) is its summer stage, the gametophyte phase of *Laminaria* is its summer stage and grows best at 3000–4000 lux. A juvenile sporophyte smaller than approximately 800 μm also has its best growth at 3000–4000 lux but afterwards when it grows to over 1 cm in length it becomes unhealthy and dies, whereas those cultivated below 2000 lux grow well (Wu 1962). The number of days required for the gametophyte to effect sexual reproduction and develop to the sporophyte is inversely proportional to the number of hours of illumination per day. For example when the illumintion is 2 h per day, it takes 44 days for the sporophyte to appear and 54 days for the sporophytes to reach 50% of the total number of gametophytes, but when the illumination is 19 h per day, it takes only 8 days to develop to the sporophytes and 11 days for the sporophytes to reach 50% of the total number of gametophytes (Tseng 1981). It was also discovered that a certain dark period is necessary for the discharge of eggs and sperm in *Laminaria* gametophytes. In general, about one hour of total darkness is required for this discharge (Tseng *et al.* 1959).

Inorganic nutrients

In the early 1950s, kelp cultivation in China was confined to the vicinity of sewage outflows and harbours in a few cities, such as Dalian, Yantai and Qingdao. Experiments with growing kelp in the so-called outer sea regions such as Taipingjiao of Qingdao failed. It was found that the nitrogenous nutrient concentration was rather low, generally less than 5 mg of nitrate nitrogen and less than 50 mg of total nitrogen, including ammonium salts·m^3 seawater. Under these cirumstances there was a need for fertilizer and this was first effected by the clay bottle method of application. Thus, in the late 1950s and early 1960s, unglazed clay bottles containing a solution of the desired nitrogenous fertilizer, usually ammonium sulphate, were hung at certain intervals on the raft. The porosity of the clay bottles effectively controlled diffusion of the fertilizer which became available to the kelp in the immediate vicinity and loss into the open sea was minimized. Under these contitions, kelp was grown commercially in formerly infertile regions of the Yellow Sea (Tseng and Wu 1966; Tseng 1981). In the 1960s, the area of cultivation became larger and kelp farms extended to several hectares, even several tens of hectares per farm, and the limitations of this method became evident. Experiments showed that nitrogen-starved fronds of kelp were able to absorb large quantities of fertilizer in a relatively short time and that this was sufficient to provide for the need of the plant for some time (Wu *et al.* 1959; Tseng *et al.* 1962). A 'soaking method' was therefore devised to immerse the kelp fronds in fertilizer solution once every several days, and some good results were obtained (Wu 1962). This method, however, is practical only with small fronds since, soaking cultivation ropes, each overgrown with 30 or more kelp fronds a few metres in length, is a very laborious job. Later, periodic sprinkling of fertilizer solution using manual labour was practised and, finally, a mechanical spraying method was developed, which is time-saving and effective. It is now the standard method of fertilizer application. The spraying of fertilizer solution to a given raft occurs once every one or two days, and spraying from a fertilizer boat rotates among the different rafts of a farm. Since a kelp farm is generally of a large size, usually several tens of hectares, the sprayed fertilizer solution remains in the area for some time and the loss to the open sea is not serious (Tseng 1981).

In the case of purple laver cultivation, the farms are classified into three groups on the basis of the nitrogenous nutrient content of the sea water. The first group has less than 50 mg of total nitrogenous nutrients·m^3 of seawater; this is regarded as infertile for purple laver cultivation and in order to cultivate purple laver there, nitrogenous fertilizers must be supplied by spraying. The second group has about 100 mg of total nitrogenous nutrients·m^3 of seawater; this is regarded as semifertile and is able to support the growth of the purple laver, producing products of medium grade if the seawater is not fertilized. The third group has either 200 mg or more of total nitrogenous nutrients·m^3 of seawater and is regarded as fertile; no fertilizer application is necessary and the product is of high quality and with good colour and taste (IOEP 1976; IOESP 1978; Tseng 1981).

Algal weeds

Like land-based agriculture, marine phycoculture also has its weed problems. In the case of kelp cultivation, traditional spore collecting takes place in autumn, generally in mid-October in the Qingdao region and the resulting sporelings are known as autumn sporelings. When the seeded ropes were placed in the sea, the spores of such weed algae as *Ectocarpus*, *Enteromorpha* and *Licmophora* would quickly adhere to them and within a few days grow to macroscopic thalli, densely covering the kelp gametophytes on the ropes. Under normal conditions, the kelp spores take about 20 days to germinate, pass through the gametophyte phase, and give rise to young sporophytes. Before this, however, the kelp gametophytes would be covered by various weed algae and, because of the lack of sufficient light, they were unable to proceed with their normal development. Thus, it would be in December, when the weed algae had matured and dropped away from the seeding ropes, that the kelp sporophytes would appear. They generally grew to transplantation size of 10–15 cm by January–February and so transplantation of the sporelings to the cultivation ropes would have to take place in the coldest season of the year. When summer sporelings are cultivated in artificially cooled seawater of about 10°C, spore collection takes place in early summer instead of mid-autumn and in about 12 days the spores germinate and develop to sporelings which grow without any interference from the nuisance weed algae. By autumn, when the seawater temperature drops to about 20°C, the seeding cords are taken out and put into the sea. Spores of the weed algae, of course, would also adhere to the spore-cords but they grow much more slowly than the sporophytes and the young sporophytes grow readily to transplantation size in a month or so. Transplantation will therefore take place in November–December when the working conditions are much better with water temperatures of about 10°C. There is also the advantage of at least two months extra growth, resulting in an increased production of 30–50% or more (Tseng *et al.* 1955a; Tseng 1986).

The algal weed problem in purple laver cultivation is much more complicated. The attachment of weed algae, such as *Monostroma*, *Enteromorpha*, *Urospora* and *Licmophora,* may be prevented by three methods. First, in the seeding process, the attached spores of the purple laver should be packed as densely as possible so that there will be little space for the spores of the weed algae. Second, in the manipulation of the cultivation nets, care should be taken not to scrape off the germlings. Third, in the harvesting process, attention should be paid to see that only large thalli are harvested and smaller thalli left intact. When there are already quantities of weed algae growing on the nets, the method of control is to expose the nets to the sun for a definite number of hours. The weed algae are more susceptible to desiccation than the purple laver. With the correct amount of exposure to the air, the weed algae can be killed and the purple laver left intact (IOEP 1976, IOESP 1978; Tseng 1981).

Disease

With the domestication of a wild plant, followed by its large-scale commercial cultivation, the new crop plant is inevitably sooner or later attacked by some diseases. Three different types of diseases have been recognized—physiological, pathogenic and pests.

The most common physiological diseases in kelp cultivation are green rot and white rot diseases, both related to light intensity. Green rot usually occurs in over-crowded fronds and it starts with the lower plants on the cultivation ropes, gradually extending upwards. The marginal portions of the diseased fronds turn greenish, become soft, decay, and disintegrate. Afterwards, the apical parts are involved, and finally the entire frond succumbs. This is due to the lack of available light to the fronds and can be controlled by inverting the cultivation ropes so that the lower over-shaded fronds can receive more light (Zhang *et al.* 1962; Tseng 1981). White rot, on the other hand, is due to excessive light and generally starts from the upper fronds downwards, especially in places where the water is not fertile enough. It is believed that a combination of three factors is involved: strong light, high water temperature and low nutrient content. To control this disease, it is recommended that the cultivation level be lowered and fertilizer applied (Zhang *et al.* 1962; Tseng 1981).

The most common pathogenic disease involves malformed sporelings, characterized by plasmolyzed oogonia, which subsequently die and drop off the cultivation ropes. It was concluded that the malformation was due to the presence of hydrogen sulphide in the culture solution as a result of the activities of sulphate-reducing bacteria and hydrogen sulphide-producing saprophyticbacteria such as *Micrococcus*. Control of the disease is effected by separating the sporeling cultivation system from the mature sporophyte cultivating system and by sterilizing the water system with bleaching powder before the spore-collecting process (Wu *et al.* 1979).

Another well-studied case is the 'frond-twist' disease of raft-cultivated kelp, first observed in the winter of 1973 in the Dalian region, North Yellow Sea. The diseased plants had abnormally twisted fronds with greatly swollen stipes and very much shortened rhizoidal holdfasts. Carefully planned experiments on contact infection confirmed the contagious nature of the disease with a rather long latent period of 60-70 days (Li *et al.* 1981). Electron microscopic examination showed that the pathogens involved is a mycoplasm-like organism (Wang *et al.* 1980).

Alginic acid-decomposing bacteria were found to be the dominating bacterial inhabitants of the fronds of the cultivated kelp. The bacteria as well as the crude enzyme preparation were observed to be able to decompose the fronds in 3-5 days (Chen *et al.* 1979). Further studies of the alginic acid-decomposing bacteria showed that they were the causative factor of the common destructive falling-off disease of the summer sporelings.

In mariculture of the purple laver, an etiological study of the green rot disease was conducted and the pathogenic bacteria isolated were found to belong to the genus *Pseudomonas*. The purple laver fronds inoculated with these bacteria were quickly attacked and irregular green spots occurred in two days (Chen *et al.* 1983). In the early 1950s, when autumn sporelings were collected, fronds of the kelp had to be oversummered in deep water and grazing by sea urchins was a serious problem. Similarly, during the cultivation of purple laver and *Kappaphycus* in Guangdong and Hainan provinces, certain herbivorous fish feeding on them is a very serious problem.

Genetic improvement and breeding of new strains

Genetic studies of the natural stock of the Japanese kelp in China showed its hybrid nature. This conclusion was derived from the following experimental evidence: (1), under the same environmental conditions gametophytes can have somewhat different morphologies and growth rates; (2), different female gametophytes react differently under X-ray treatment; (3), different gametophytes react differently to temperature and (4), partheno-sporophytes have different morphologies and growth rates. It has also been proved that frond length, frond thickness, stipe length and even the iodine content of the kelp under cultivation are all quantitative characteristics controlled by both environmental factors and poly-genes (Fang 1983).

The above evidence forms the basis for selection work. Since the Japanese kelp is a hybrid, it can be subjected to selection and X-ray treatment during breeding to develop more desirable strains. It has been pointed out that the harmful effect of continual inbreeding is relative and conditional; in some inbred lines there are harmful effects, while in others no harmful effects are found. Therefore Chinese geneticists have employed methods of continual inbreeding and selection in developing new strains. In the inbreeding process, single fronds of the kelp are used to produce the zoospores instead of several fronds as in the commercial production of the summer sporelings. In this way, the gametophytes and the resulting sporophytes all come from one single kelp frond (Fang 1983).

In the 1960s, three strains of kelp were selected, one with broad fronds, one with long fronds and one with thick fronds. In the 1970s, two strains with both high production and high iodine content were selected. The selection of the high iodine content characteristic was effected by the so-called half-frond method. In 1970, Chinese phycologists conducted large scale selection work in the nine cultivation regions of the five coastal provinces. They selected many mature fronds and, using half of the frond for iodine anslysis, they found 19 plants with high production and high iodine content. The other half of each of these plants was left to mature and eventually zoospores were collected from them. Breeding was carried out by repeated inbreeding and selection and then the offspring of a single frond were treated by X-radiation. After a few years of cultivation and examination of genetic characteristics, two new strains with high production and high iodine content were successfully produced. These answered better to the demand of the industry and are now under cultivation in large areas where they have won the approval of the kelp farmers (IOC & QMF 1976). Recently a hybrid between these two strains has been bred successfully; it shows even higher production rates and a higher iodine content.

Recent studies have shown that kelp partheno-sporophytes can complete their life-histories without the help of any male gametophyte. It is therefore suggested that the monoecious sporophyte of the Japanese kelp is really dioecious in nature. It is also suggested that there might be a sex chromosome in the gametophytic cells. No high percentage of natural doubling of chromosome number from haploid to diploid has been observed in any higher plant. The success in monocloning the haploid gametophyte phases makes *Laminaria* desirable for further genetic investigation (Fang 1983).

Fundamental types of algal mariculture techniques

The success of the commercial cultivation of economically valuable algae depends upon good culturing techniques that may differ to some extent from country to country and region to region. The scientific bases for successful algal mariculture should be universal, but the techniques actually used should be adapted to the specific conditions concerned. A certain technique may be successful in one place but a total failure in another. The techniques now popularly employed in China in the commercial cultivation of the Japanese kelp are, so far, a success and account for an increase in production from a mere 10 tons dry weight in 1952, when the raft method was first initiated, to a peak of over 250,000 tons dry weight in recent years. But if these same techiques were to be introduced into the United States, the result could be a total failure because of economic and other differences. There are three fundamental types of algal mariculture, the rock and stone type, the pond type and the raft type.

The rock and stone type

This type of algal mariculture is the primitive and archaic type which originated several hundred years ago in the southern part of Fujian Province. It was first employed to enhance the production of the glueweed *Gloiopeltis furcata* in Jinmen (Quemoy) County, near Xiamen (Amoy) City. The rocks were cleaned by scraping, just before the growing season of the glueweed. The loosened material was carried away by tides and on the following day lime was sprayed on the cleaned rocks to make more complete the destruction of the invading seaweeds, barnacles and other forms of life. The glueweed first apears in November and matures in about two months. However harvesting of the glueweed is not formally started until March (Tseng 1933).

The same method has also been employed in the production of purple laver in eastern Fujian Province for the last two to three hundred years, somewhat later than the glueweed. It is probable that the people of Pingtan County where this originated borrowed the idea from those of Jinmen County. The rocks are cleaned generally before 24 August. Limewater spraying takes place once or twice, or occasionally thrice, between 24 August and 8 September. On the basis of long years of experience, three different kinds of rocks are distinguished which are classified on the basis of the appearance time of the purple laver. First, there are the 'early purple laver rocks', facing north or northeast and vigorously washed by stormy waves; germlings of the purple laver appear on these rocks in early September. Second, there are the 'mid purple laver rocks', facing east or southeast and also washed by stormy waves; germlings of the purple laver appear somewhat later, generally in late September. Third, there are the 'late purple laver rocks', facing west, southwest or northwest, and hardly washed by the stormy waves; germlings appear generally after early October (Tseng and Chang 1956).

Formerly, the algal farmers depended on nature for the 'seeds' of the purple laver. At present, they spray sea water containing conchospores over the cleaned rocks. Harvesting the seaweed may start in late October for the early purple laver rocks, in early November for the mid purple laver rocks and in late November for the late purple laver rocks. Afterwards, harvesting may take place once every two weeks. Purple lavers of the earlier harvest up to February are most tender in texture and more delicious in taste and sell for a better price. Purple lavers of the later harvest after February are coarser in texture, not as delicious in taste and sell for a lower price. The purple laver of the later harvest now serves as raw materials, used for the extraction of agar.

Production of *Eucheuma gelatinae* in Hainan is simple. First, 'seed' thalli are selected; they must be thick, sturdy and without epiphytes. These thalli are then divided up into branch systems, about 40 such systems from each kilogram of the thalli. The 'seeds' are tied to a branch of dead coral by means of rubber rings and scattered on a selected sea bottom at a density of about 75,000 branches per hectare. Arrangement of the 'seed' thalli on the sea bottom is done by professional divers, and harvesting is conducted once a year (Tseng 1981).

In the cultivation of the kelps *Laminaria* and *Undaria*, the traditional way was to throw stones into the subtidal regions when zoospores of these kelps were released. The stones provided places for the zoospores to settle and germinate. This was the way that the kelps were propagated in the 1930s and 1940s. At present, cultivation ropes made of synthetic fibres hanging from floating ropes are employed as the substrate for the kelp sporelings. However, in places like Dalian, stone throwing is still practiced to increase natural growth of the kelp.

The pond type

This is the current method of cultivating the microalgae *Dunaliella*, *Isochrysis*, *Phaeodactylum*, *Spirulina* and *Tetraselmis* and the macroalgae *Gracilaria*. The ponds are generally rectangular in shape from about 20 m² to about one tenth of a hecture in area. They are from 20 cm to 80 cm or 100 cm in depth, depending upon the algae under cultivation. For commercial purposes the ponds are generally uncovered and covered only when raining, manually or mechanically stirred.

A *Dunaliella* farm for beta-carotene was started in 1984 in a salt field at Tianjin (Tientsin). At present the total area of production is 14,000 m² with 3 different kinds of tanks, 1,350 m², 500 m² and 10 m², all rectangular in shape. The ponds are lined with a plastic membrane to prevent contact of the culture solution with the soil. Stirring is effected by rotating wheels, and brine water of 15–20 Be is used for the cultivation to enhance the production of carotene and to inhibit multiplication of pests in the open cultures. Carbon dioxide is employed both as the carbon source and to regulate the pH. High salinity is necessary for *Dunaliella* to produce more carotene; when it rains, therefore, plastic film is used to cover the tanks. It floats on the water, thus separating the rain water from the culture solution and, by means of a specially built sluice gate, the rain water automatically drains off. The plastic film can be recovered mechanically. When the *Dunaliella* has reached a certain concentration it is harvested by a gas floatation method. A coagulating agent is added and a specially designed gas float equipment is employed. Two types of this equipment have been devised, a 3.5 $m^3 \cdot h^{-1}$ and a 30 $m^3 \cdot h^{-1}$ model. A carotene extraction experimental workshop with an annual production of 100–200 kg has been designed and four kinds of products are produced for food grade natural colour: (1), 1.5% carotene in oil solution; (2), 30% carotene in oil suspension; (3), carotene in crystalline form and (4) 1–24% water soluble carotene powder.

Isochrysis, Phaeodactylum, Spirulina, and *Tetraselmis* are microalgae which have been cultivated indoors to serve as feeds for marine animals, especially the juveniles of scallops, shrimps and other animals. They are generally cultured in tanks of 10–20 m^2 or more which are stirred manually from time to time. Because of the present large-scale production of scallops and shrimps in China, these microalgae (except *Spirulina*) are widely cultivated in all the maritime provinces of China. In the early 1960s when China was suffering from agricultural difficulties, *Tetraselmis* was cultivated in salt water fields of several hectares to see if production for human consumption was feasible. This was given up, however, because the agricultural crisis was soon over and it was also found to be economically impossible because of the high cost of harvesting and drying involved. Trial experiments for *Spirulina* cultivation on a large scale were started only a few years ago. *Spirulina* has very high protein content, mostly 60–70%, and is highly appreciated as a health food. As an animal feed it is unexcelled because of its high protein content. However, for ordinary marine animals it is far too expensive but, for the juvenile stages of the more expensive forms such as shrimps, abalones and scallops, *Spirulina* has been employed successfully. Cultivation methods for these microalgae are similar, generally consisting of a series of cement tanks or earthern dugouts lined with a plastic membrane or film.

Pond culture is also employed in the commercial cultivation of macroalgae such as *Gracilaria*. In China, cultivation of *Gracilaria* started in 1958 in different provinces by using raft and split bamboo culture. Unit area production was less than 2 tons dry algae per hectare. It is labour-intensive and has difficulty competing against other more profitable businesses. Cultivation of *Gracilaria* started in Taiwan in 1962 as a pond culture, and unit area production was about 10 tons per hectare, 5 times that of raft culture and split bamboo culture in mainland China. According to Shang (1976), the polyculture ponds of Taiwan Province on the average yielded 9 tons *Gracilaria* and 6.3 tons of grass shrimp and crab per hectare. Total annual production was about $4438, yielding a profit of $2381·ha^{-1}. The production cost, according to Shang was only $135·t^{-1} comparing favourably with the import price from Japan ($500·t^{-1}). It was therefore concluded that 'the culture and export of raw *Gracilaria* to Japan appears to be a profitable business'(Shang 1976). *Gracilaria* grows most rapidly in waters of about 25‰ salinity and at temperature of 20–25°C and the plant begins to die when salinity exceeds 35‰. Therefore, in the cultivation of *Gracilaria*, fresh water should be available for diluting seawater where increases in salinity can occur due to evaporation. The ponds are usually rectangular in shape and one hectare in area. The depth of water in the ponds is generally 20–30 cm during March to June and, after June, 60–80 cm. *Gracilaria* fragments are introduced to the ponds in April at a density of 5000 kg·ha^{-1}. They are strewn evenly on the bottom and held in place either with upright bamboo sticks fixed to the bottom, or the plants may be covered with old fish nets to prevent them from drifting. The best planting time is early or late in the day and in cloudy weather. Water in the pond is exchanged every 2–3 days after planting. Weeds must be removed at least three times a year. Milkfish and tilapias are usually stocked at about 300–400 fish·ha^{-1} in the *Gracilaria* ponds, not for profit, but to browse on and control the green and bluegreen algae. When these weeds are consumed the fish should be removed to prevent them from eating the *Gracilaria*. The ponds are usually fertilized with urea or fermented pig manure to accelerate growth of the plants. The harvesting period ranges from June to November and takes place every 10 days by hand or by the use of scoop nets. Harvesting stops after November since the plants stop growing between December and March. Harvested plants are washed and sundried and about 7 kg of the plants yield 1 kg of dry seaweed (Shang 1976).

This tank type of cultivation is also used for the culture of the juveniles of marine algae with a biphasic type of life history in which one is microscopic, such as the conchocelis phase of *Porphyra* and the gametophytic phase of *Laminaria*.

This conchocelis of *Porphyra* may be cultured free-living or on the shells of various molluscs. Culture of the free living conchocelis is similar to ordinary microbial culture. In the case of growth on shells, cultivation takes place in large shallow indoor concrete tanks containing sea water 20–30 cm in depth. The seawater has previously been subjected to sedimentation in the dark for a few days and nitrogenous and phosphate nutrients added. Water temperature is not controlled but light intensity is controlled by a series of screens to give best growth for the conchocelis and to produce the maximal number of conchospores per unit area. For the seeding process, nets are placed in the tank with shells and water is agitated to help liberation of the conchospores (IOEP 1976; IOESP 1978).

In the case of *Laminaria* gametophytes, the partially air-dried fronds of the mature sporophytes are placed in water 10–15 cm deep in elongated concrete tanks in a specially built greenhouse. The pressure resulting from the quick absorption of water breaks the sporangial wall and liberates large masses of zoospores. When a sufficient number of zoospores have been obtained, the parent fronds are taken out, new water added and the spore collectors, in the form of frames with seeding cords, are placed in the spore water and the actively swimming zoospores soon adhere to the collectors, thus completing the seeding process. These seeding frames are arranged in shallow tanks containing sea water previously cooled to 8–10°C and enriched with nitrogenous and phosphate nutrients. The seeded frames, eventually with young sporophytes, remain in the cool house until mid-October when the seawater temperature drops to about 20°C and the juvenile sporophytes are about 1–2 cm high. These summer sporelings are then sold to the kelp farmers who will bring them to their own farms and hang them on rafts set for kelp cultivation (Tseng 1981).

The raft type

A raft is a flat structure of logs and ropes fastened together and floated on water. In aquaculture there are two general types of floating rafts, the net type and the long line type, the former for principally tidal forms such as *Porphyra* and the latter for principally subtidal forms such as *Laminaria*, *Undaria*, *Eucheuma* and *Gelidium*.

In the net-raft for *Porphyra* cultivation, three methods have been practiced in China, the pillar method, the semi-floating raft method and the floating raft method (Fig. 1)

In the pillar method, pillars are driven into the ground to serve as supports for the cultivation nets which are fastened tightly to the pillars with short binding cords at a definite level within the tidal range and are held in this fixed position. This is the fixed type method. In places with a greater tidal range, the net is furnished on its upper surfaces with cylindrical floats made of bamboo or synthetic pipes. It is fastened to the poles at a definite level within the tidal range by binding cords of a certain length so that the net can go up and down, floating on the water surface with the change of tidal levels within a definite range, controlled by the length of the binding cords (Fig. 1A).

The intertidal semi-floating raft cultivation method is an improvement made in China to take the place of the pillar method, combining the strong points of the pillar method and the floating method, especially for intertidal organisms. At high tide, the raft floats on the water, giving the *Porphyra* the opportunity of receiving sufficient light and at low tide the raft rests on the ground by short legs (Fig. 1B). By this method, the sporelings appear earlier and grow better, and the final production is about double the production by the pillar method.

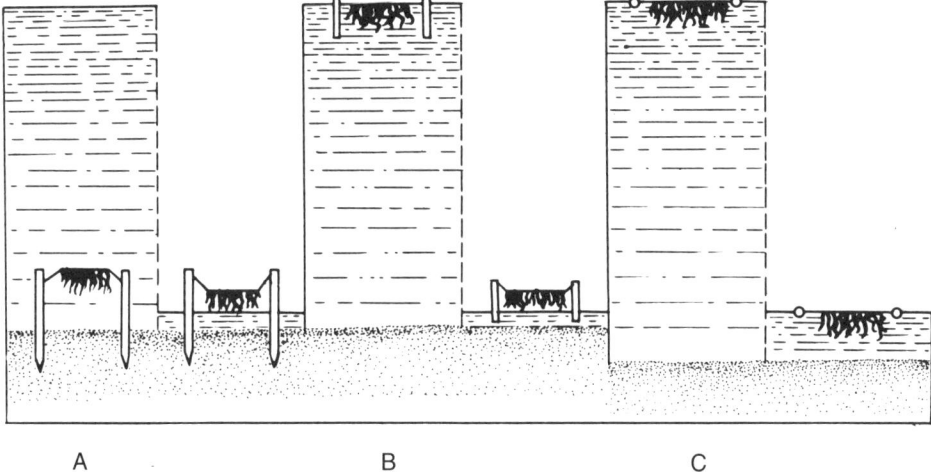

Fig. 1. Diagrammatic sections of the three methods of *Porphyra* cultivation. A, Lift type of the pillar method. B, Semifloating method. C, Floating method. Note that in each of the methods, the diagram on the left represents the position of the net at high tide and that on the right represents its position at low tide (after IOEP 1976).

The floating raft method is adapted for production of *Porphyra* in deep water in subtidal regions (Fig. 1C). The floating rafts, made of synthetic fibres, are 60 m long and 180 cm broad with an elongate anchor rope 18.25 m long. The method is similar to the cultivation of kelp in which there are many kelp ropes hanging down from the floating rope. The germination of the conchospores and the growth of the sporelings are not as good as in the intertidal region and, when the sporelings reach 1–3 cm in length, the nets are cultivated by the floating method (IOEP 1976; IOESP 1978).

The floating raft method for kelp cultivation consists of a long rope made of synthetic fibre, which is 1–1.5 cm in diameter and 30–60 m long, attached to two wooden stakes with two anchor cables also made of synthetic fibre about 2 cm in diameter. The main floating rope is kept afloat with bamboo or glass balls 15–20 cm in diameter. The cultivation ropes are also of synthetic fibres, 8 mm in diameter and 1–1.5 m in length. They are attached to the floating rope and a stone or some other weight is attached to the lower end of the cultivation rope to keep it from floating to the surface with the kelps. In general, to each cultivation rope are attached 30 kelps. The distance between

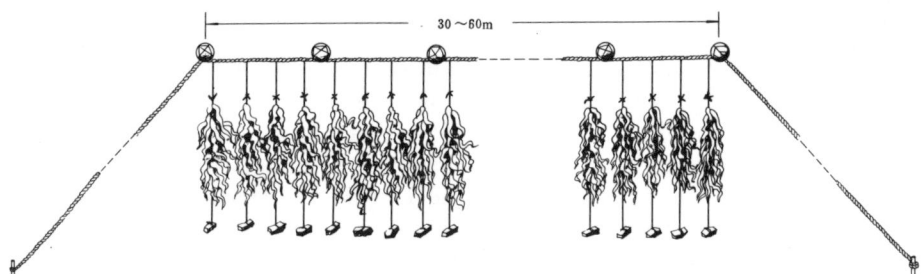

Fig. 2. Sketch of a *Laminaria* cultivation raft. Note that each cultivation rope bearing kelps has its upper end tied to a hanging rope attached to the floating rope and its lower end tied to a weighting stone (after Tseng 1981).

two cultivation ropes is 70–140 cm and that between two rafts abot 6–7 m. The total number of kelp plants cultivated in one hectare differs from place to place, averaging 150,000–300,000 plants·ha^{-1} (Fig. 2).

There are two kinds of arrangement for the cultivation ropes, and beside the hanging type just mentioned above there is also the horizontal type, which is parallel to the sea surface. The hanging type is the usual form employed. In the course of cultivation for a few months there will be quite a difference in growth between the upper and lower plants on the same rope. To equalize the growth, a method of rope inversion was devised in which the lowest plant becomes the highest one. Another method to help equalize the growth is to level the two adjacent ropes by tying them together so that they become horizontally disposed. By these methods the production and quality of the product are greatly improved (Tseng 1964, 1981, 1986; Cheng 1964).

Cultivation of *Macrocystis pyrifera* started in 1985 when the Mexican plant was transplanted to China. Trial cultivation by the ordinary raft method was practised and some production has been made for abalone feed and other uses. Cultivation of the Philippine eucheumoid alga *Kappaphycus alvarezii* in China also relies on the raft method. The plants are tied to knots in the hanging cultivation ropes. *Gelidium* and *Gracilaria* are also cultivated by similar methods. *Eucheuma*, *Gelidium* and *Gracilaria* are cultivated by using fragments of their thalli which grow asexually very well. At present these seaweeds are widely cultivated by vegetative multiplication.

Marine algae under cultivation or suggested for cultivation in the northern South China Sea region

(a) In the South China Sea region of China, only four seaweed taxa, i.e., *Gracilaria tenuistipatata*, *Gracilaria tenuistipatata* var. *liui*, *Eucheuma gelatinae* and *Kappaphycus alvarezii*, have been subjected to commercial cultivation. The three microalgae for feed are also cultivated.

Cultivation of Gracilaria

Gracilaria has three different phases of plants, the tetrasporophyte producing tetraspores which are asexual, the male gametophytes producing spermatia and the female gmetophytes producing carpospores. The two kinds of spores for reproduction are the asexual tetraspores and the carpospores resulting from sexual fusion of the gametes. Experiments show that the maximal quantity of spores is released at 8–10 a.m., then gradually decreasing so that the minimum quantity is released between 10 p.m. and 6 a.m. the following day. The quantity of spores released is also dependent on ambient environmental factors such as desiccation, temperature and salinity.

Gracilaria spores are generally 30 μm in diameter and the tetraspores are somewhat larger than the carpospores. Although *Gracilaria* are generally euryhaline species, their spores are still quite sensitive to salinity changes and will generally break up and die in seawater of specific gravity below 1.010 (Zeng 1987). Germination of the spores and growth of the seedlings are similar for both tetraspores and carpospores. and the most favourable temperature is 20–30°C, though in some cases it may be as low as 15°C, but the tendency is towards higher temperature (Tables 1 and 2). When *G. asiatica* is cultured in nutrient solution and exposed to 400 luxes for 10 hr. per day for 50 days, tetraspores at 15°C, 20°C, and 28°C and carpospores at 20°C and 28°C give rise to discs 95 x 82–85 um broad with cells beginning to differentiate, the central ones beginning to form on erect branches (Tables 1 and 2). Erect branches begin to be formed 20 days after germination (Zeng 1987).

Table 1
Germination of *Gracilaria* tetraspores at different temperatures.

Temperature °C / μm / Time (days)	7	10	15	20	28
10	39.6 x 39.6	36.3 x 36.3	39.6 x 39.6	36.0 x 36.0	39.1 x 39.1
20	39.6 x 39.6	42.9 x 42.9	49.5 x 49.5	42.9 x 42.9	42.9 x 42.9
30	46.2 x 46.2	62.7 x 62.7	62.8 x 62.8	52.8 x 52.8	52.8 x 52.8
40	52.8 x 49.8	69.3 x 62.7	75.9 x 61.9	75.9 x 66.0	75.9 x 66.0
50	49.5 x 42.9	66.0 x 59.0	95.7 x 82.5	95.9 x 85.0	99.0 x 82.5

After Zeng *et al.* 1987

Table 2
Germination of *Gracilaria* carpospores at different temperatures.

Temperature °C / μm / Time (days)	7	10	15	20	28
10	39.6 x 39.6	42.9 x 42.9	46.2 x 46.2	36.3 x 36.3	42.9 x 42.9
20	39.6 x 39.6	45.9 x 45.9	52.8 x 52.8	59.4 x 59.4	49.5 x 42.5
30	46.2 x 46.2	59.4 x 59.4	59.4 x 59.4	56.1 x 56.1	56.1 x 56.1
40	56.9 x 49.5	62.7 x 59.0	69.3 x 62.7	75.3 x 75.9	72.6 x 59.4
50	56.9 x 49.5	66.0 x 59.4	66.0 x 66.0	95.7 x 82.5	99.0 x 82.5

After Zeng *et al.* 1987

Germination of the spores is also affected by light intensity. Generally speaking, the spores germinate better at 3000 lux (Table 3). It may be that germination would be even better above 3000 lux (Zeng 1987).

Spore germination is also affected by salinity, and seawater with a specific gravity of 1.018–1.025 appears to be the most favourable. Fertility of the water is evidently also important.

Table 3
Germination of *Gracilaria* spores under different light intensities.

Light intensity (lux) \ Time (days) μm	10	15	20	25
3000	69	78	93	112
1500	52	63	85	104
200	40	48	60	76
Darkness	Poor germination	Poor germination	Death	—

After Zeng et al. 1987

Growth of the *Gracilaria* thallus is similar to that of the spores. Salinity is, however, somewhat different as mentioned above. Optimal seawater temperature of our southern species, *G. tenuistipitata*, is similar to that of our northern species, *G. asiatica* and *G. lemaneiformis*. When the water temperature is 30°C, its daily growth is 0.1–0.2 cm but, as the temperature drops to 28°C, the growth rate increasse to 0.4–0.5 cm and, at 15–25°C, it can be higher than 1 cm. Their growth requires comparatively high light and varies with the tidal level (Table 4). This is due to the fact that photosynthesis of *Gracilaria* is more active the deeper the water. At 3 m, although photosynthesis is still very active, the respiratory intensity exceeds the photosynthetic intensity and the plants will not only stop growing but also start rotting (Table 5).

In the farming of *Gracilaria*, spores must be collected and sporelings produced as mentioned above. At present the most common method for farming *Gracilaria* is pond culture, which is practiced in Taiwan and Hainan and the species involved is *G. tenuistipitata* var. *liui*. The method started in Taiwan where phycologists and farmers tried to raise *Gracilaria* in fish pond with milk fish in 1962. Unexpectedly good results were obtained so that many farms gradually shifted to growing the *Gracilaria* which give a good source of agar. The stock seaweeds are cut into pieces and spread in the fish pond at a density of 5–6 tons of fresh thalli·ha^{-1}. Chemical fertilizers or manure is applied regularly. Every 30–45 days, most parts of the seaweeds can be harvested and the rest left in the ponds as stock. The harvesting period lasts for about six months from June to November in North China and longer in the south (Chen 1990).

In the recent experiments of Wu et al. (1990), it was found that *Gracilaria tenuistipitata*, under a favourable temperature of 20–30°C, has a daily growth rate reaching as high as 3.3%, and the mean annual growth rate as 2.4% per day. Salinity has an important influence with peak growth at 21‰ salinity and with a broad plateau between

Table 4
Growth of *Gracilaria* thalli at different water depths.

Depth (cm)	0.5	1.0	1.5	2.0	2.5	3.0	3.5	4.0
L_0 (cm)	22.0	22.5	27.3	15.3	19.5	27.7	19.8	12.8
L_t (cm)	27.0	28.0	28.7	16.0	20.5	26.5	18.8	10.7
$L_t - L_0$ (cm)	+5.0	+5.5	+1.4	+0.7	+1.0	-1.5	-1.0	-2.1
$\dfrac{L_t - L_0}{L_0 \cdot 10} \cdot 100$	+2.3	+2.4	+0.5	+0.5	+0.5	-0.5	-0.5	-1.6

L_0 = initial length; L_t = terminal length after 10 days
Mean water temperature = 17°C
Mean specific gravity of seawater = 1.020 (25.5–30.1‰)
Transparency of seawater = 3 m
After Zeng et al. 1987

Table 5
Photosynthetic intensity of *Gracilaria* at different water depths ($mg \cdot O_2 L^{-1}$).

Depth (cm)	Control	0	0.5	1.0	1.5	2.0	2.5	3.0	3.5	4.0
II*	8.25	11.20	9.77	9.19	9.10	8.96	8.00	8.72	7.68	7.64
III*	8.25	10.90	10.50	10.60	9.24	9.10	8.24	8.16	8.00	7.12
Mean	8.25	11.06	10.23	9.84	9.17	9.03	8.42	8.24	7.84	7.38

* II and III are the same experiments run on different dates
** Seawater without seaweeds
After Zeng et al. 1987

7–27‰. Total nitrogen concentration of 4 µm is sufficient to enable the plant to maintain a daily growth rate of 2.7%. The best growth was obtained at a culture density of 0.5–1 kg·m^{-2} and a culture depth of 30 cm in the pond (Wu et al. 1991).

Unpublished results from experiments in northern and southeastern China show that raft culture of *Gracilaria* will give as good or better results than pond culture. It is estimated that about 2000 tons of *Gracilaria* are produced each year.

Cultivation of eucheumoid algae

In China, the only eucheumoid species under cultivation since 1960 is *Eucheuma gelatinae*, now cultivated in eastern Hainan. The thallus is 10–20 cm long, growing horizontally on coral chips in the sublittoral region, and best at 4–5 metres below sea level, branching irregularly with spinous projections from the edges, and adhering to the substrate by a discoid holdfast. The branches adhere to each other, forming a mass. This species grows in tropical China in Taiwan, Hainan and Xisha Islands, and in water with high salinity. Cultivation is effected by selecting fast growing thallus fragments of 25–30 gm, fastening them to coral chips by rubber rings and throwing them into the coral flats. A cultivation worker may deal with more than 800 thallus fragments each

Table 6
Effect of cultivation depth on growth of *Kappaphucus alvarezii*.

Cultivation layer (cm) Fresh weight (kg) Date	50		90		130		170		210	
	Average weight per cutting	Average daily growth in weight (%)	Average weight per cutting	Average daily growth in weight (%)	Average weight per cutting	Average daily growth in weight (%)	Average weight per cutting	Average daily growth in weight (%)	Average weight per cutting	Average daily growth in weight (%)
25 May	0.08	4.80	0.09	5.30	0.11	6.50	0.08	3.90	0.10	1.80
6 June	0.26	10.32	0.31	10.86	0.31	9.02	0.22	8.80	0.22	6.79
22 June	0.48	3.91	0.65	4.74	0.61	4.32	0.39	3.64	0.33	2.57
2 July	0.92	6.72	0.97	4.08	0.86	3.49	0.52	2.92	0.40	1.94

(Experiment started on 13 May 1986)
After Wu *et al.* 1989.

morning. Each *mu* (one fifteenth of a hectare) of the sea needs about 5,000 thallus fragments and 1 kg of rubber rings, Divers are sent down to arrange the thallus fragments, about 9–10 fragments in a square metre, the distance between fragments being about 30 cm. Each worker plants about 0.12 *mu* a day, and each *mu* needs about 50 kg of stock. In one year, these fragments will be ready for harvest. 300 tons of *Eucheuma gelationae* is produced annually by this method.

In recent years *Kappaphycus alvarezii* (formerly called '*Eucheuma striatum*') has been introduced from the Philippines and cultivation experiments started in Hainan. Growth is promising and average daily growth in weight reached 10% at favourable temperature of about 26°C. Experiments show that timely cutting of the plant was effective to obtain new cuttings for cultivation and to accelerate growth. New cuttings 0.05 kg in weight are suggested to be used as seed stocks and concurrently the old plant should be harvested. Artificial cultivation was effected with a type of underwater raft, applicable in places with strong current.

The effect of light intensity on the growth of *Kappaphycus* was investigated. Cuttings grew fast from April to September in Hainan, when the water transparency was as high as 5–6 metres. The results show that the cuttings grow best in shallower waters (Table 6). Analysis of some hereditary characteristics show quite a difference between individuals (Table 7).

Table 7
Differences in growth of individuals of *Kappaphycus alvarezii*.

Plant No. Fresh weight (kg)	1–70	2–71	3–53	2–68	3–64	1–54	3–58
Weight per plant 14 June 1985	0.06	0.05	0.05	0.06	0.07	0.06	0.03
Weight per plant 13 August 1985	5.20	4.40	13.10	5.30	4.60	4.10	3.20
Increment in weight per plant	5.14	4.35	13.05	5.24	4.53	4.04	3.17
Growth in weight (%)	85.67	87.00	261.00	87.33	64.71	67.33	105.67

After Wu *et al.* 1989

Cultivation of microalgae

Microalgae has been successfully cultivated as feed for the young stages of marine animals such as the shrimps since the late 1950s to early 1960s. At present, the same three species, namely, *Isochrysis galbana*, *Phaeodactylum triocornutum* and *Tetraselmis subcordiformis*, are most commonly employed. Indoor rectangular tanks and nutrient solution were employed as mentioned above.

In addition to *Gracilaria*, *Eucheuma*, *Kappaphycus*, and the microalgae, *Isochrysis*, *Phaeodactylum* and *Tetraselmis*, a few other marine algae have been subjected to biotechnological studies and very probably will be commercially cultivated. These are *Porphyra*, *Gelidium* and the two microalgae, *Spirulina* and *Dunaliella*.

Porphyra guangdongensis has been subjected previously to cultivation experiments, but unsuccessfully. Fang *et al.* (1984) experimented with *P. yezoensis* and *P. haitanensis* in North China, utilizing their cells and protoplasts as 'seeds' for mariculture and obtaining fairly good results. Somewhat later, Wang *et al.* (1986) cultivated vegetative cells of *Porphyra* in the East China Sea and obtained thalli reaching 58 cm in length. In their 1989 experiments, Wang *et al.* (1990) obtained an experimental production of 74 kg·mu^{-1} or 1110 kg·ha^{-1}. They separated the cells of *Porphyra* using enzymes from molluscs. This work will probably help to revolutionalize the classical method of *Porphyra* production by conchospores.

Gelidium has been a difficult group to cultivate successfully because of its slow growth. Methods for its commercial cultivation involve vegetative propagation and a great number of thalli must be employed. Pei *et al.* (1987) cut the thalli of *Gelidium pacificum*, scattered them on substrates such as ropes and cultured them in the laboratory for one month. The fragments became attached to the substrate, grew and sent out filaments. These became the seed-stocks of *Gelidium*. Sun *et al.* (1990) worked with *Gelidium amansii* by similar methods and grew them in the laboratory for only two weeks. They were then taken out to the sea and grew well. This has an important bearing on *Gelidium* cultivation, since by tissue culture, the amounts of thalli employed in producing seedstocks are mininized. In spite of its slow growth, total production is quite enormous.

The microalga *Spirulina platensis* has been successfully cultivated in sea water in ponds. The experiments in Guangdong and Hainan were very successful with maximal production reaching 20 gm·m^{-2}·day^{-1}, whereas in North China production of only 7 gm was achieved. A pilot plant of about 3000 m^2 has been built in Guangdong Province. *Spirulina* powder has a high protein content (about 65%) and it is not only good for animal feeds but also valuable as a health food for man. Undoubtedly the South China Sea region will serve as an excellent place for the commercial growing of *Spirulina*.

The other microalga under cultivation is *Dunaliella salina*, which is now grown in the salt fields of Tanggu, Tianjin in North China for its beta-carotene. Its growing season there is about five months from late May to early November and North China is evidently not ideal for growing *Dunaliella*. Although no experiments have been reported in the south, there is no doubt that the South China Sea region will provide an ideal place for *Dunaliella* culture because of its much higher temperature and, in some places, less rainy days.

In conclusion, there are, at present, only four seaweeds and three microalgae under cultivation in the vast northern South China Sea region. *Gracilaria tenuistipitata* var. *liui* yields about 2000 tons dry weight each year in Taiwan and Hainan and *Eucheuma gelatinae*, about 300 tons in Hainan. In the South China Sea, the eucheumoid algae *Kappaphycus alvarezii* and *Eucheuma denticulatum* have been cultivated on a large scale in the Philippines for about 20 years and in Thailand and Indonesia in recent years. There is no question at all that these eucheumoid algae can be successfully farmed in the northern part of the South China Sea. In recent experiments, Wu and his colleagues have successfully grown *Kappaphycus alvarezii* in Hainan and achieved a daily growth rate in weight of 13.7% (Wu *et al.* 1989), many times the daily growth rate of the local *Eucheuma*. Carrageenan extracted from the eucheumoid algae is an important phycocolloid, popularly employed in the West in the food and cosmetic industries. At present its use in China is still very limited, but with the progress of China's industrialization, it will definitely find broader utilization. Great expansion of China's eucheumoid algae farming is to be expected.

As for *Gracilaria* farming, there is no doubt that further expansion of the industry will be expected. *Gracilaria* is an important agarophyte and, at present, the world's market for agar and agarose is far from being saturated. Beside *G. tenuistipitata* var. *liui* a few more species of *Gracilaria* especially *G. tenuistipitata*, *G. lemaneiformis* and *G. asiatica* will undoubtedly become important phycoculture subjects.

Beside the above mentioned seaweeds, farming of other marine algae will most probably be achieved soon. Cell cultivation of *Porphyra* and tissue cultivation of *Gelidium* have been experimented with in North and East China with good results. There is no doubt that their cultivation will also be successful in South China. *Gelidium* is a very important agarophyte and the success of its farming in South China will help greatly in China's agar industry. *Porphyra* is one of the most important food algae and the Fujian species, *P. haitanensis*, will undoubtedly grow well in northern South China sea region. Besides, there are other subtropical species of *Porphyra* in the South China Sea which are worthy of trial cultivation. The two microalgae, *Spirulina* and *Dunaliella*, will also undoubtedly grow better in some places in the Northern part of the South China Sea region. *Gloiopeltis furcata*, the first marine alga to be cultivated in China, will no doubt be submitted to modern phycoculture technique and resume its important role in marine algae farming.

ACKNOWLEDGEMENTS

This is Contribution No. 2007 from the Institute of Oceanology, Chinese Academy of Sciences, Qingdao, China. The author wishes to thank Mr Zhou Xiantong for his tireless effort in typing the manuscript and checking the references for me.

REFERENCES

Chen, D., Lin, G.H. and Shen, S.Z. 1979. Studies on alginic acid decomposing bacteria, I. Action of alginic acid decomosing bacteria and alginase on *Laminaria japonica*. *Oceanologia et Limnologia Sinica.* 10:329–33.

Chen, D., Yu, Y.D. and Yang, Z.H. 1983. Studies on the etiology of green rot disease of cultivated *Porphyra*. In *Proceedings of the First Chinese Phycological Symposium*, 35–44. Beijing: Science Press.

Chen, J.X. 1990. *Gracilaria* culture in China. mss. 16pp.

Cheng, T.H. 1979. Production of Kelp — a major aspect of China's exploitation of the sea. *Economic Botany* 23:215–36.

Fang, T.C. 1983. A summary of the genetic studies of *Laminaria japonica* in China. In *Proceedings of Joint China-US. Phycology Symposium* (ed. C.K. Tseng), 123–6.

Fang, T.C., Dai, J.X., Tang, Y.L., Liu, W.S. and Bao, Z.M. 1986. Isolation of the vegetative cells of *Porphyra yezoensis* Ueda with enzymes and its application in aquaculture. *Marine Science* 10:46–7.

Li, J.J., Peng, Z.S., Xue, Z.F. and Huang, Z.Y. 1981. Contagious experiments of the twisted frond disease in *Laminaria japonica* Aresch. *Oceanologia et Limnologia Sinica (Supplement)*. pp. 222–9.

Liang, L. 1990. Status of Production and Utilization of Seaweed in China. mss. 20 pp.

McHugh, D.J. 1987 Production, properties and uses of alginates. In *Production and Utilization of Products from Commercial Seaweeds* (ed. D.J. McHugh). FAO Fisheries Technical Paper 288:58–115.

Pei L.Q., Fei, Z., Ma, G., Zhou, J. and Zhu, Y. 1988. A preliminary study of seedling of *Gelidium pacificum* Okam. obtained by regeneration of thallus fragments. *Journal of Zhejiang College of Fisheries*, 99–105.

Richards-Rajadurai, H. 1990. Production, marketing and trade of seaweeds. In First Asia Pacific Workshop on Culture and Utilization of Seaweeds. mss. 15pp.

Section of Experimental Phyco-ecology, Institute of Oceanology, Academia Sinica (IOEP). 1976. All-artificial spore-collecting cultivation of *Tiaoban-zicai* (*Porphura yezoensis* Ueda). *Scientia Sinica* 19:253–9.

Section of Experimental Phyco-ecology and Section of Systematic Phycology, Institute of Oceanology, Academia Sinica (IOESP). 1978. Cultivation of *Zicai* (*Porphyra yezoensis* Ueda). Beijing: Science Press. (In Chinese)

Section of Seaweed Genetics and Breeding, Institute of Oceanology, Academia Sinica and Qingdao Institute of Marine Fisheries (IOG & QMF). 1976. The breeding of new varieties of *Haidai* (*Laminaria japonica* Aresch.) with high production and high iodine content. *Scientia Sinica* 19:243–52.

Shang, Y.C. 1976. Economic aspects of *Gracilaria* culture in Taiwan. *Aquaculture* 8:1–7.

Sun, J.Z, Yu, H., Rao, D.Z. and Wu, L.P. 1990. Studies on the cultivation technique of *Gelidium amansii* by regeneration of thallus fragments. In *Third Conference of Chinese Phycological Society*, Abstract No. 240. (In Chinese).

Tseng, C.K. 1933. *Gloiopeltis* and the other economic seaweeds of Amoy, China. *Lingnan Science Journal* 12:43–63.

Tseng, C.K. 1964. Kelp farming, a new industry. *China Reconstructs* 13:36–38.

Tseng, C.K. 1981. Commercial Cultivation. In *Botanical Monographs Vol. 17: The Biology of Seaweeds* (ed. C.S. Lobban and M.J. Wynne), 680–725.

Tseng, C.K. 1986. *Laminaria* mariculture in China. In *Case Studies of Seven Commercial Seaweed Resources* (ed. M.S. Doty, J.F. Caddy and B. Santelices). FAO Fisheries Technical Paper 281:239–63.

Tseng, C.K. and Chang C.F. 1956. On China's *Porphyra* and its cultivation. *Shengwuxue Tongbao* 3:29–33. (In Chinese)

Tseng, C.K. and Chang T.J. 1955. Studies on the life history of *Porphyra tenera* Kjellm. *Scientia Sinica* 4:375–98.

Tseng, C.K., Ren, G.Z. and Wu, C.Y. 1959. On the discharge of egg and spermatozoids of *Laminaria japonica* and the morphology of spermatozoids. *Kexue Tongbao* 4:129–30. (In Chinese)

Tseng, C.K., Sun, K.Y. and Wu, C.Y. 1955. On the cultivation of *haidai* (*Laminaria japonica* Aresch.) by summering young sporophytes at low temperature. *Acta Botanica Sinica* 4:255–64.

Tseng, C.K. and Wu, C.Y. 1966. Studies on fertilizer application in the cultivation of *haidai* (*Laminaria japonica* Aresch.). In *Papers of the Nineth Meeting of the Western Pacific Fisheries Research Commission*, 37–40. Beijing: Science Press. (In Chinese)

Tseng, C.K., Wu, C.Y., Wang, Z.M., Zheng, S.Q., Jiang, B.Y., Li, P.L., Peng, Z.S. and Zou, S.H. 1962. Studies on the absorption of nitrate and ammonium nitrogen by *Laminaria japonica* Aresch. In *Collected Papers of the Fifth Meeting of the Western Pacific Fisheries Research Commission*, 21–32. Beijing: Science Press. (In Chinese)

Wang, Q., Xu, S., Liu, R., Qiao, B., Zhang, Z., and Sun, G. 1980. Studies on the frond twist disease of the *haidai* (*Laminaria japonica* Aresch.) — electron microscope examination of the pathogen. *Scientia Sinica* 6:587–91. (In Chinese)

Wang, S.J., Sun, Y. and Liu, A. 1987. A study of the cultivation of the vegetative cells and protoplasts of *Porphyra haitanensis*. II. The cultivation of seedlings in the sea. *Marine Science* 1:1–7.

Wang, S.J., Zhang, X., Xu, Z.D. and Sun, Y.L. 1986. A study on the utilization of the vegetative cells and protoplasts of *Porphyra haitanensis*. I. *Oceanologia et Limnologia Sinica* 16:217–21.

Wang, S.J., He, P. and Sun, Y. 1990. Development of seedling production technique of *Porphyra* by using vegetative cells as seeds. In *Third Conference of Chinese Phycological Society*, Abstract No. 183. (In Chinese)

Wu, C.Y. 1962. Growth and development of the sporophyte (of *Laminaria japonica*) in relation to the environmental factors. In *Manual of Cultivation of Haidai (Laminaria japonica)* (ed. C.K. Tseng and C.Y. Wu), 34–71. Beijing: Science Press. (In Chinese)

Wu, C.Y., Tseng, C.K., Wang, Z.M., Jiang, B.Y. and Sun, G.Y. 1959. Experiment on intermittently fertilizing *Laminaria japonica*. *Kexue Tongbao* 24:829–30. (In Chinese)

Wu, C.Y., Gao, N.S., Chen, D.C., Chou, B.C., Cai, P.X., Dong, S.X., Wen, Z.C. and Cong, R.Y. 1979. On the malformation disease of *Laminaria* sporelings. *Oceanologia et Limnologia Sinica* 10:238–50.

Wu, C.Y., Li, J.J., Xia, E.Z., Peng, Z.S., Li, J., Wen, Z.C., Huang, X.H., Cai, Z.L. and Chen, G.J. 1989. On the transplantation and cultivation of *Kappaphucus alvarezii* in China. *Chinese Journal of Oceanology and Limnology* 7:327–34.

Wu, C.Y., Li, R.Z., Lin, G.H., Wen, Z.C., Dong, L.F., Zhang, J.P., Huang, X.H., Wei, S.Q. and Lan, G.B. 1991. Some aspects of the growth of *Gracilaria tenuistipitata* in pond culture. mss. 5 pp.

Zeng, C.K. (C.K. Tseng) 1984. Phycological research in the developmet of the Chinese seaweed industry. *Hydrobiologia* 116/117, 7–18.

Zhang, J.C., Suo, R.Y. and Zhang, D.M. 1962. Diseases and pests in *haidai* (*Laminaria japonica*) cultivation. In *Manual of Cultivation of Haidai (Laminaria japonica)*, (ed. C.K. Tseng and C.Y. Wu), 230–6. Beijing: Science Press. (In Chinese)

FISHERIES
SESSION PAPERS

The Marine Biology of the South China Sea
(ed. B. Morton). Proceedings of the First
International Conference on the Marine Biology
of Hong Kong and the South China Sea,
Hong Kong, 28 October – 3 November 1990.
Hong Kong: Hong Kong University Press, 1993.

THE SPECIES COMPOSITION OF PENAEID PRAWNS AND CARIDEAN SHRIMPS IN A *GEI WAI* AT THE MAI PO MARSHES NATURE RESERVE, HONG KONG

S.F. Leung

Department of Zoology, The University of Hong Kong, Hong Kong

ABSTRACT

The species composition of penaeids and carideans was investigated in a Mai Po Marshes *gei wai* from September 1986 to January 1989. The catches comprised four species of penaeid prawns (56.72%) and three species of caridean shrimps (43.82%). The penaeids were *Metapenaeus ensis* (96.0%), *Metapenaeus affinis* (1.13%), *Penaeus penicillatus* (2.77%) and *Penaeus monodon* (0.11%). The carideans comprised two palaemonids, *Exopalaemon styliferus* (87.39%) and *Macrobrachium nipponense* (12.51%) and one alpheid, *Alpheus paludicola* (0.1%). Two more carideans, *Coutierella tonkinensis* (Palaemonidae) and *Caridina nilotica* (Atyidae), inhabit the trailing vegetation along the drainage channels of the *gei wai*. All the carideans were caught throughout the year whereas the penaeids, except *M. ensis*, were caught seasonally. Monthly variations in species composition have been shown. Annual species composition of the catch and species diversity values were, however, relatively stable over the study period.

Though sympatric, the carideans and the penaeids have different life histories. The carideans mature, breed and commence their life cycles inside the *gei wai* whereas the penaeids do not and recruitment relies upon spawning stocks in saline waters and immigration of postlarvae.

INTRODUCTION

Despite the wide fluctuations in environmental conditions that affect estuarine mangrove areas and which cause stress to the organisms present, a diverse faunal assemblage is adapted to the highly variable conditions that occur in the Mai Po Marshes Nature Reserve (Lee 1988). It is almost an article of faith amongst estuarine scientists that coastal wetlands, such as highly productive mangrove forests, are important nursery sites for postlarvae and juveniles of fish and crustaceans (Haines 1979; Weinstein 1979; Boesch and Turner 1984; Robertson and Duke 1987).

Adult penaeid prawns migrate to fully marine conditions offshore to spawn. Subsequently, postlarvae use flood tides to move into estuarine areas to feed, grow and reach adulthood (Copeland and Truitt 1965; Young and Carpenter 1977; Staples 1980). Such habitats are, as a consequence, important nurseries for penaeid prawns, especially species of *Penaeus* and *Metapenaeus* (Kutkuhn 1966; Parker 1970; Glaister 1977; Edwards 1978; De Freitas 1986; Potter *et al.* 1986). This is related to the high survival rate of juveniles, promoted by an abundance of protective cover and high concentrations of food in such brackish-water habitats (Hoese 1960; Barrett and Gillespie 1973; Zimmerman *et al.* 1984). Soft, estuarine, muds also provide a favourable substratum for juvenile prawns to burrow into.

Caridean shrimps are also common in estuarine mangroves. Species of Palaemonidae, Alpheidae and Atyidae are common inhabitants of polyhaline waters in mangrove creeks and prawn ponds (Johnson 1965; Manuputty 1984). Most species are euryhaline and commence their life cycles in mangroves. In addition to the bottom mud, *gei wai*s also provide an abundance of trailing vegetation along drainage channels and the grass *Paspalum distichum* Ridley and the reed *Phragmites communis* (L.) Trin. provide furthur favourable habitat for carideans.

Because of the dependence of some commercially important penaeids on mangrove-dominated habitats, many such areas have been converted into tidal prawn ponds. Culture is based on the tidal flow of postlarvae and juvenile prawns into the ponds where they remain and grow to marketable size. Such a system of marine prawn cultivation has been in existence for most of the present century in Southeast Asia (Delmendo and Rabanal 1956; Tham 1968) and the *gei wai*'s at Mai Po are a good example of the practice.

In the Mai Po *gei wai*, penaeid prawns are the target species whereas caridean shrimps are ignored by the fishermen. Because prawn production relies on natural stocks of larvae and juveniles, the structure of prawn and shrimp communities may be variable. In this study, seasonal variations in the species composition of penaeids and carideans in the *gei wai* have been investigated.

MATERIALS AND METHODS

The prawns and shrimps in *gei wai* No. 18 at Mai Po were sampled monthly from September 1986 to January 1989 with a net of 10 mm mesh secured over the sluice gate. Traditional prawn-harvesting methods were employed, i.e., the sluice gate opening and trapping method. Sampling was undertaken at night during spring low tide periods. When there was a low tide such that the water level in the sluice channel was lower than in the *gei wai*, the gate was opened and the prawns and shrimps were carried by the draining current into the net. The net was emptied frequently by untying the knot at the cod-end until a sample of about 500 prawns and shrimps were caught. All individuals collected were frozen for temporary storage. After transfer to the laboratory, the prawns and shrimps were identified to species and numbers recorded.

Species diversity was calculated using the Shannon-Wienner information function (H') and Evenness (J) (Pearson and Rosenberg 1978).

RESULTS

Species composition

A total of 41,647 individuals, representing four species of penaeid prawns and three species of caridean shrimps, was collected during the study period. Penaeids constituted 56.72% of the total catch, carideans 43.28% (Table 1). The penaeids comprised *Metapenaeus ensis* (De Haan) (96.00%), *Metapenaeus affinis* (H. Milne-Edwards) (1.13%), *Penaeus penicillatus* (Alcock) (2.77%) and *Penaeus monodon* (Fabricius) (0.11%). The caridean shrimps comprised two palaemonids, i.e., *Exopalaemon* aff. *styliferus* (H. Milne-Edwards) (87.39%) and *Macrobrachium nipponense* (De Haan) (12.51%), and one alpheid, i.e., *Alpheus* cf. *paludicola* (Kemp) (0.10%). *M. ensis* was the dominant penaeid, *E. styliferus* the dominant caridean. Ranked in order of abundance (by numbers) (Table 2), the species fell into the following sequence: *M. ensis* (54.45%), *E. styliferus* (37.82%), *M. nipponense* (5.41%), *P. penicillatus* (1.57%), *M. affinis* (0.64%), *P. monodon* (0.62%) and *A. paludicola* (0.43%). Ranked according to biomass (Table 3), the species fell into the following sequence: *M. ensis* (78.58%), *E. styliferus* (14.94%), *P. penicillatus* (2.53%), *M. nipponense* (2.51%), *P. monodon* (1.20%), *M. affinis* (0.18%) and *A. paludicola* (0.07%).

Annual variations in species composition

The relative abundance of penaeids and carideans changed from 1986–87 to 1987–89. Carideans were more numerous (61.56%) than the penaeids (38.35%) in 1986–87 while the reverse was true in the following year (penaeids, 71.75%; carideans 28.85%). Species composition remained relatively stable over the two years. Of the penaeids, *Metapenaeus ensis* was dominant (> 94%) in both years, followed by *Penaeus penicillatus*, *Metapenaeus affinis* and *Penaeus monodon* (Fig. 1). For the carideans, the dominance of *Exopalaemon styliferus* decreased from 94.56% in 1986–87 to 75.36% in 1987–89 while that of *Macrobrachium nipponense* increased from 5.31% in 1986–87 to 24.59% in 1987–89. *Alpheus paludicola* was encountered only occasionally in both years (Fig. 1).

Table 1
The species composition of prawn and shrimp catches from *gei wai* 18 over the study period.

Species	Catch (% of total catch)	Group composition (% frequency)
Penaeidae	56.72	
Metapenaeus ensis		95.99
Metapenaeus affinis		1.13
Penaeus penicillatus		2.77
Penaeus monodon		0.11
Caridea	43.28	
Exopalaemon styliferus		87.39
Macrobrachium nipponense		12.51
Alpheus paludicola		0.10

Table 2
The species composition (by numbers) of penaeids and carideans caught from *gei wai* 18 over the study period.

Species	% Frequency
Metapenaeus ensis	54.45
Exopalaemon styliferus	37.82
Macrobrachium nipponense	5.41
Penaeus penicillatus	1.57
Metapenaeus affinis	0.64
Penaeus monodon	0.62
Alpheus paludicola	0.43

Table 3
The species composition (by biomass) of penaeids and carideans caught from *gei wai* 18 over the study period.

Species	% Frequency
Metapenaeus ensis	78.58
Exopalaemon styliferus	14.94
Penaeus penicillatus	2.53
Macrobrachium nipponense	2.51
Penaeus monodon	1.20
Metapenaeus affinis	0.18
Alpheus paludicola	0.07

Seasonal variation in species composition

The relative abundance of penaeids and carideans fluctuated from month to month (Fig. 2) with the penaeids more numerous from September to February, but less so from March to August.

Variations in penaeid species composition showed a seasonal pattern (Fig. 3). *Metapenaeus ensis* was dominant throughout the year accounting for > 97% of the penaeids from December to May but less so from June to November (70–97%). The other three species, i.e., *Metapenaeus affinis*, *Penaeus penicillatus* and *Penaeus monodon*, were caught seasonally. *M. affinis* was caught from June to November with peaks of 26.41%, 3.95% and 5.05% in September 1986, October 1987 and September 1988, respectively. *P. penicillatus* occurred in small numbers (< 3%) in all months of both years except June, July and August and constituted a higher proportion of the penaeid catch (7–14% in 1987 and 5–8% in 1988). *P. monodon* was relatively uncommon (< 1%) and was caught mainly from October to March.

Variations in caridean species composition showed no seasonal trend. *Exopalaemon styliferus* and *Macrobrachium nipponense* occurred year round while *Alpheus paludicola* was only caught occasionally. *E. styliferus* was the major species throughout the year (60%) except in February 1987 and from February to March 1988 when its dominance decreased (< 60%). This was attributed to the increased relative abundance of *M. nipponense* which fluctuated between 0–51.38% of the total caridean catch (Fig. 4).

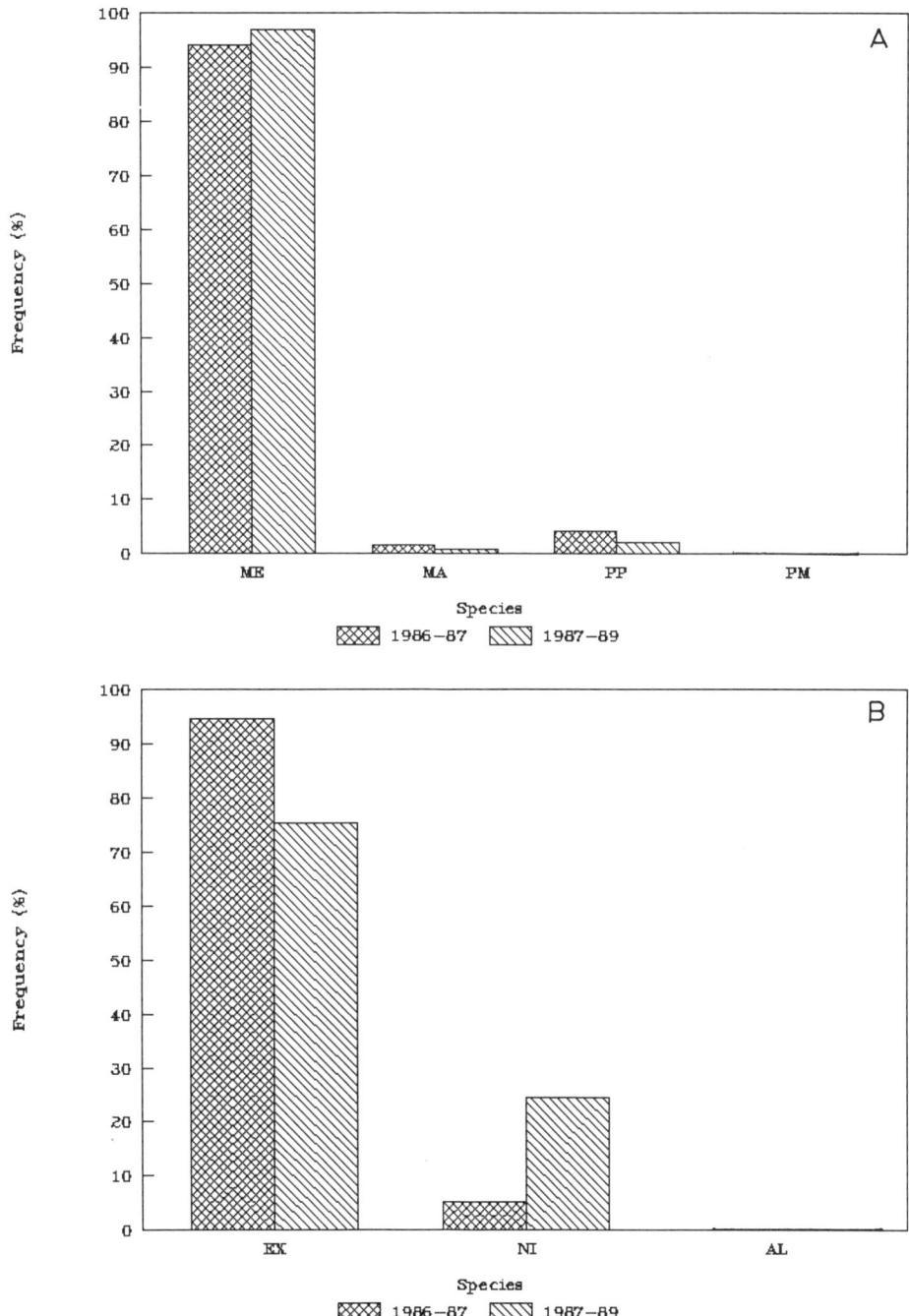

Fig. 1. Annual variations in species composition (by numbers) of A, penaeids (ME, *Metapenaeus ensis*; MA, *Metapenaeus affinis*; PP, *Penaeus penicillatus*; PM, *Penaeus monodon*) and B, carideans *(EX, Exopalaemon styliferus;* NI, *Macrobrachium nipponense;* AL, *Alpheus pauludicola)* in *gei wai* 18 over the study period.

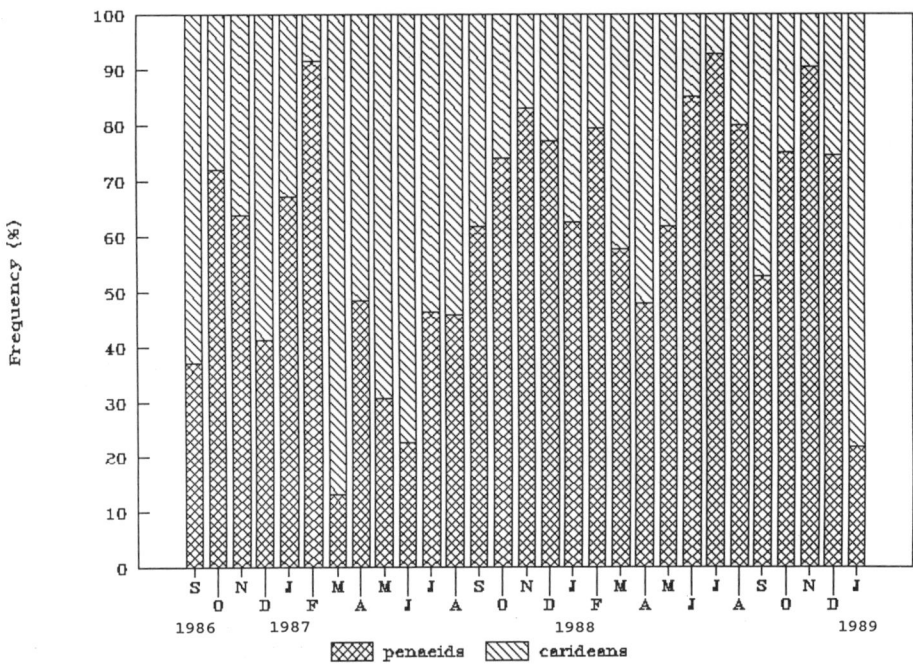

Fig. 2. Monthly variations in the relative abundance of penaeids and carideans in *gei wai* 18 over the study period.

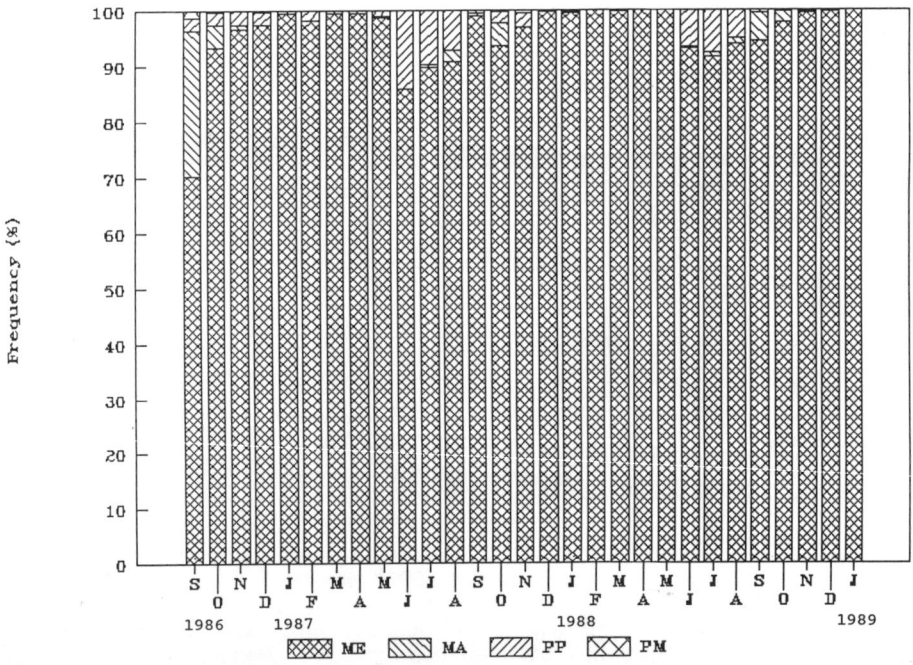

Fig. 3. Monthly variations in species composition of penaeids in *gei wai* 18 over the study period. (ME, *Metapenaeus ensis*; MA, *Metapenaeus affinis*; PP, *Penaeus penicillatus*; PM, *Penaeus monodon*).

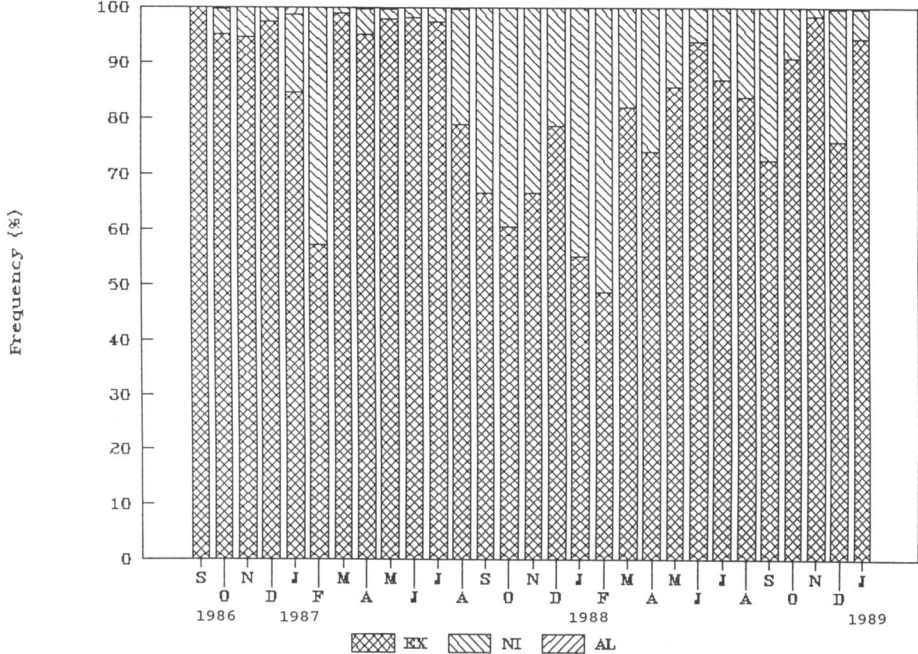

Fig. 4. Monthly variations in species composition of carideans in *gei wai* 18 over the study period. (EX, *Exopalaemon styliferus*; NI, *Macrobrachium nipponense*; AL, *Alpheus paludicola*).

Other species

In addition to the three carideans mentioned above, one more palaemonid, *Coutierella tonkinensis* (Sollaud) and one more atyid, *Caridina nilotica* (de Man) occurred in the *gei wai*. Both are inhabitants of the trailing vegetation along the drainage channels; *C. tonkinensis* was, however, relatively more abundant than *C. nilotica*.

Species diversity

The mean species diversity (H) and evenness (J) values were respectively 1.122 ± 0.260 and 0.472 ± 0.096 for 1986–87 and 1.135 ± 0.280 and 0.504 ± 0.132 for 1987–89, again respectively. There was no significant difference in diversity values between the years ($P > 0.05$).

DISCUSSION

A total of nine species of prawns and shrimps were recorded from the *gei wai* during the study period. Mean species diversity was 1.1. The diversity of the prawn and shrimp community appears limited by the variability in environmental conditions (Sanders 1968; Wade 1972) and the pollution (Pearson and Rosenberg 1978; Wu 1982) of Deep Bay. A progressive decline in prawn production has been reported by the cultivators at Mai Po in recent years. Increased levels of pollution in Deep Bay (Environmental Protection Department 1989) have been proposed as one of the reasons (Irving and Morton 1988). Individual species, such as *Metapenaeus affinis* and *Penaeus penicillatus*, which occurred in high numbers in the past, constituted only a small proportion of the catch in the present study.

The prawn fauna of the Mai Po *gei wai* included two species of *Metapenaeus* and two species of *Penaeus*, all of which are Indo-West Pacific penaeids of well established commercial importance (Racek 1970). Locally, *Metapenaeus ensis*, *Metapenaeus affinis* and *Penaeus penicillatus* are distributed widely throughout the territorial waters of Hong Kong while *Penaeus monodon* occurs only in the western coastal waters of Hong Kong (Cheung 1960). As is true for most *Penaeus* and *Metapenaeus* species, the postlarvae and juveniles of these four species move into estuaries and mangrove waters where they find food and shelter. *M. ensis* and *M. affinis* are well known mangrove associates, consistently being recorded from the mangrove waters of the Indo-Pacific region (Macintosh 1982; Robertson and Duke 1987). *P. monodon* also occurs in the mangrove community, but in smaller numbers (Macintosh 1982).

Metapenaeus ensis was the most abundant prawn, with *Penaeus penicillatus*, *Metapenaeus affinis* and *Penaeus monodon* ranked subordinately. This may be attributed to differences in the densities of offshore spawning stocks which results in differences in larval densities among different species (Crocos and Kerr 1983). Cheung (1960) recorded for the four species here obtained, that *M. ensis* was more abundant in the western coastal waters of Hong Kong, followed by *P. penicillatus*, *M. affinis* and *P. monodon*. Such information agrees well with the species composition of penaeids in *gei wai* 18. The recruitment of postlarval and juvenile penaeids may also be influenced by habitat availability, notably the choice of substratum (Branford 1981; Aziz and Greenwood 1982), the presence or absence of submerged vegetation (Young 1978; Coles *et al.* 1987), turbidity (Hughes 1966) and salinity (Hughes 1969; Young and Carpenter 1977; Garcia and Le Reste 1981).

Although *gei wai* tidal culture practices have many disadvantages in that stocking is uncontrolled and dependent on the seasonal availability of postlarvae so that stock species composition may vary greatly, the annual species composition actually remained relatively stable. Seasonal variations in penaeid species composition can be mainly attributed to the seasonal recruitment of postlarvae into and the seasonal migration of adults out of the *gei wai*.

Unlike penaeids, carideans are residents of the *gei wai* where they reach sexual maturity, breed and commence their life cycle. Representatives of three families of carideans, i.e., Palaemonidae, Alpheidae and Atyidae, occurred in the *gei wai*. All the species obtained, except *Caridina nilotica*, are oligohaline and inhabit estuarine habitats. Species of *Exopalaemon* and *Palaemon* are brackish-water inhabitants and many are associated with mangroves (Marine Fisheries Information Services, India 1979; Robertson and Duke 1987). *Exopalaemon styliferus* occurred in high numbers in the *gei wai* and this author believes that it is a mangrove-associate. *Macrobrachium nipponense* commonly inhabits the brackish waters of coastal estuaries and lagoons but its occasional occurrence in inland waters, such as the pools of upper rivers and lakes, has also been reported upon (Kamita 1970, pp. 96-129; Mashiko 1983). *Coutierella tonkinensis* is another brackish-water species which extends marginally into freshwaters. In the *gei wai*, it occurred in high numbers and was associated with the grass *Paspalum distichum* along the drainage channels. Another species, *Caridina nilotica*, occurred with

C. tonkinensis and belongs to the Atyidae which is an important family of largely warm freshwater shrimps (Hart 1980; 1981) largely inhabitants of vegetated littoral habitats (Hart 1979). *C. nilotica* occurred, however, in much smaller numbers than *C. tonkinensis* in the *gei wai*.

The mangrove crustaceans of the Mai Po *gei wai* are thus dominated by juvenile and subadult penaeids and resident palaemonids. They are the major source of secondary production in the *gei wai*. In addition to being important consumers which depend on the mangrove habitat for food (Odum and Heald 1972), juvenile penaeids and carideans provide an important food for many predatory fishes and migrant and resident birds at Mai Po. Moreover, penaeid prawns, especially the dominant *Metapenaeus ensis*, are economic species and are harvested heavily by man during the fishing season from April to October each year.

The commercial success of tidal prawn ponds is attributed to the association between penaeid prawns and the mangrove habitat (Hall 1962; Macnae 1974). Macnae (1974) demonstrated that high prawn yields were derived from waters bordering mangrove coastlines in East Africa and Southeast Asia. Conversion of mangrove forests into tidal prawn ponds, however, destroys the natural communities which, in turn, destroys the penaeid nursery grounds. As a result, the recruitment of mangrove-associated penaeids into such areas and the survivorship of postlarvae and juveniles is adversely affected. In El Salvador, the destruction of mangroves was determined to be a factor contributing to a decline in prawn catches (Daugherty 1975). Hence, conservation of mangroves is important not only for maintaining a good yield of prawns from tidal ponds and surrounding waters, but also for ensuring sustainable yields by providing nursery grounds.

ACKNOWLEDGEMENTS

I would like to thank World Wide Fund For Nature Hong Kong for giving me the opportunity to work at Mai Po Marshes Nature Reserve. Thanks are also extended to the staff of WWFHK who helped in various way throughout the study. In particular, Mr K.H. Wong and W.C. Chong helped in routine *gei wai* operations and shrimp collection. I am grateful to Dr A.J. Bruce, Museums and Art Galleries of the Northern Territory, Australia, Dr Alain Crosnier, Laboratoire De Zoologie, Museum National D'Histoire Naturelle, Paris, France and Dr X.Q. Liang, Shanghai Fisheries University, People's Republic of China, for identifying the carideans and penaeids here reported upon. I would also like to express my sincere thanks to Prof. Brian Morton for his support and constructive criticisms of the first drafts of the manuscript of this paper.

REFERENCES

Aziz, K.A. and Greenwood, J.G. 1982. Response of juvenile *Metapenanaeus bennettae* Racek and Dall 1965 (Decapoda: Penaeidae) to sediments of differing particle size. *Crustaceana* 43:121–6.

Barrett, B.B. and Gillespie, M.C. 1973. Primary factors which influence commercial shrimp production in coastal Louisiana. *Louisiana Wildlife and Fishery Commission Technical Bulletin* 9:1–28.

Bosech, D.F. and Turner, R.E. 1984. Dependence of fishery species on salt marshes: the role of food and refuge. *Estuaries* 7:460–8.

Branford, J.R. 1981. Sediment and the distribution of penaeid shrimp in the Sudanese Red Sea. *Estuarine, Coastal and Shelf Science* 13:349–54.

Cheung, T.S. 1960. The natural history of the commercial species of Hong Kong Penaeidae. M.Sc. Thesis, The University of Hong Kong.

Coles, R.G., Lee Long, W.J., Squire, B.A., Squire, L.C. and Bibby, J.M. 1987. Distribution of seagrasses and associated juvenile commercial penaeid prawns in north-eastern Queensland waters. *Australian Journal of Marine and Freshwater Research* 38:103–20.

Copeland, B.J. and Truitt, M.V. 1965. Fauna of the Aransas Pass inlet, Texas. II. penaeid shrimp postlarvae. *Texas Journal of Science* 18:65–74.

Crocos, P.J. and Kerr, J.D. 1983. Maturation and spawning of the banana prawn *Penaeus merguiensis* de Man (Crustacea: Penaeidae) in the Gulf of Carpentaria, Australia. *Journal of Experimental Marine Biology and Ecology* 69:37–59.

Daugherty, H.E. 1975. Human impact on the mangrove forests of El Salvador. In *Proceedings of International Symposium on Biology and Management of Mangroves, 1974* (ed. G.E. Walsh, S.C. Snedaker and H.J. Teas), 816-24. Gainesville: University of Florida.

De Freitas, A.J. 1986. Selection of nursery areas by six southeast African Penaeidae. *Estuarine, Coastal and Shelf Science* 23:901–8.

Delmendo, M.N. and Rabanal, H.R. 1956. Cultivation of "sugpo" (jumbo tiger shrimp), *Penaeus monodon* Fabricius, in the Philippines. *Proceedings of the Indo-Pacific Fisheries Council* 18:424–31.

Edwards, R.R.C. 1978. The fishery and fisheries biology of penaeid shrimp on the Pacific coast of Mexico. *Oceanography and Marine Biology Annual Review* 16:145–80.

Environmental Protection Department. 1989. *Marine water quality in Hong Kong*. Marine Section, Water Policy Group, Environmental Protection Department, Hong Kong Government.

Garcia, S. and Le Reste, L. 1981. Life cycles, dynamics, exploitation and management of coastal penaeid shrimp stock. *FAO Fisheries Technical Paper* 203:1–215.

Glaister, J.P. 1977. Ecological studies on *Metapenaeus macleayi* (Haswell) (Crustacea, Decapoda, Penaeidae) in the Clarence River region, northern N.S.W. M.Sc. Thesis, University of New England.

Haines, E.B. 1979. Interactions between Georgia salt marshes and coastal waters: a changing paradigm. In *Ecological processes in coastal and marine systems* (ed. R.J. Livingston), 35-46. New York: Plenum Press.

Hall, D.N.F. 1962. Observations on the taxonomy and biology of some Indo-West-Pacific Penaeidae (Crustacea, Decapoda). *Colonial Office Fishery Publications No. 17*. London: Her Majesty's Stationary Office.

Hart, R.C. 1979. The invertebrate communities: zooplankton, zoobenthos and littoral fauna. In *Lake Sibaya* (ed. B.R. Allanson). *Monographiae Biologicae* 36:108–61.

Hart, R.C. 1980. Embryonic duration and post-embryonic growth rates of the tropical freshwater shrimp *Caridina nilotica* (Decapoda: Atyidae) under laboratory and experimental field conditions. *Freshwater Biology* 10:297–315.

Hart, R.C. 1981. Population dynamics and production of the tropical freshwater shrimp *Caridina nilotica* (Decapoda: Atyidae) in the littoral of Lake Sibaya. *Freshwater Biology* 11:531–47.

Hoese, H.D. 1960. Juvenile penaeid shrimp in the shallow Gulf of Mexico. *Ecology* 41:592–3.

Hughes, D.A. 1966. Investigations of the "nursery areas" and habitat preferences of juvenile penaeid prawns in Mozambique. *Journal of Applied Ecology* 3:349–54.

Hughes, D.A. 1969. Responses to salinity change as a tidal transport mechanism of pink shrimp, *Penaeus duorarum*. *Biological Bulletin* 136:45–53.

Irving, R.T.A. and Morton, B. 1988. *A Geography of the Mai Po Marshes*. Hong Kong: Hong Kong University Press.

Johnson, D.S. 1965. A review of the brackish water prawns of Malaya. *Bulletin of the National Museum of Singapore* 33:7–11.

Kamita, T. 1970. *Studies on the freshwater shrimps, prawns and crawfishes of Japan*. Matsue: Sonoyama Shoten.

Kutkuhn, J.H. 1966. The role of estuaries in the development and perpetuation of commercial shrimp resources. In *A Symposium on estuarine fisheries* (ed. R.F. Smith, A.H. Swartz and W.H. Massman). *Special Publication of the American Fisheries Society* 3:16–36.

Lee, S.Y. 1988. The ecology of a traditional tidal shrimp pond in Hong Kong, the production and fate of macrodetritus, and its implications for management. Ph.D. Thesis, The University of Hong Kong.

Macintosh, D.J. 1982. Fisheries and aquaculture significance of mangrove swamps, with special reference to the Indo-West Pacific region. In *Recent Advances in Aquaculture* (ed. J.F. Muir and R.J. Roberts), 5-85. London: Croom Helm.

Macnae, W. 1974. Mangrove forests and fisheries. *Indian Ocean Programme Publication No. 34.* Indian Ocean Fishery Commission, Rome, 1 OFC/DEV/74/75. 35 pp.

Manuputty, A.E.W. 1984. Some notes on the crustacean fauna around mangrove areas of Pancer Balok, Cimanuk River Estuary, West Java. In *Proceedings of the Asian Symposium on Mangrove Environment, Research and Development* (ed. E. Soepadmo, A.N. Rao and D.J. Macintosh), 231-40. University of Malaya and Unesco.

Marine Fisheries Information Services, India. 1979. Synopsis of marine prawn fishery of India– 1978. *Technical and Extension Series No. 10.*

Mashiko, K. 1983. Differences in the eggs and clutch sizes of the prawn *Macrobrachium nipponense* (de Haan) between brackish and fresh waters of a river. *Zoological Magazine (Tokyo)* 92:1–9.

Odum, W.E. and Heald, E.J. 1972. Trophical analysis of an estuarine mangrove community. *Bulletin of Marine Science* 22:671–738.

Parker, J.C. 1970. Distribution of juvenile brown shrimp (*Penaeus aztecus* Ives) in Galveston Bay, Texas, as related to certain hydrographic features and salinity. *Contributions in Marine Science, University of Texas* 5:1–12.

Pearson, T.H. and Rosenberg, R. 1978. Macrobenthic succession in relation to organic enrichment and pollution of the marine environment. *Oceanography and Marine Biology Annual Review* 16:229–331.

Potter, I.C., Penn, J.W. and Brooker, K.S. 1986. Life cycle of the western school prawn, *Metapenaeus dalli* Racek, in a Western Australian estuary. *Australian Journal of Marine and Freshwater Research* 37:95–103.

Racek, A.A. 1970. Indo-West Pacific penaeid prawns of commercial importance. In *Coastal Aquaculture in the Indo-Pacific Region* (ed. T.V.R. Pillay), 152-72. Fishing News (Books) Limited.

Robertson, A.I. and Duke, N.C. 1987. Mangroves as nursery sites: comparisons of the abundance and species composition of fish and crustaceans in mangroves and other nearshore habitats in tropical Australia. *Marine Biology* 96:193–205.

Sanders, H.L. 1968. Marine benthic diversity: a comparative study *American Naturalist* 102:243–82.

Staples, D.J. 1980. Ecology of juvenile banana prawns, *Penaeus merguiensis*, in a mangrove estuary and adjacent offshore area of the Gulf of Carpentaria. I. Immigration and settlement of postlarvae. *Australian Journal of Marine and Freshwater Reaearch* 31:635–52.

Tham, A.K. 1968. Prawn culture in Singapore. Contribution to the FAO World Scientific Conference on the Biology and Culture of Shrimps and Prawns, New Mexico, June 1967. *FAO Fisheries Report* 57:85–93.

Wade, B.A. 1972. A description of a highly diverse soft-bottom community in Kingston Harbour, Jamaica. *Marine Biology* 13:57–69.

Weinstein, M.P. 1979. Shallow marsh habitats as primary nurseries for fishes and shellfish, Cape Fear River, North Carolina. *Fisheries Bulletin* 77:339–57.

Wu, R.S.S. 1982. Periodic defaunation and recovery in a subtropical community in relation to organic pollution. *Journal of Experimental Marine Biology and Ecology* 64:253–69.

Young, P.C. 1978. Moreton Bay, Queensland: a nursery area for juvenile penaeid prawns. *Australian Journal of Marine and freshwater Research* 29:55–75.

Young, P.C. and Carpenter, S.M. 1977. Recruitment of postlarval penaeid prawns to nursery areas in Moreton Bay, Queensland. *Australian Journal of Marine and Freshwater Research* 28:745–73.

Zimmerman, R.J., Minello, T.T. and Zamora, G. 1984. Selection of vegetated habitat by brown shrimp, *Penaeus aztecus*, in a Galveston Bay salt marsh. *Fishery Bulletin of the United States* 82:325–34.

The Marine Biology of the South China Sea
(ed. B. Morton). Proceedings of the First
International Conference on the Marine
Biology of Hong Kong and the South China Sea,
Hong Kong, 28 October – 3 November 1990.
Hong Kong: Hong Kong University Press, 1993.

ECOLOGICAL CHARACTERISTICS OF THE FISH FAUNA OF THE SOUTH CHINA SEA

Wang Cunxin

Institute of Oceanology, Academia Sinica, Qingdao, China

ABSTRACT

Based on samples collected over the last 35 years, the distributions of South China Sea fishes are summarized. 1787 species of fishes have been recorded, belonging to 37 orders, 234 families and 774 genera. More species occur in the southern than the northern region. Only a few endemic species have been recorded from the South China Sea. The Indo-Malaysian zoogeographical sub-region includes the southern and the Sino-Japan sub-region includes the northern parts of the South China Sea. Some commercial fishes are now extremely rare. The largest fish populations comprise smaller species of lower commercial value.

INTRODUCTION

The South China Sea, including the Taiwan Strait, is one of the largest marginal seas in the western north Pacific Ocean. It is mostly tropical and is connected with the Pacific Ocean by the Bashi Channel, Taiwan and the Mindolo Straits; with the Indian Ocean by the Straits of Malacca. The Kuroshio Current and cold deep-water masses can exchange water with this area through the Bashi Channel. The fish fauna of the South China Sea is highly diverse.

There are at least 1787 species, belonging to 37 orders, 234 families and 774 genera, occurring in the South China Sea. Of these, 139 species (7.8% of the total) are chondrichthian and 1648 (92.2% of the total) are osteichthian. The chondrichthian fishes are represented by 13 orders, 38 families, 76 genera and 139 species. Of these, the carcharhiriform fishes are the most abundant, with 5 families, 20 genera and 51 species. The myliobatiform fishes have eight families, 13 genera and 29 species. The osteichthian fishes are represented by 24 orders, 196 families, 698 genera and 1648 species, among which the perciform fishes are dominant in terms of species numbers, including 83 families, 293 genera and 928 species.

The South China Sea is a spawning, feeding and overwintering area for many commercial fishes. Both migratory and resident fishes occur alternately throughout the year, thus forming good fishing grounds. Of the 1787 species of fishes in this area, about 80% of the total are demersal. Of these, the predominant species include *Muraenesox cinereus* (Forsskål), *Pseudosciaena crocea* (Richardson), *Argyrosomus argentatus* (Houttuyn), *Argyrosomus macroscephalus* (Tang), *Nibea albiflora* (Richardson), *Johnius belengerii* (Cuvier and Valenciennes), *Miichthys miiuy* (Basilewsky), *Collichthys lucidus* (Richardson), *Pagrosomus major* (Temminck and Schlegel), *Parargyrops edita* Tanaka, *Taius tumiforons* (Temminck and Schlegel), *Upeneus moluccensis* (Bleeker), *Epinephelus akaara* (Temminck and Schlegel), *Epinephelus awoara* (Temminck and Schlegel), *Sillago sihama* (Forsskål), *Trichiurus haumela* (Forsskål), *Lethrinus haematopterus* (Temminck and Schlegel), *Lutjanus sanguineus* (Cuvier and Valenciennes), *Arius thalassinus* (Rüppell), *Mugil cephalus* Linneaus, *Priacanthus macracanthus* Cuvier, *Priacanthus tayenus* Richardson, *Platycephalus indicus* (Linnaeus), *Nemipterus virgatus* (Houttuyn), *Nemipterus bathybius* (Snyder) and *Navodon tesselatus* (Günther). *Navodon tessellatus* (Günther), *Pseudosciaena crocea* (Richardson) and *Trichiurus haumela* (Forsskål) are the most important in terms of yield and value of catch. About 20% of the total number of fishes in this area are pelagic. The predominant species consist of *Decapterus maruadsi* (Temminck and Schlegel), *Decapterus lajing* Bleeker, *Trachurus japonicus* (Temminck and Schlegel), *Pneumatophorus japonicus* (Houttuyn), *Rastrelliger kanagurta* (Cuvier), *Ilisha elongata* (Bennett), *Sardinella aurita* Valenciennes, *Scomberomorus guttatus* (Bloch and Schneider), *Scomberomorus commersoni* (Lacépède), *Thunnus thynnus* (Linnaeus), *Thunnus albacora* (Lowe), *Thunnus tonggol* (Bleeker), *Auxis thazard* (Lacépède), *Katsuwonus pelamis* (Linnaeus), *Euthynnus yaito* Kishinouye, *Pampus argenteus* (Euphrasen), *Coryphaena hippurus* Linnaeus, and *Formio niger* (Bloch). Among these species, *Decapterus maruadsi* (Temminck and Schlegel), *Trachurus japonicus* (Temminck and Schlegel), *Sardinella aurita* Valenciennes, *Ilisha elongata* (Bennett), *Pampus argenteus* (Euphrasen) and *Scomberomorus guttatus* (Bloch and Schneider) are of relatively greater economic importance.

FAUNAL CHARACTERISTICS AND GEOGRAPHIC DISTRIBUTION OF THE FISHES OF THE SOUTH CHINA SEA

There are warm-water, warm-temperate and cold-temperate species occurring in the South China Sea. About 65% are warm-water species and include *Prionace glauca* (Linnaeus), *Rhina ancylostoma* Bloch and Schneider, *Chanos chanos* (Forsskål), *Synodus variegatus* (Lacépède), *Myrichthys maculosus* (Cuvier), *Conger cinereus* Rüppell, *Echidna polyzona* (Richardson), *Gymnothorax pictus* (Ahl), *Aulostomus chinensis* (Linnaeus), *Adioryx diadema* (Lacépède), *Myrichthys murdjan* (Forsskål), *Variola louita* (Forsskål), *Epinephelus merra* (Bloch), *Caesio coerulaureus* Lacépède, *Gnathodentex aurolineatus* (Lacépède), *Mulloidichthys samoensis* (Günther), *Chaetodon auripes* Jordan and Snyder, *Amphiprion akallopisus* Bleeker, *Anampses diadematus* Rüppell, *Cheilinus rhodochrous* Günther, *Thalassoma fuscum* (Lacépède), *Scarops rubroviolaceus* (Bleeker), *Siganus vulpinus* (Schlegel and Müller), *Acanthurus olivaceus* Bloch and Schneider, *Psettodes erumei* (Schneider), *Balistes vetula* Linnaeus, *Arothron hispidus* (Linnaeus), *Diodon hystrix* Linnaeus and *Gastrophysus spadiceus* (Richardson). Warmtemperate species include *Dasyatis akajei* (Müller and Henle), *Coilia ectens* Jordan and Seale, *Saurida elongata* (Temminck and Schlegel), *Hippocampus japonicus* Kaup, *Liza haematocheila* (Temminck and Schlegel), *Lateolabrax japonicus* (Cuvier and Valenciennes), *Apogonichthys lineatus* (Temminck and Schlegel), *Hapalogenys nitens* (Richardson), *Nibea albiflora* (Richardson), *Miichthys miiuy* (Basilewsky), *Sparus macrocephalus* (Basilewsky), *Pagrosomus major* (Temminck and Schlegel), *Chaeturichthys stigmatias* Richardson, *Paralichthys olivaceus* (Temminck and Schlegel), *Pleuronichthys cornutus* (Temminck and Schlegel), *Cynoglossus semilaevis* Günther, *Fugu vermicularis* (Temminck and Schlegel), *Fugu xanthopterus* (Temminck and Schlegel). In winter, cold-temperate species such as *Eopsetta grigorjewi* (Herzenstein) and *Liparis tanakae* (Gilbert and Burke) occasionally occur in the northern Taiwan Strait.

Cosmopolitan species include *Hexanchus griseus* (Bonnaterre), *Galeocerdo cuvier* (Lesueur), *Prionace glauca* (Linnaeus), *Caetorhinus maximus* (Gunner), *Rhincodon typus* Smith, *Chanos chanos* (Forsskål), *Ablennes hians* (Cuvier and Valenciennes), *Exocoetus volitans* Linnaeus, *Caranx sexfasciatus* Quoy and Gaimard), *Selar crumenophthalmus* (Bloch), *Naucrates ductor* (Linnaeus), *Elagatis bipinnulatus* (Quoy and Gaimard), *Coryphaena hippurus* Linnaeus, *Promethichthys prometheus* (Cuvier and Valenciennes), *Acanthocybium solandi* (Cuvier and Valenciennes), *Auxis thazard* (Lacépède), *Katsuwonus pelamis* (Linnaeus), *Thunnus thynnus* Linnaeus, *Echeneis naucrates* Linnaeus, *Remora remora* (Linnaeus), *Remora albescens* (Temminck and Schlegal), *Canthidermis maculatus* (Bloch), *Diodon holacanthus* Linnaeus, *Chilomycterus orbicularis* (Bloch), *Gastrophysus spadiceus* (Richardson), and *Mola mola* (Linnaeus). Occurring in the northern part of the South China Sea, most of the above species are eurythermal warm-water. Only a few endemic species, i.e., *Bahaba flavolabiata* (Linnaeus), *Nibea semifasciata* Chu Lo and Wu, *Pomadasys unimaculatus* Tian, *Plectorhynchus sinensis* Zhu, Wu and Jin, *Hemipteronotus caerulopunctatus* Yu, have been described.

Many species belonging to the Muraenidae, Holocentridae, Chaetodontidae, Pomacentridae, Labridae, Scaridae, Acanthuridae, Zanclidae and Balistidae are typical warm-water coral reef fishes. Of 522 fish species recorded from the South China Sea Islands, 224 species are warm-water coral reef fishes. There are only 29 warm-water coral reef species occurring in the Southern Taiwan Strait, and 9 species in the north.

According to information in the literature, a total of 124 species of deep-pelagic fishes, belonging to 7 orders, 21 families and 58 genera, have been recorded from the South China Sea. Of these, 76 species are myctophiform and 36 species are salmoniform. The majority of the deep-pelagic fishes (78 species, 4.4% of the total) in the South China Sea, such as *Cyclothene obscura* Brauer, *Opisthoproctus soleatus* Vaillant, *Stomias affinis* Günther, *Omosudis lowei* Günther and *Barathronus diaphanus* Brauer, have a world-wide distribution. Twenty species (1.2% of the total), such as *Stomias nebulosus* Alcock, *Myctophum spinosum* (Steindachner), and *Diaphus richardsoni* Taning have been recorded from the Pacific and Indian Oceans, but not the Atlantic Ocean. Only five species (0.3% of the total) such as *Bolinichthys longipes* (Brauer), *Lampanyctus omostigma* Gilbert, *Diaphus burtoni* Fowler, *Diaphus malayanus* Weber and *Vitiziella cubiceps* Rass are restricted to the western Pacific.

CONCLUSIONS

Based on the characteristics of the fish fauna and the distribution of the 20°C surface isotherm in winter, I consider that the boundary between the subtropical Sino-Japanese and tropical Indo-Malaysian subregions may be located along the eastern coast of Hainan Island and include the inshore areas of the mainland coastline, the outer margin of the southeastern coast of Taiwan and the Ryukyu Islands. The fish fauna to the north of this boundary is subtropical, to the south of this boundary it is tropical. The Sino-Japanese subregion includes the mainland coastal area of the northern South China Sea and the western part of the East China Sea, of which the northern boundary reaches the mouth of the Yangtze River and Quelpart Island (Korea).

THE FISHES OF THE SOUTH CHINA SEA

Hexanchiformes
  Hexanchoideae
    Hexanchidae
      Hexanchus
        Hexanchus griseus (Bonnaterre)
      Notorhynchus
        Notorhynchus platycephalus (Tenore)
      Heptranchias
        Heptranchias perlo Bonnaterre
        Heptranchias dakini Whitley
Heterodontiformes
  Heterodontoidea
    Heterodontidae
      Heterodontus
        Heterodontus zebra (Gray)
Isuriformes
  Carcharioidea
    Carchariidae
      Carcharias
        Carcharias arenarias Ogilby
  Isurioidea
    Isuridae
      Isurus
        Isurus glaucua (Müller and Henle)
      Carcharodon
        Carcharodon carcharias (Linnaeus)
  Cetorhinoidea
    Cetorhinidae
      Cetorhinus
        Cetorhinus maximus (Gunner)
  Alopioidea
    Alopiidae
      Alopias
        Alopias pelagicus Nakamura
        Alopias vulpinus (Bonnaterre)
        Alopias profundus Nakamura

Orectolobiformes
  Orectoloboidei
    Orectolobidae
      Orectolobus
        Orectolobus japonicus Regan
        Orectolobus maculatus (Bonnaterre)
      Stegotoma
        Stegotoma fasciatus (Hermann)
      Chiloscyllium
        Chiloscyllium plagiosum (Bennett)
        Chiloscyllium griseum (Müller and Henle)
        Chiloscyllium punctatum (Müller and Henle)
        Chiloscyllium colax (Meuachen)
      Ginglymostoma
        Ginglymostoma ferrugineum Lesson
      Nebrius
        Nebrius macrurus (Garman)
    Cirrhoscyllidae
      Cirrhoscyllium
        Cirrhoscyllium expolitum Smith and Radcliffe
  Rhincodontoidei
    Rhincodontidae
      Rhincodon
        Rhincodon typus Smith
Carcharhiniformes
  Scyliorhinoidei
    Scyliorhinidae
      Galeus
        Galeus eastmani (Jordan and Snyder)
        Galeus niphonenais Nakaya
        Galeus sauteri Jordan and Richardson

Cephaloscyllium
  Cephaloscyllium fasciatum Chan
  Cephaloscyllium umbratile Jordan
    and Fowler
Halaelurus
  Halaelurus burgeri (Müller and
    Henle)
Apristurus
  Apristurus microps (Gilchrist)
  Apristurus platyrhynchus (Tanaka)
  Apristurus verweyi (Fowler)
  Apristurus longicephalus Nakaya
  Apristurus sinensis Chu and Wu
  Apristurus macrorhynchus (Tanaka)
Atelomycterus
  Atelomycterus marmoratus (Bennett)
Proscyllium
  Proscyllium habereri (Hilgendorf)
Triakoidei
  Pseudotriakidae
    Pseudotriakis
      Pseudotriakis acrages Jordan and
        Snyder
  Triakidae
    Triakis
      Triakis venustum (Tanaka)
      Triakis scyllium Müller and Henle
    Galeorhinus
      Galeorhinus japonicus (Müller and
        Henle)
    Mustelus
      Mustelus griseus Peitschmann
      Mustelus kanekonis (Tanaka)
Carcharhinoidei
  Carcharhinidae
    Triaenodon
      Triaenodon obesus (Rüppell)
    Galeocerdo
      Galeocerdo cuvier Fowler
    Negogaleus
      Negogaleus microstoma (Bleeker)
      Negogaleus brachygnathus Chu
      Negogaleus balfouri (Day)
      Negogaleus macroatoma (Bleeker)
    Paragaleus
      Paragaleus acutiventralis Chu
    Scoliodon

    Scoliodon sorrakowah (Cuvier)
    Scoliodon walbeehmi Bleeker
    Scoliodon palasorrah (Cuvier)
    Scoliodon dumerili (Bleeker)
    Negaprion
      Negaprion queenslandicus (Whitley)
    Aprionodon
      Aprionodon brevipenna (Müller and
        Henle)
    Hypoprion
      Hypoprion macloti (Müller and
        Henle)
      Hypoprion atripinnis Chu
    Carcharhinus
      Carcharhinus gangeticus (Müller
        and Henle)
      Carcharhinus albimarginatus
        (Rüppell)
      Carcharhinus microphthalmus Chu
      Carcharhinus pleurotaenia (Bleeker)
      Carcharhinus menisorrah (Müller
        and Henle)
      Carcharhinus dussumieri (Müller
        and Henle)
      Carcharhinus melanopterus (Quoy
        and Gaimard)
      Carcharhinus longimanus (Poey)
      Carcharhinus brachyurus (Günther)
      Carcharhinus sorrah (Müller and
        Henle)
      Carcharhinus atrodorsus Deng et al.
    Physodon
      Physodon mulleri (Müller and
        Henle)
    Prionace
      Prionace glauca (Linnaeus)
  Sphyrnoidei
    Sphyrnidae
      Sphyrna
        Sphyrna tiburo (Linnaeus)
        Sphyrna lewini (Linnaeus)
        Sphyrna mokarran (Rüppell)
        Sphyrna blochi (Cuvier)
Squaliformes
  Squaloidei
    Squalidae
      Squalus

Squalus mitsukurii Jordan
Squalus brevirostris Tanaka
Pseudocentrophorus
  Pseudocentrophorus isodon Chu et al.
Centrophorus
  Centrophorus acus Garman
Andmopterus
  Andmopterus lucifer Jordan and Snyder
Dalatiidae
Dalatias
  Dalatias licha (Bonnaterre)
Echinorhinidae
Echinorhinus
  Echinorhinus brucus (Bonnaterre)
Squatiniformes
Squatinoidei
Squatinidae
Squatina
  Squatina nebulosa Regan
Pristiophoriformes
Pristiophoroidei
Pristiophoridae
Pristiophorus
  Pristiophorus japonicus Günther
Pristiformes
Pristoidei
Pristidae
Pristis
  Pristis cuspidatus Latham
  Pristis microdon Latham
Rajiformes
Rhinobatoidei
Rhinidae
Rhina
  Rhina ancylostoma Bloch and Schneider
Rhynchohobatidae
Rhynchobatus
  Rhynchobatus djiddensis (Forsskål)
Rhinobatidae
Scobatus
  Scobatus granulatus (Cuvier)
  Scobatus halavi (Forsskål)
Rhinobatus
  Rhinobatus hynnicephalus Richardson
  Rhinobatus schlegeli Müller and Henle
Platyrhinidae
Platyrhina
  Platyrhina sinensis (Bloch and Schneider)
  Platyrhina limboonkengi Tang
Rajoidei
Rajidae
Raja
  Raja kenojei Müller and Henle
  Raja hollandi Jordan and Richardson
  Raja kwangtungensis Chu
Breviraja
  Breviraja tobitukai Hiyama
Anacanthobatidae
Anacanthobatis
  Anacanthobatis borneensis Chan
Springeria
  Springeria nanhaiensis Meng and Li
  Springeria melanosoma Chan
Myliobatiformes
Dasyatoidei
Hexatrygonidae
Hexatrygon
  Hexatrygon bickelli Heemstra and Smith
Urolophidae
Urolophus
  Urolophus marmoratus Chu et al.
Dasyatidae
Urogymnus
  Urogymnus africanus (Bloch and Schneider)
Taeniura
  Taeniura melanospilos Bleeker
Dasyatis
  Dasyatis atratus Ishiyama
  Dasyatis uarank (Forsskål)
  Dasyatis gerrardi (Gray)
  Dasyatis imbricatus (Bloch and Schneider)
  Dasyatis bennetti (Müller and Henle)
  Dasyatis microphthalmus Chen
  Dasyatis zugei (Müller and Henle)

Dasyatis kuhli (Müller and Henle)
　　Dasyatis akajei (Müller and Henle)
　Gymnuridae
　　Gymnura
　　　Gymnura bimaculata (Norman)
　　　Gymnura poecilura (Shaw)
　　　Gymnura japonica (Temminck and Schlegel)
　　Aetoplatea
　　　Aetoplatea zonura Bleeker
Myliobatoidei
　Myliobatidae
　　Myliobatis
　　　Myliobatis tobijei Bleeker
　　Aetomylaeus
　　　Aetomylaeus maculatus (Gray)
　　　Aetomylaeus vespertilio (Bleeker)
　　　Aetomylaeus nilvus (Müller and Henle)
　　Aandomylaeus
　　　Aandomylaeus nichofi (Bloch and Schneider)
　Aetobatidae
　　Aaetobatus
　　　Aetobatus guttatus (Shaw)
　　　Aetobatus flagellum (Bloch and Schneider)
Rhinopteroidei
　Rhinopteridae
　　Rhinoptera
　　　Rhinoptera hainanica Chu
　　　Rhinoptera javanica Müller and Henle
Mobuloidei
　Mobuloidae
　　Mobula
　　　Mobula japonica (Müller and Henle)
　　　Mobula diabolus (Shaw)
　　Manta
　　　Manta birostris (Walbaum)
Torpediniformes
　Torpedinoidei
　　Torpedinidae
　　　Narcine
　　　　Narcine maculata (Shaw)
　　　　Narcine timlei (Bloch and Schneider)
　　　　Narcine lingula Richardson
　　　Benthobatis
　　　　Benthobatis moresbys Alcock
　　　Torpedo
　　　　Torpedo macnilli (Whitley)
　　Narkidae
　　　Narke
　　　　Narke japonica (Temminck and Schlegel)
　　　Crassinarke
　　　　Crassinarke dormitor Takagi
Chimaeriformes
　Chimaeroidei
　　Chimaeridae
　　　Chimaera
　　　　Chimaera phantasma Jordan and Snyder
　　Rhinochimaeridae
　　　Rhinochimaera
　　　　Rhinochimaera pacific (Mitsukuri)
Acipenseriformes
　Acipenseridae
　　Acipenser
　　　Acipenser sinensis Gray
Elopiformes
　Elopidae
　　Elops
　　　Elops saurus Linnaeus
　Megalopidae
　　Megalops
　　　Megalops cyprinoides (Broussonet)
　Albulidae
　　Albula
　　　Albula vulpes (Linnaeus)
Gonorhynchiformes
　Gonorhynchidae
　　Gonorhynchus
　　　Gonorhynchus abbreviatus Temminck and Schlegel
　Chanidae
　　Chanos
　　　Chanos chanos (Forsskål)
Clupeiformes
　Clupeidae
　　Dussumieria
　　　Dussumieria hasselti Bleeker
　　Etrumeus
　　　Etrumeus micropus (Temminck and

Schlegel)
Kowala
  Kowala coval (Cuvier)
Sardinella
  Sardinella aurita Valenciennes
  Sardinella sirm (Walbaum)
  Sardinella clupeoides (Bleeker)
  Sardinella melanura (Cuvier)
  Sardinella jussieu (Lacépède)
Sardinops
  Sardinops sagax melanosticta (Temminck and Schlegel)
Macrura
  Macrura kelee (Cuvier)
  Macrura reevesi (Richardson)
Clupanodon
  Clupanodon thrissa (Linnaeus)
  Clupanodon punctatus (Temminck and Schlegel)
Nematalosa
  Nematalosa nasus (Bloch)
Anodontostoma
  Anodontostoma chacunda (Hamilton)
Ilisha
  Ilisha indica (Swainson)
  Ilisha elongata (Bennett)
Opisthopterus
  Opisthopterus tardoore (Valenciennes)
Engraulidae
Anchoviella
  Anchoviella heteroloba (Rüppell)
  Anchoviella zollingeri (Bleeker)
  Anchoviella commersoni (Lacépède)
  Anchoviella tri (Bleeker)
  Anchoviella chinensis (Günther)
  Anchoviella indica (Van Hasselt)
Thrissa
  Thrissa kammalensis (Bleeker)
  Thrissa hamiltoni (Gray)
  Thrissa mystax (Bloch and Schneider)
  Thrissa vitirostris (Gilchrist and Thompson)
  Thrissa dussumieri (Valenciennes)
  Thrissa setirostris (Broussonet)
Setipinna
  Setipinna taty (Valenciennes)
Coilia
  Coilia grayii Richardson
  Coilia mystus (Linnaeus)
Chirocentridae
Chirocentrus
  Chirocentrus dorab (Forsskål)
  Chirocentrus nudus (Swainson)
Salmoniformes
Osmeroidei
Plecoglossidae
Plecoglossus
  Plecoglossus altivelis Temminck and Schlegel
Salangidae
Neosalanx
  Neosalanx tangkahkeii (Wu)
Leucosoma
  Leucosoma chinensis (Osbeck)
Argentidae
Argentina
  Argentina kagoshimae Jordan and Snyder
Opisthoproctidae
Opisthoproctus
  Opisthoproctus soleatus Vaillant
Stomiatoidei
Gonostomatidae
Gonostoma
  Gonostoma atlanticus Norman
  Gonostoma elongatus Günther
Polymetme
  Polymetme illustris (McCulloch)
Cyclothone
  Cyclothone obscura Brauer
  Cyclothone alba Brauer
  Cyclothone acclinidens Garman
  Cyclothone pseudopallida Mukacheva
  Cyclothone pallida Brauer
Valenciennellus
  Valenciennellus tripunctulatus (Esmark)
Vinciguerria
  Vinciguerria nimbara (Jordan and Williams)
Stenoptychidae

Argyropelecus
  Argyropelecus affinis Garman
  Argyropelecus hemigymnus Cocco
  Argyropelecus sladeni Regan
  Argyropelecus aculeatus
    Valenciennes
Sternoptyx
  Sternoptyx obscura Garman
  Sternoptyx diaphana Hermann
  Sternoptyx pseudobadura Baird
Polyipnus
  Polyipnus tridentifer McCulloch
  Polyipnus spinosus Günther
Stomiatidae
 Stomias
  Stomias nebulosus Alcock
  Stomias affinis Günther
Idiacanthidae
 Idiacanthus
  Idiacanthus fasciola Peters
Melanostomiatidae
 Eustomias
  Eustomias longibarba Parr
Photonectes
  Photonectes albipennis (Doderlein)
Leptostomias
  Leptostomias robustus Imai
Melanostomias
  Melanostomias melanopogon Regan
    and Trewavas
Bathophilus
  Bathophilus longipinnis
    (Pappenheim)
Pachystomias
  Pachystomias microdon (Günther)
 Astronesthoidei
  Astronesthidae
   Astronesthes
    Astronesthes lucifer Gilbert
    Astronesthes indicus Brauer
  Chauliodontidae
   Chauliodus
    Chauliodus sloani Schneider
Alepocephaloidei
 Alepocephalidae
  Alepocephalus
   Alepocephalus bicolor Alcock

Myctophiformes
 Myctophoidei
  Synodidae
   Synodus
    Synodus kaianus (Günther)
    Synodus macrops Tanaka
    Synodus hoshinonis Tanaka
    Synodus indicus (Day)
    Synodus variegatus (Lacépède)
    Synodus englemani Schultz
   Trachinocephalus
    Trachinocephalus myops (Bloch and
     Schneider)
   Saurida
    Saurida gracilis (Quoy and
     Gaimard)
    Saurida undosquamis (Richardson)
    Saurida tumbil (Bloch and
     Schneider)
    Saurida filamentosa Ogilby
    Saurida elongata (Temminck and
     Schlegel)
  Harpodontidae
   Harpodon
    Harpodon nehereus (Hamilton)
  Aulopodidae
   Hime
    Hime japonicus (Günther)
  Chlorophthamidae
   Chlorophthalmus
    Chlorophthalmus acutifrons Hiyama
    Chlorophthalmus nigromarginatus
     (Kamohara)
    Chlorophthalmus oblongus
     Kamohara
    Chlorophthalmus albatrossis Jordan
     and Starks
  Neosopelidae
   Scopelengys
    Scopelengys tristis Alcock
  Myctophidae
   Diogenichthys
    Diogenichthys atlanticis (Taning)
    Diogenichthys laternatus (Garman)
    Diogenichthys panurgus Bolin
   Benthosema
    Benthosema suborbitale Gilbert

Hygophum
  Hygophum proximum Becker
  Hygophum atratum (Garman)
Myctophum
  Myctophum nitidulum Garman
  Myctophum obtusirostris Taning
  Myctophum aurolaternatum Garman
  Myctophum lychnobium Bolin
  Myctophum brachgnathum (Bleeker)
  Myctophum asperum Richardson
  Myctophum spinosum (Steindachner)
Symbolophorus
  Symbolophorus boops (Richardson)
  Symbolophorus evermanni (Gilbert)
Gonichthys
  Gonichthys coccoi (Cocco)
Centrobranchus
  Centrobranchus andreae (Lutken)
  Centrobranchus choerocephalus Fowler
Diaphus
  Diaphus richardsoni Taning
  Diaphus fulgens (Brauer)
  Diaphus parri Taning
  Diaphus perspicillatus (Ogilby)
  Diaphus burtoni Fowler
  Diaphus luetkeni (Brauer)
  Diaphus suborbitalis Weber
  Diaphus diademophilus Nafpaktitis
  Diaphus problematius Parr
  Diaphus jenseni Taning
  Diaphus malayanus Weber
  Diaphus garmani Gilbert
Lampadena
  Lampadena luminosa Garman
Bolinichthys
  Bolinichthys longipes (Brauer)
Ceratoscopelus
  Ceratoscopelus warmingi (Lutken)
Lampanyctus
  Lampanyctus alatus Goode and Bean
  Lampanyctus macropterus (Brauer)
  Lampanyctus omostigma Gilbert
  Lampanyctus niger Günther
Triphoturus
  Triphoturus micropterus (Brauer)
  Triphoturus nigrescens (Brauer)

Alepisauroidei
  Scopelarchidae
    Scopelarchus
      Scopelarchus guentheri Alcock
      Scopelarchus analis (Brauer)
    Scopelarchoides
      Scopelarchoides danae Johnson
  Alepisaurusidae
    Alepisaurus
      Alepisaurus ferox Lowe
  Evermannellidae
    Evermannella
      Evermannella indica Brauer
  Omosudidae
    Omosudis
      Omosudis lowei Günther
Cetomimiformes
  Cetomimoidei
    Megalomycteridae
      Vitiaziella
        Vitiaziella cubiceps Rass
  Ateleopodooidei
    Ateleopidae
      Ateleopus
        Ateleopus purpureus Tanaka
      Ijimaia
        Ijimaia dofleini Sauter
Anguilliformes
  Anguillidae
    Anguilla
      Anguilla marmorata Quoy and Gaimard
  Congridae
    Coloconger
      Coloconger scholesi Chan
    Conger
      Conger cinereus Rüppell
    Anago
      Anago anago (Temminck and Schlegel)
    Rhynchocymba
      Rhynchocymba nystroms (Jordan and Snyder)
      Rhynchocymba sivicola (Matsubara and Ochiai)
    Rhynchoconger
      Rhynchoconger ectenurus (Jordan

and Richardson)
Uroconger
 Uroconger lepturus (Richardson)
Muraenesocidae
 Muraenesox
  Muraenesox cinereus (Forsskål)
  Muraenesox yamaguchiensis
   Katayama and Takai
  Muraenesox talabonoides (Bleeker)
  Muraenesox talabon (Cuvier)
 Oxyconger
  Oxyconger leptoganathus Bleeker
Nandtastomidae
 Chlopsis
  Chlopsis fierasfer Jordan and Snyder
  Chlopsis taiwanensis Chen and
   Weng
Muraenidae
 Echidna
  Echidna zebra (Shaw)
  Echidna polyzona (Richardson)
  Echidna nebulosa (Ahl)
  Echidna delicatula (Kaup)
 Gymnomuraena
  Gymnomuraena tigrina (Lesson)
  Gymnomuraena concolor (Rüppell)
 Gymnothorax
  Gymnothorax pictus (Ahl)
  Gymnothorax thyrsoideus
   (Richardson)
  Gymnothorax meleagris (Shaw)
  Gymnothorax polyuranodon
   (Bleeker)
  Gymnothorax flavimarinatus
   (Rüppell)
  Gymnothorax boschi Bleeker
  Gymnothorax reticularis Bloch
  Gymnothorax petelli (Bleeker)
  Gymnothorax richardsoni (Bleeker)
  Gymnothorax punctofasciatus
   Bleeker
  Gymnothorax kidako (Temminck
   and Schlegel)
  Gymnothorax melanospilus
   (Bleeker)
  Gymnothorax fimbriata (Bennett)
  Gymnothorax favagineus (Bloch and
   Schneider)
  Gymnothorax reevesi (Richardson)
  Gymnothorax leucostigma Jordan
   and Richardson
  Gymnothorax undulatus (Lacépède)
  Gymnothorax pseudothyrsoideus
   Bleeker
Moringuidae
 Moringua
  Moringua macrocephalus (Bleeker)
  Moringua macrochir (Bleeker)
Nemichthyidae
 Nemichthys
  Nemichthys scolopaeus Richardson
Dysommidae
 Dysomma
  Dysomma anguillaris Barnard
  Dysomma melanurum Chen and
   Weng
Echelidae
 Myrophis
  Myrophis cheni Chen and Weng
 Muraenichthys
  Muraenichthys macropteus Bleeker
  Muraenichthys malabonensis Herre
  Muraenichthys gymnopterus Bleeker
Ophichthyidae
 Caecula
  Caecula longipinnis Kner and
   Steindachner
 Bascanichthys
  Bascanichthys kirki (Günther)
 Brachysomophis
  Brachysomophis cirrhochilus
   (Bleeker)
  Brachysomophis crocodilinus
   (Bennett)
 Cirrhimuraena
  Cirrhimuraena chinensis Kaup
 Leiuranus
  Leiuranus semicinctus (Lay and
   Bennett)
 Myrichthys
  Myrichthys maculosus (Cuvier)
  Myrichthys colubrinus (Boddaert)
 Pisodonophis
  Pisodonophis cancrivorugs

(Richardson)
Pisodonophis boro (Hamilton)
Pisodonophis rubicandus Chen
Xyrias
  Xyrias revulsus Jordan and Richardson
Ophichthyus
  Ophichthyus evermanni Jordan and Richardson
  Ophichthyus apicalis (Bennett)
  Ophichthyus urolophus (Temminck and Schlegel)
  Ophichthyus celebicus Bleeker
Notacanthiformes
  Halosauridae
    Halosaurus
      Halosaurus sinensis Abe
    Halosauropsis
      Halosauropsis affinis (Günther)
Siluriformes
  Plotosidae
    Plotosus
      Plotosus anguillaris (Bloch)
  Pangasidae
    Sinopangasius
      Sinopangasius semicultratus Chang and Wu
  Ariidae
    Arius
      Arius sinensis (Lacépède)
      Arius leiotetocephalus Bleeker
      Arius thalassinus (Rüppell)
Atheriniformes
  Atherinidae
    Allanetta
      Allanetta bleekeri (Günther)
      Allanetta woodwardi (Jordan and Starks)
      Allanetta forsskål (Rüppell)
    Pranesus
      Pranesus insularum (Jordan and Evermann)
Beloniformes
  Belonidae
    Belone
      Belone platyura Bennett
    Ablennes
      Ablennes anastomella (Cuvier and Valenciennes)
      Ablennes hians (Cuvier and Valenciennes)
    Tylosurus
      Tylosurus giganteus (Temminck and Schlegel)
      Tylosurus melanotus (Bleeker)
      Tylosurus crocodilus (Le Sueur)
      Tylosurus leiurus (Bleeker)
  Exocoetoidei
    Hemiramphidae
      Hemiramphus
        Hemiramphus georgii Cuvier and Valenciennes
        Hemiramphus sinensis (Günther)
        Hemiramphus intermedius Cantor
        Hemiramphus melanurus Cuvier and Valenciennes
        Hemiramphus quoyi Cuvier and Valenciennes
        Hemiramphus dussumieri Cuvier and Valenciennes
        Hemiramphus far (Forsskål)
      Euleptorhamphus
        Euleptorhamphus viridis (Van Hasselt)
      Zenarchopterus
        Zenarchopterus buffoni (Cuvier and Valenciennes)
    Oxyporhamphidae
      Oxyporhamphus
        Oxyporhamphus micropterus (Cuvier and Valenciennes)
    Exocoetidae
      Fodiator
        Fodiator acutus pacificus Brunn
      Parexocoetus
        Parexocoetus mento (Cuvier and Valenciennes)
        Parexocoetus brachyptorus (Richardson)
      Exocoetus
        Exocoetus monocirrhus (Richardson)
        Exocoetus volitans Linnaeus
      Cypselurus
        Cypselurus speculiger (Cuvier and

Valenciennes)
　Cypselurus oxycephalus (Bleeker)
　Cypselurus poecilopterus (Cuvier and Valenciennes)
　Cypselurus suttoni (Whitley and Colefax)
　Cypselurus atrisignis Jenkins
　Cypselurus katoptron (Bleeker)
　Cypselurus arcticeps (Günther)
　Cypselurus brevis Weber and Beaufort
　Cypselurus pinnatibarbatus japonicus (Franz)
　Cypselurus bahiensis (Ranzani)
　Cypselurus cyanopterus (Cuvier and Valenciennes)
　Cypselurus nigripennes (Cuvier and Valenciennes)
　Cypselurus simus (Cuvier and Valenciennes)
　Cypselurus oligolepis (Bleeker)
　Cypselurus starksi Abe
　Cypselurus hiraii Abe
　Cypselurus spilopterus Cuvier and Valenciennes
　Cypselurus naresi (Günther)
　Cypselurus opisthopus (Bleeker)
　Prognichthys
　　Prognichthys rondeleti (Cuvier and Valenciennes)
　　Prognichthys albimaculatus (Fowler)
　　Prognichthys brevipinnis (Cuvier and Valenciennes)
Gadiformes
　Gadoidei
　　Moridae
　　　Physicucus
　　　　Physicucus japonicus Hilgendorf
　　　　Physicucus maximowiczi (Herzenstein)
　　　　Physicucus nigrscens Smith and Radcliffe
　　　　Physicucus jordani Bohlke and Mead
　　Bregmacerotidae
　　　Bregmaceros
　　　　Bregmaceros macclellandi Thompson
　　　　Bregmaceros atlanticus Goode and Bean
　　　　Bregmaceros rarisquamosus Munro
　　　　Bregmaceros nectabanus White
　　　　Bregmaceros arabicus D'Ancona and Cavinato
　Macrouroidei
　　Macrouridae
　　　Gadomus
　　　　Gadomus multifilis (Günther)
　　　Hymenocephalus
　　　　Hymenocephalus longiceps Smith and Radcliffe
　　　　Hymenocephalus striatissimus Jordan and Gilbert
　　　　Hymenocephalus lethonemus Jordan and Gilbert
　　　Ventrifossa
　　　　Ventrifossa nigrodorsalis Gilbert and Hubbs
　　　　Ventrifossa divergens Gilbert and Hubbs
　　　　Ventrifossa garmani (Jordan and Gilbert)
　　　Coelorhynchus
　　　　Coelorhynchus kamoharai Matsubara
　　　　Coelorhynchus formosanus Okamura
　　　　Coelorhynchus cingulatus Gilbert and Hubbs
　　　　Coelorhynchus kishinouyei Jordan and Snyder
　　　　Coelorhynchus commutabilis Smith and Radcliffe
　Ophidioidei
　　Carapidae
　　　Carapus
　　　　Carapus lumbricoides (Bleeker)
　　　　Carapus parvipinnis (Kaup)
　　　　Carapus homei (Richardson)
　　　　Carapus kagoshimanus (Steindachner and Doderlein)
　　　　Carapus owasianus Matsubara
　　Ophidiidae
　　　Brotula

Brotula multibarbata Temminck and
    Schlegel
Ophidion
    Ophidion asiro (Jordan and Fowler)
    Ophidion muraenolensis Günther
Sirembo
    Sirembo imberbis (Temminck and
        Schlegel)
    Sirembo marmoratum (Goode and
        Bean)
Hoplobrotula
    Hoplobrotula armata (Temminck
        and Schlegel)
Pycnocraspedum
    Pycnocraspedum microlepis
        (Matsubara)
Luciobrotula
    Luciobrotula bartschi Smith and
        Radcliffe
Homostolus
    Homostolus japonicus Matsubara
Monomitopus
    Monomitopus longiceps Smith and
        Radcliffe
Neobythites
    Neobythites nigromaculatus
        Kamohara
    Neobythites fasciatus Smith and
        Radcliffe
Dicrolene
    Dicrolene tristis Smith and Radcliffe
Bassozetus
    Bassozetus robustus Smith and
        Radcliffe
Bythitidae
Diplacanthopoma
    Diplacanthopoma brunnea (Smith
        and Radcliffe)
Saccogaster
    Saccogaster tubercularis (Chan)
Oligopus
    Oligopus robustus (Smith and
        Radcliffe)
Dinematichthys
    Dinematichthys iluocoeteoides
        Bleeker
Brotulina

Brotulina fusca Fowler
Aphyonidae
Aphyonus
    Aphyonus bolini Nielsen
Barathronus
    Barathronus diaphanus Brauer
Beryciformes
Stephanoberycoidei
Melamphaidae
Scopeloberyx
    Scopeloberyx robustus (Günther)
Scopelogadus
    Scopelogadus mizolepis (Günther)
Poromitra
    Poromitra oscitans Ebeling
Berycoidei
Polymixiidae
Polymixia
    Polymixia berndti Gilbert
    Polymixia japonicus Günther
Diretmidae
Diretmus
    Diretmus argenteus Johnson
Berycidae
Beryx
    Beryx splendens Lowe
Centroberyx
    Centroberyx lineatus (Cuvier and
        Valenciennes)
Trachichtyidae
Gephyroberyx
    Gephyroberyx japonicus (Doderlein)
Hoplostethus
    Hoplostethus mediterraneus Cuvier
        and Valenciennes
Paratraicchthys
    Paratraicchthys prosthemius Jordan
        and Fowler
Holocentridae
Ostichthys
    Ostichthys japonicus (Cuvier and
        Valenciennes)
Myripristis
    Myripristis pralinius Cuvier and
        Valenciennes
    Myripristis adustus Bleeker
    Myripristis hexagonus (Lacépède)

Myripristis murdjan (Forsskål)
Myripristis violaceus Bleeker
Myripristis parvidens Cuvier and Valenciennes
Flammeo
  Flammeo opercularis (Cuvier and Valenciennes)
  Flammeo sammara (Forsskål)
  Flammeo argenteus (Cuvier and Valenciennes)
Adioryx
  Adioryx spinifer (Forsskål)
  Adioryx spinossimus (Temminck and Schlegel)
  Adioryx cornutus (Bleeker)
  Adioryx violaceus (Bleeker)
  Adioryx furcatus (Günther)
  Adioryx caudimacuatus (Cuvier and Valenciennes)
  Adioryx lacteoguttatus (Cuvier and Valenciennes)
  Adioryx tiere (Cuvier and Valenciennes)
  Adioryx microstomus (Günther)
  Adioryx diadema (Lacépède)
Dispinus
  Dispinus ruber (Forsskål)
Monocentridae
Monocentris
  Monocentris japonicus (Houttuyn)
Zeiformes
  Grammicolepidae
    Xenolepidichthys
      Xenolepidichthys dalgleishi Gilchrist
  Zeidae
    Zeus
      Zeus japonicus Cuvier and Valenciennes
    Cyttomimus
      Cyttomimus affinis Weber
    Zenion
      Zenion holopis (Goode and Bean)
    Parazen
      Parazen pacificus Kamohara
  Antigonidae
    Antigonia
      Antigonia capros Lowe
      Antigonia rubescens (Günther)
Lampridiformes
  Veliferoidei
    Veliferidae
      Velifer
        Velifer hypselopterus Bleeker
  Trachipteroidei
    Trachipteridae
      Zu
        Zu cristatus (Bonelli)
    Regalecidae
      Regalecus
        Regalecus russelli (Shaw)
Gasterosteiformes
  Aulostomoidei
    Fistulariidae
      Fistularia
        Fistularia commersoni Rüppell
        Fistularia petimba Lacépède
    Aulostomidae
      Aulostomus
        Aulostomus chinensis (Linnaeus)
    Centriscidae
      Centriscus
        Centriscus scutus Linnaeus
  Syngnthoidei
    Solenostomidae
      Solenostomus
        Solenostomus armatus Weber
    Syngnathidae
      Urocampus
        Urocampus nanus Günther
      Ichthyocampus
        Ichthyocampus belcheri Kaup
      Doryrhampus
        Doryrhampus melanopleura (Bleeker)
      Halicampus
        Halicampus koiomatodon Bleeker
      Trachyrhamphus
        Trachyrhamphus serratus Temminck and Schlegel
      Yozia
        Yozia bicoarctatus Bleeker
      Syngnatus
        Syngnatus djarong Bleeker
        Syngnatus spicifer Rüppell

Syngnatus argyrostictus Kaup
Syngnatus cyanospilus Bleeker
Syngnatus acus Linnaeus
Corythoichthys
  Corythoichthys fasciatus (Gray)
Syngnathoides
  Syngnathoides biaculeatus (Bloch)
Solegnathus
  Solegnathus hardwicki (Gray)
Hippocampus
  Hippocampus coronatus Temminck and Schlegel
  Hippocampus histrix Kaup
  Hippocampus japonicus Kaup
  Hippocampus kuda Bleeker
  Hippocampus trimaculatus Leach
  Hippocampus kelloggi Jordan and Snyder
Mugiliformes
  Sphyraenoidei
    Sphyraenidae
      Sphyraena
        Sphyraena helleri Jenkins
        Sphyraena japonica Cuvier and Valenciennes
        Sphyraena barracuda (Walbaum)
        Sphyraena forsteri Cuvier and Valenciennes
        Sphyraena jello Cuvier and Valenciennes
        Sphyraena obtusata Cuvier and Valenciennes
        Sphyraena pinguis Günther
  Mugiloidei
    Mugilidae
      Mugil
      Mugil cephalus Linnaeus
      Osteomugil
        Osteomugil strongylocephalus (Richardson)
        Osteomugil ophuyseni (Bleeker)
      Valamugil
        Valamugil seheli (Forsskål)
        Valamugil buchanani (Bleeker)
      Liza
        Liza carinatus (Cuvier and Valenciennes)
        Liza dussumieri (Cuvier and Valenciennes)
        Liza tade (Forsskål)
        Liza haematocheila (Temminck and Schlegel)
        Liza macrolepis (Smith)
      Ellochelon
        Ellochelon vaigiensis (Quoy and Gaimard)
      Plicomugil
        Plicomugil labiosus (Cuvier and Valenciennes)
      Crenimugil
        Crenimugil crenilabis (Forsskål)
Polynemoidei
  Polynemidae
    Eleutheronema
      Eleutheronema tetradactylum (Shaw)
    Polynemus
      Polynemus plebeius Broussonet
      Polynemus sextarius Bloch and Schneider
Perciformes
  Percoidei
    Ambassidae
     Ambassis
      Ambassis kopsi Bleeker
      Ambassis miops Günther
      Ambassis urotaenia Bleeker
      Ambassis gymnocephalus (Lacépède)
    Latidae
     Lates
      Lates calcarifer (Bloch)
     Psammoperca
      Psammoperca waigiensis (Cuvier and Valenciennes)
    Serranidae
     Malakichthys
      Malakichthys elogans Matsubara
      Malakichthys griseus Doderlein
     Grammistes
      Grammistes sexlineatus Thünberg
     Pogonoperca
      Pogonoperca ocellatus Günther
     Lateolabrax

Lateolabrax japonicus (Cuvier and
    Valenciennes)
Diploprion
  Diploprion bifasciatum (Kuhl and
    Van Hasselt)
Synagrops
  Synagrops japonicus (Steindachner
    and Doderlein)
  Synagrops philippinensis (Günther)
  Synagrops serratospinosus Smith
    and Radcliffe
Plectropomus
  Plectropomus oligacanthus Bleeker
  Plectropomus truncatus Fowler and
    Bean
  Plectropomus leopardus (Lacépède)
Variola
  Variola louti (Forsskål)
Gracila
  Gracila albomarginatus (Fowler and
    Bean)
Aethaloperca
  Aethaloperca rogaa (Forsskål)
Cephalopholis
  Cephalopholis pachycentron (Cuvier
    and Valenciennes)
  Cephalopholis boenack (Bloch)
  Cephalopholis leopardus (Bloch and
    Schneider)
  Cephalopholis urodelus (Bloch and
    Schneider)
  Cephalopholis sonnerati (Cuvier and
    Valenciennes)
  Cephalopholis aurantius (Cuvier
    and Valenciennes)
  Cephalopholis miniatus (Forsskål)
  Cephalopholis argus (Bloch and
    Schneider)
Anyperodon
  Anyperodon leucogrammicus
    (Cuvier and Valenciennes)
Trisotropis
  Trisotropis dermopterus (Temminck
    and Schlegel)
Promicrops
  Promicrops lanceolatus (Bloch)
Epinephalus

Epinephelus hoedti (Bleeker)
Epinephelus undulosus (Quoy and
    Gaimard)
Epinephelus areolatus (Forsskål)
Epinephelus chlorostigma (Cuvier
    and Valenciennes)
Epinephelus truncatus Katayama
Epinephelus latifasciatus (Temminck
    and Valenciennes)
Epinephelus cometae Tanaka
Epinephelus morrhua (Cuvier and
    Valenciennes)
Epinephelus septemfasciatus
    (Thünberg)
Epinephelus moara (Temminck and
    Valenciennes)
Epinephelus fasciatus (Forsskål)
Epinephelus sexfasciatus (Cuvier
    and Valenciennes)
Epinephelus awoara (Temminck and
    Schlegel)
Epinephelus fasciatomaculatus
    (Peters)
Epinephelus amblycephalus
    (Bleeker)
Epinephelus diacanthus (Cuvier and
    Valenciennes)
Epinephelus hexagonatus (Cuvier
    and Valenciennes)
Epinephelus tauvina (Forsskål)
Epinephelus malabaricus (Bloch and
    Schneider)
Epinephelus maculatus (Bloch)
Epinephelus akaara (Temminck and
    Schlegel)
Epinephelus fario (Thünberg)
Epinephelus megachir (Richardson)
Epinephelus rhyncholepis (Bleeker)
Epinephelus summana (Forsskål)
Epinephelus merra (Bloch)
Epinephelus spilotoceps Schultz
Epinephelus corallicola (Cuvier and
    Valenciennes)
Epinephelus tukula Morgana
Epinephelus fuscoguttatus (Forsskål)
Epinephelus microdon (Bleeker)
Epinephelus caeruleopunctatus

(Forsskål)
Epinephelus macrospilos (Bleeker)
Epinephelus epistictus (Temminck and Schlegel)
Epinephelus bleekeri (Vaillant and Bocourt)
Cromileptes
  Cromileptes altivelis (Cuvier and Valenciennes)
Chorististium
  Chorististium latifasciata (Tanaka)
Chelidoperca
  Chelidoperca margaritifera Weber
Zalanthias
  Zalanthias azumanus (Jordan and Richardson)
Sayonara
  Sayonara satsumae Jordan and Seale
Selenanthias
  Selenanthias analis Tanaka
Caprodon
  Caprodon schlegeli (Günther)
Tosama
  Tosama niwae Smith and Pope
Sacura
  Sacura margaritacea (Hilgendorf)
Anthias
  Anthias squamipinnis (Panders)
Pseudanthias
  Pseudanthias elongatus (Franz)
  Pseudanthias cichlops (Bleeker)
Mirolabrichthys
  Mirolabrichthys tuka Herre
Glaucosomidae
 Glaucosoma
  Glaucosoma hebraicum Richardson
Pseudochromidae
 Dampieria
  Dampieria melanotaenia (Bleeker)
Plesiopidae
 Plesiops
  Plesiops melas Bleeker
Pseudochromis
  Pseudochromis fuscus Müller and Troschel
Kuhliidae
 Kuhlia

Kuhlia taeniura (Cuvier and Valenciennes)
Kuhlia marginata (Cuvier and Valenciennes)
Kuhlia rupestris (Lacépède)
Priacanthidae
 Pseudopriacanthus
  Pseudopriacanthus niphonivus (Cuvier and Valenciennes)
  Pseudopriacanthus multifasciatus (Yoshino and Iwai)
Priacanthus
  Priacanthus boops (Bloch and Schneider)
  Priacanthus hamrur (Forsskål)
  Priacanthus tayenus Richardson
  Priacanthus cruentatus (Lacépède)
  Priacanthus macracanthus Cuvier and Valenciennes
  Priacanthus blochi Bleeker
Acropomidae
 Acropoma
  Acropoma japonicum Günther
  Acropoma hanedai Matsubara
Apogonidae
 Papillapogon
  Papillapogon auritus (Cuvier and Valenciennes)
Cheilodipterus
  Cheilodipterus macrodon (Lacépède)
Paramia
  Paramia quinquelineatus (Cuvier and Valenciennes)
Archamia
  Archamia macropterus (Cuvier and Valenciennes)
  Archamia lineolata (Cuvier and Valenciennes)
Apogonichthys
  Apogonichthys perdix Bleeker
  Apogonichthys striatus (Smith and Radcliffe)
  Apogonichthys lineatus (Temminck and Schlegel)
  Apogonichthys arafurae (Günther)
  Apogonichthys niger Doderlein
  Apogonichthys albomarginatus

Radcliffe
Apogonichthys ellioti (Day)
Apogonichthys carinatus (Cuvier and Valenciennes)
Apogonichthys brachygrammus (Jenkins)
Apogon
  Apogon orbicularis Cuvier and Valenciennes
  Apogon amboinensis Bleeker
  Apogon kiensis Jordan and Snyder
  Apogon taeniatus Cuvier and Valenciennes
  Apogon trimaculatus Cuvier and Valenciennes
  Apogon erythrinus Snyder
  Apogon endekataenia (Bleeker)
  Apogon fusca (Quoy and Gaimard)
  Apogon semilineatus Temminck and Schlegel
  Apogon fraenatus Cuvier and Valenciennes
  Apogon doederleini Jordan and Snyder
  Apogon robustus (Smith and Radcliffe)
  Apogon fleurieu (Lacépède)
  Apogon bandanensis Bleeker
  Apogon quadrifasciatus Cuvier and Valenciennes
  Apogon novemfasciatus Cuvier and Valenciennes
Lactariidae
  Lactarius
    Lactarius lactarius (Bloch and Schneider)
Sillaginidae
  Sillago
    Sillago maculata Quoy and Gaimard
    Sillago japonica Temminck and Schlegel
    Sillago sihama (Forsskål)
Branchiostegidae
  Branchiostegus
    Branchiostegus japonicus (Houttuyn)
    Branchiostegus auratus (Kishinouye)
    Branchiostegus argentatus (Cuvier and Valenciennes)
  Malacanthus
    Malacanthus hoedti Bleeker
    Malacanthus latovittatus (Lacépède)
Carangidae
  Alectis
    Alectis ciliaris (Bloch)
    Alectis indica (Rüppell)
  Atropus
    Atropus atropus (Bloch and Schneider)
  Caranx
    Caranx chrysophrys Cuvier and Valenciennes
    Caranx malabaricus (Bloch and Schneider)
    Caranx talamparoides (Bleeker)
    Caranx coeruleopinnatus Rüppell
    Caranx armatus (Forsskål)
    Caranx plumbeus (Quoy and Gaimard)
    Caranx oblongus Cuvier and Valenciennes
    Caranx dinema (Bleeker)
    Caranx helvolus (Forsskål)
    Caranx equula Temminck and Schlegel
    Caranx praeustus Bennetdi
    Caranx plagiotaenia (Bleeker)
    Caranx ferdau (Forsskål)
    Caranx sexfasciatus Quoy and Gaimard
    Caranx oshimai Wakiya
    Caranx melampygus Cuvier and Valenciennes
    Caranx stellatus Eydoux and Souleyt
    Caranx ishikawai Wakiya
    Caranx ignobilis (Forsskål)
    Caranx bucculentu Alleyne and Macleay
    Caranx sansun (Forsskål)
    Caranx hippos (Linnaeus)
    Caranx kalla Cuvier and Valenciennes
    Caranx mate Cuvier and

Valenciennes
Caranx malam (Bleeker)
Caranx pectoralis Chu and
 Cheng
Caranx macrurus (Bleeker)
Caranx djeddaba (Forsskål)
Caranx platessa (Cuvier and
 Valenciennes)
Caranx delicatissimus (Doderlein)
Gnathanodon
Gnathanodon speciosus (Forsskål)
Selaroides
Selaroides leptolepis (Cuvier and
 Valenciennes)
Ulua
Ulua mandibularis (Macleay)
Selar
Selar crumenophthamus (Bloch)
Selar boops Cuvier and
 Valenciennes
Decapterus
Decapterus maruadsi (Temminck
 and Schlegel)
Decapterus fasciatus Bleeker
Decapterus kurroides Bleeker
Decapterus russelli (Rüppell)
Decapterus maruadsi (Temminck
 and Schlegel)
Decapterus lajang Bleeker
Decapterus macrosoma Bleeker
Megalaspis
Megalaspis cordyla (Linnaeus)
Trachurus
Trachurus japonicus
 (Temminck and Schlegel)
Trachinotus
Trachinotus ovatus (Linnaeus)
Trachinotus bailloni (Lacépède)
Trachinotus russelli Cuvier and
 Valenciennes
Seriola
Seriola dumerili (Risso)
Seriola aureovittata Temminck and
 Schlegel
Seriola quinqueradiata Temminck
 and Schlegel
Zonichthys
Zonichthys nigrofasciata (Rüppell)
Naucrates
Naucrates ductor (Linnaeus)
Elagatis
Elagatis bipinnulatus (Quoy and
 Gaimard)
Chorinemus
Chorinemus lysan (Forsskål)
Chorinemus tala (Cuvier and
 Valenciennes)
Chorinemus hainanensis Chu and
 Cheng
Chorinemus sanctiperi Cuvier and
 Valenciennes
Chorinemus tolooparah (Rüppell)
Chorinemus orientalis Temminck
 and Schlegel
Chorinemus moadetta Cuvier and
 Valenciennes
Chorinemus formosanus (Wakiya)
Menidae
Mene
Mene maculata (Bloch and
 Schneider)
Formionidae
Formio
Formio niger (Bloch)
Rachycentridae
Rachycentron
Rachycentron canadum (Linnaeus)
Coryphaenidae
Coryphaena
Coryphaena hippurus Linnaeus
Sciaenidae
Johnius
Johnius amblycephalus (Bleeker)
Johnius fasciatus Chu et al.
Johnius belengeri (Cuvier and
 Valenciennes)
Johnius dussumieri (Cuvier and
 Valenciennes)
Johnius carutta Bloch
Wak
Wak coitor (Hamilton)
Wak soldado (Lacépède)
Wak tingi (Tang)
Wak sina (Cuvier and Valenciennes)

Megalonibea
  Megalonibea fusca Chu *et al.*
Bahaba
  Bahaba flavolabiata (Lin)
Macrospinosa
  Macrospinosa cuja (Hamilton)
Panna
  Panna microdon (Bleeker)
Umbrina
  Umbrina russelli Cuvier and Valenciennes
Otolithes
  Otolithes argenteus (Cuvier and Valenciennes)
  Otolithes ruber (Bloch and Schneider)
Chrysochir
  Chrysochir aureus (Richardson)
Paranibea
  Paranibea semiluctuosa (Cuvier and Valenciennes)
Nibea
  Nibea chui Trewavas
  Nibea albiflora (Richardson)
  Nibea semifasciata Chu *et al.*
  Nibea diacanthus (Lacépède)
  Nibea miichthioides Chu *et al.*
  Nibea japonica (Temminck and Valenciennes)
Argyrosomus
  Argyrosomus aneus (Bloch)
  Argyrosomus macrocephalus (Tang)
  Argyrosomus pawak Lin
  Argyrosomus argentatus (Houttuyn)
Atrobucca
  Atrobucca nibe (Jordan and Thompson)
Miichthys
  Miichthys miiuy (Basilewsky)
Pseudosciaena
  Pseudosciaena croacea (Richardson)
Collichthys
  Collichthys lucidus (Richardson)
Leiognathidae
  Leiognathus
    Leiognathus insidiator (Bloch)
    Leiognathus ruconius (Hamilton)
    Leiognathus elongatus (Günther)
    Leiognathus leuciscus (Günther)
    Leiognathus aplendens (Cuvier)
    Leiognathus bindus (Cuvier and Valenciennes)
    Leiognathus lineolatus (Cuvier and Valenciennes)
    Leiognathus berbis (Cuvier and Valenciennes)
    Leiognathus fasciatus Lacépède
    Leiognathus dussumieri (Cuvier and Valenciennes)
    Leiognathus equulus (Forsskål)
    Leiognathus rivulatus (Temminck and Schlegel)
    Leiognathus brevirostris (Cuvier and Valenciennes)
    Leiognathus daura (Cuvier)
  Gazza
    Gazza minuta (Bloch)
Gerridae
  Pentaprion
    Pentaprion longimanus (Cantor)
  Gerres
    Gerres filamentosus Cuvier
    Gerres oblongus Cuvier
    Gerres acinaces Bleeker
    Gerres oyena (Forsskål)
    Gerres macrosoma Bleeker
    Gerres abbreviatus Bleeker
    Gerres lucidus Cuvier
    Gerres poeti Cuvier and Valenciennes
    Gerres argyreus (Bloch and Schneider)
  Gerreomorpha
    Gerreomorpha japonica (Bleeker)
Lutiianidae
  Etelis
    Etelis carbunculus Cuvier and Valenciennes
  Pristipomoides
    Pristipomoides typus Bleeker
    Pristipomoides microlepis (Bleeker)
  Aprion
    Aprion virescens Cuvier and

Valenciennes
Aphareus
  Aphareus furcatus (Lacépède)
Tangia
  Tangia carnolabrum Chan
Paracaesio
  Paracaesio xanthurus Bleeker
Macolor
  Macolor niger (Forsskål)
Lutjanus
  Lutjanus johni (Bloch)
  Lutjanus argentimaculatus (Forsskål)
  Lutjanus vitta (Quoy and Gaimard)
  Lutjanus chrysotaenia (Bleeker)
  Lutjanus lineolatus (Rüppell)
  Lutjanus kasmira (Forsskål)
  Lutjanus spilurus (Bennett)
  Lutjanus vaigiensis (Quoy and Gaimard)
  Lutjanus lutjanus Bloch
  Lutjanus fulviflamma (Forsskål)
  Lutjanus fulvus (Forster)
  Lutjanus monostigma (Cuvier and Valenciennes)
  Lutjanus russelli Bleeker
  Lutjanus rivulatus (Cuvier and Valenciennes)
  Lutjanus bohar (Forsskål)
  Lutjanus sanguineus (Cuvier and Valenciennes)
  Lutjanus gibbus (Forsskål)
  Lutjanus sebae (Cuvier and Valenciennes)
  Lutjanus altifrontalis Chan
Pinjalo
  Pinjalo pinjalo (Bleeker)
Glabrilutjanus
  Glabrilutjanus nematophorus (Bleeker)
Symphorus
  Symphorus spilurus Günther
Caesio
  Caesio tile Cuvier and Valenciennes
  Caesio chrysozona Cuvier and Valenciennes
  Caesio diagramma Bleeker
  Caesio coerulaureus Lacépède
  Caesio lunaris Cuvier and Valenciennes
  Caesio xanthonotus Bleeker
  Caesio erythrogaster Cuvier and Valenciennes
Emmelichthyidae
 Erythrocles
  Erythrocles schlegeli (Richardson)
 Dipterygonotus
  Dipterygonotus leucogrammicus (Bleeker)
Lethrinidae
 Lethrinus
  Lethrinus nematacanthus Bleeker
  Lethrinus miniatus (Bloch and Schneider)
  Lethrinus kallopterus Bleeker
  Lethrinus variegatus Cuvier and Valenciennes
  Lethrinus haematopterus Temminck and Schlegel
  Lethrinus rhodopterus Bleeker
  Lethrinus ornatus Cuvier and Valenciennes
  Lethrinus nebulosus (Forsskål)
  Lethrinus leutjanus (Lacépède)
Sparidae
 Taius
  Taius tumifrons (Temminck and Schlegel)
 Monotaxis
  Monotaxis grandoculis (Forsskål)
 Evynnis
  Evynnis japonicus Tanaka
 Pagrosomus
  Pagrosomus major (Temminck and Schlegel)
  Pagrosomus edita Tanaka
 Argyrops
  Argyrops beleekeri Oshima
 Rhabdosargus
  Rhabdosargus sarba (Forsskål)
 Sparus
  Sparus macrocephalus (Basilewsky)
  Sparus berda Forsskål
  Sparus latus Houttuyn

Lobotidae
Lobotes
  Lobotes surinamensis (Bloch)
Banjosidae
Banjos
  Banjos banjos (Richardson)
Nemipteridae
Nemipterus
  Nemipterus tolu (Cuvier and Valenciennes)
  Nemipterus virgatus (Houttuyn)
  Nemipterus bathybius (Snyder)
  Nemipterus oveni (Bleeker)
  Nemipterus hexodon (Quoy and Gaimard)
  Nemipterus japonicus (Bloch)
Pentapodidae
Gnathodentex
  Gnathodentex aurolineatus (Lacépède)
Gymnocranius
  Gymnocranius griseus (Temminck and Schlegel)
Pentapus
  Pentapus setosus Cuvier and Valenciennes
Scolopsidae
Scolopsis
  Scolopsis eriomma Jordan and Richardson
  Scolopsis inermis (Temminck and Schlegel)
  Scolopsis cancellatus (Cuvier and Valenciennes)
  Scolopsis taeniopterus (Cuvier and Valenciennes)
  Scolopsis bimaculatus Rüppell
  Scolopsis margaritifer (Cuvier and Valenciennes)
  Scolopsis temporalis Cuvier
  Scolopsis ciliatus (Lacépède)
  Scolopsis bilinaetus (Bloch)
  Scolopsis vosmeri (Bloch)
Pomadasyidae
Pomadays
  Pomadays furcatus (Bloch and Schneider)
  Pomadays grunniens (Bloch and Schneider)
  Pomadays arganteus (Forsskål)
  Pomadays hasta (Bloch)
  Pomadays maculatus (Bloch)
  Pomadays unimaculatus Tian
Hapalogenys
  Hapalogenys mucroinatus (Eydoux and Souleyand)
  Hapalogenys kishinouyei Smith and Pope
  Hapalogenys nitens (Richardson)
Parapristipoma
  Parapristipoma trilineatus (Thünberg)
Plectorhynchus
  Plectorhynchus pictus (Thünberg)
  Plectorhynchus nigrus (Cuvier)
  Plectorhynchus cinctus (Temminck and Schlegel)
  Plectorhynchus sinensis Zhu et al.
  Plectorhynchus chaetodontoides Lacépède
  Plectorhynchus punctatissimus (Playfair)
  Plectorhynchus goldmanni (Bleeker)
  Plectorhynchus orientalis (Bloch)
  Plectorhynchus diagrammus (Linnaeus)
  Plectorhynchus lineatus (Cuvier and Valenciennes)
  Plectorhynchus foetela (Forsskål)
  Plectorhynchus reticulatus (Günther)
Theraponidae
Helotes
  Helotes sexlineatus (Quoy and Gaimard)
  Helotes cancellatus (Cuvier and Valenciennes)
Therapon
  Therapon oxyrhynchus Temminck and Schlegel
  Therapon theraps (Cuvier and Valenciennes)
  Therapon jarbua (Forsskål)
Pelates
  Pelates quadrilineatus (Bloch)

Kyphosidae
Kyphosus
  Kyphosus lembus (Cuvier and Valenciennes)
  Kyphosus cinerascens (Forsskål)
Girellidae
Girella
  Girella punctata Gray
Mullidae
Upeneus
  Upeneus bensasi (Temminck and Schlegel)
  Upeneus luzoninus Jordan and Seale
  Upeneus tragula Richardson
  Upeneus subvittatus (Temminck and Schlegel)
  Upeneus vittatus (Forsskål)
  Upeneus sulphureus Cuvier and Valenciennes
  Upeneus moluccensis (Bleeker)
  Upeneus quadrilineatus Cheng and Wang
Parupeneus
  Parupeneus pleurostigma (Bennett)
  Parupeneus barberinus (Lacépède)
  Parupeneus indicus (Shaw)
  Parupeneus bifasciatus (Lacépède)
  Parupeneus trifasciatus (Lacépède)
  Parupeneus fraterculus (Cuvier and Valenciennes)
  Parupeneus chryserdros (Lacépède)
  Parupeneus chrysopleuron (Temminck and Schlegel)
  Parupeneus luteus (Cuvier and Valenciennes)
  Parupeneus megalops (Tanaka)
Mulloidichthys
  Mulloidichthys samoensis (Günther)
  Mulloidichthys auriflamma (Forsskål)
  Mulloidichthys vanicolensis Cuvier and Valenciennes
Pempherididae
Pempheris
  Pempheris japonicus Doderlein
  Pempheris nyctereutes Jordan and Evermann
  Pempheris oualensis Cuvier and Valenciennes
  Pempheris xanthopterus Tominaga
Parapriacanthus
  Parapriacanthus ransonneti Steindachner
Ephippidae
Ephippus
  Ephippus orbis (Bloch)
Platax
  Platax teira (Forsskål)
  Platax orbicularis (Forsskål)
  Platax batavianus Cuvier and Valenciennes
Drepanidae
Drepane
  Drepane punctata (Linnaeus)
  Drepane longimana (Bloch and Schneider)
Psettidae
Monodactylus
  Monodactylus argenteus (Linnaeus)
Scatophagidae
Scatophagus
  Scatophagus argus (Linnaeus)
Scorpidae
Microcanthus
  Microcanthus strigatus (Cuvier and Valenciennes)
Chaetodontidae
Forcipiger
  Forcipiger longirostris (Broussonet)
Chelmon
  Chelmon rostratus (Linnaeus)
Heniochus
  Heniochus varius (Cuvier)
  Heniochus monoceros Cuvier and Valenciennes
  Heniochus singularius Smith and Radcliffe
  Heniochus acuminatus (Linnaeus)
  Heniochus permutatus Cuvier and Valenciennes
Coradion
  Coradion chrysozonus (Cuvier and Valenciennes)
Hemitaurichthys

Hemitaurichthys zoster (Bennett)
Parachaetodon
  Parachaetodon ocellatus (Cuvier and Valenciennes)
Chaetodon
  Chaetodon stragangulus Gmelin
  Chaetodon plebeius Gmelin
  Chaetodon ephippium Cuvier and Valenciennes
  Chaetodon auriga Forsskål
  Chaetodon semeion Bleeker
  Chaetodon ornatissimus Cuvier and Valenciennes
  Chaetodon trifasciatus Mungo Park
  Chaetodon triangulum Cuvier and Valenciennes
  Chaetodon modestus Temminck and Schlegel
  Chaetodon reticulatus Cuvier and Valenciennes
  Chaetodon kleini Bloch
  Chaetodon bennetti Cuvier and Valenciennes
  Chaetodon unimaculatus Bloch
  Chaetodon speculum Cuvier and Valenciennes
  Chaetodon falcula Bloch
  Chaetodon lineolatus Cuvier and Valenciennes
  Chaetodon punctatofasciatus Cuvier and Valenciennes
  Chaetodon octofasciatus Bloch
  Chaetodon chrysurus Desjardins
  Chaetodon rafflesi Bennett
  Chaetodon miliaris Quoy and Gaimard
  Chaetodon melanotus Bloch and Schneider
  Chaetodon citrinellus Cuvier and Valenciennes
  Chaetodon selene Bleeker
  Chaetodon lunula (Lacépède)
  Chaetodon wiebeli Kaup
  Chaetodon adiergastos Seale
  Chaetodon collare Bloch
  Chaetodon vagabundus Linnaeus
  Chaetodon argentatus Smith and Radcliffe
Euxiphipops
  Euxiphipops sexstriatus (Cuvier and Valenciennes)
Centropyge
  Centropyge heraldi Woode and Schultz
  Centropyge bicolor (Bloch)
  Centropyge tibicen Cuvier and Valenciennes
  Centropyge bispinosus (Günther)
  Centropyge vroliki (Bleeker)
  Centropyge fisheri (Snyder)
  Centropyge ferrugatus Randall and Burgess
Pygoplites
  Pygoplites diacanthus (Boddert)
Genicanthus
  Genicanthus melanospilos (Bleeker)
  Genicanthus macclesfieldiensis Chan
Holacanthus
  Holacanthus trimaculatus Cuvier and Valenciennes
Pomacanthus
  Pomacanthus imperator (Bloch)
  Pomacanthus annularis (Bloch)
  Pomacanthus semicirculatus (Cuvier and Valenciennes)
Chaetodontoplus
  Chaetodontoplus septentrionalis (Temminck and Schlegel)
  Chaetodontoplus duboulayi (Günther)
Histiopteridae
  Histiopterus
    Histiopterus typus Temminck and Schlegel
Oplegnathidae
  Oplegnathus
    Oplegnathus punctatus (Temminck and Valenciennes)
Cepolidae
  Cepola
    Cepola schlegeli (Day)
  Acanthocepola
    Acanthocepola krusensterni (Temminck and Schlegel)

Acanthocepola limbata Cuvier and
 Valenciennes
Acanthocepola indica (Day)
Labridae
 Choerodonoides
  Choerodonoides japonicus
   Kamohara
 Xiphocheilus
  Xiphocheilus typus Bleeker
  Xiphocheilus quadrimaculatus
   Günther
 Choerodon
  Choerodon nectemblema (Jordan
   and Evermann)
  Choerodon anchorago (Bloch)
  Choerodon pescadorensis Yu
  Choerodon azurio (Jordan and
   Snyder)
  Choerodon melanostigma Fowler
   and Bean
  Choerodon schoenleini (Cuvier and
   Valenciennes)
 Bodianus
  Bodianus axillaris (Bennett)
  Bodianus diana (Lacépède)
  Bodianus perditio (Quoy and
   Gaimard)
  Bodianus hirsutus (Lacépède)
  Bodianus bilunulatus (Lacépède)
  Bodianus oxycephalus (Bleeker)
 Anampses
  Anampses geographius Cuvier and
   Valenciennes
  Anampses twisti Bleeker
  Anampses caeruleopunctatus
   Rüppell
  Anampses melanurus Bleeker
  Anampses meleagrides Cuvier and
   Valenciennes
  Anampses diadematus Rüppell
 Cheilio
  Cheilio inermis (Forsskål)
 Gomphosus
  Gomphosus varius Lacépède
 Thalassoma
  Thalassoma hardwicki (Bennett)
  Thalassoma janseni (Bleeker)
  Thalassoma lunare (Linnaeus)
  Thalassoma fuscum (Lacépède)
  Thalassoma umbrostigma Rüppell
  Thalassoma cupido (Temminck and
   Schlegel)
  Thalassoma purpureum (Forsskål)
  Thalassoma quinquevittatus (Lay
   and Bennett)
  Thalassoma lutescens (Lay and
   Bennett)
  Thalassoma amblycephalus
   (Bleeker)
 Duymaeria
  Duymaeria flagellifera (Cuvier and
   Valenciennes)
 Hemigymnus
  Hemigymnus fasciatus (Bloch)
  Hemigymnus melapterus (Bloch)
 Labrichthys
  Labrichthys cyanotaenia Bleeker
 Psedolabrus
  Psedolabrus japonicus (Houttuyn)
  Psedolabrus gracilis (Steindachner)
 Labropsis
  Labropsis manabei Schmidt
 Labroides
  Labroides dimidiatus (Cuvier and
   Valenciennes)
 Stethojulia
  Stethojulia strigiventer Bennett
  Stethojulia axillaris (Quoy and
   Gaimard)
  Stethojulia interrupta (Bleeker)
  Stethojulia kalosoma (Bleeker)
  Stethojulia phekadopleura (Bleeker)
  Stethojulia trilineatus (Bloch and
   Schneider)
  Stethojulia renardi (Bleeker)
  Stethojulia linearis (Schultz)
 Macropharyngodon
  Macropharyngodon meleagris
   (Cuvier and Valenciennes)
 Halichoeres
  Halichoeres cyanopleura (Bleeker)
  Halichoeres trimaculatus (Quoy and
   Gaimard)
  Halichoeres scapularis (Bennett)

Halichoeres centiquadris (Lacépède)
Halichoeres melanuchir (Fowler and Bean)
Halichoeres marginatus Rüppell
Halichoeres melanurus (Bleeker)
Halichoeres nigrescens (Bloch and Valenciennes)
Halichoeres leparensis (Bleeker)
Halichoeres miniatus (Cuvier and Valenciennes)
Halichoeres margaritaceus (Cuvier and Valenciennes)
Halichoeres nebulosus (Cuvier and Valenciennes)
Halichoeres hyrtli (Bleeker)
Halichoeres amboinensis (Bleeker)
Halichoeres tenuispinis (Günther)
Halichoeres poecilopterus (Temminck and Schlegel)
Halichoeres hartzfeldi (Bleeker)
Halichoeres argus (Bloch and Schlegel)
Halichoeres purpurascens (Bleeker)
Hologymnosus
  Hologymnosus semidisus (Lacépède)
Pseudocoris
  Pseudocoris awayae (Schmidt)
  Pseudocoris yamashiroi (Schmidt)
Coris
  Coris aygula Lacépède
  Coris gaimard (Quoy and Gaimard)
  Coris musume (Jordan and Snyder)
Cirrhilabrus
  Cirrhilabrus solorensis Bleeker
Neocirrhilabrus
  Neocirrhilabrus oxyurus Cheng and Wang
Cymolutes
  Cymolutes lecluse (Quoy and Gaimard)
Hemipteronotus
  Hemipteronotus aneitensis (Günther)
  Hemipteronotus pentadactylus (Linnaeus)
  Hemipteronotus melanopus (Bleeker)
  Hemipteronotus caerulopunctatus Yu
  Hemipteronotus verrens (Jordan and Evermann)
  Hemipteronotus evides Jordan and Richardson
Iniistius
  Iniistius dea (Temminck and Schlegel)
  Iniistius pavo (Cuvier and Valenciennes)
Novaculichthys
  Novaculichthys taeniourus (Lacépède)
Epibulus
  Epibulus insidiator (Pallas)
Cheilinus
  Cheilinus chlorurus (Bloch)
  Cheilinus oxycephalus Bleeker
  Cheilinus trilobatus Lacépède
  Cheilinus fasciatus (Bloch)
  Cheilinus undulatus Rüppell
  Cheilinus bimaculatus Cuvier and Valenciennes
  Cheilinus diagramma (Lacépède)
  Cheilinus rhodochrous Günther
  Cheilinus mentalis Rüppell
  Cheilinus celebicus Bleeker
Pseudocheilinus
  Pseudocheilinus hexataenia (Bleeker)
Scaridae
 Calotomus
  Calotomus spinidens (Quoy and Gaimard)
  Calotomus japonicus (Cuvier and Valenciennes)
 Leptoscarus
  Leptoscarus vaigiensis (Quoy and Gaimard)
 Bolbometopon
  Bolbometopon bicolor (Rüppell)
  Bolbometopon murieatus (Cuvier and Valenciennes)
 Scarus
  Scarus gibbus Rüppell
  Scarus longiceps Cuvier and Valenciennes

Scarus venosus Cuvier and
  Valenciennes
Scarus taeniurus Cuvier and
  Valenciennes
Scarus sordidus Forsskål
Scarus forsteri Cuvier and
  Valenciennes
Scarus ovifrons (Temminck and
  Schlegel)
Scarus frenatus Lacépède
Scarus oviceps Cuvier and
  Valenciennes
Scarus fasciatus Cuvier and
  Valenciennes
Scarus globiceps Cuvier and
  Valenciennes
Scarus lepidus Jenyns
Scarus ghobban Forsskål
Scarus dimidiatus Bleeker
Scarus scaber Cuvier and
  Valenciennes
Scarus aeruginosus Cuvier and
  Valenciennes
Scarus janthochir Bleeker
Scarus niger Forsskål
Scarus chlorodon Jenyns
Scarops
  Scarops rubroviolaceus (Bleeker)
Pomacentridae
Amphiprion
  Amphiprion perideraion Bleeker
  Amphiprion akallopisus Bleeker
  Amphiprion polymnus (Linnaeus)
  Amphiprion percula (Lacépède)
  Amphiprion frenatus Brevoort
  Amphiprion bicinctus Rüppell
Daya
  Daya jordani (Rutter)
Dascyllus
  Dascylus aruanus (Linnaeus)
  Dascylius trimaculatus (Rüppell)
  Dascylius marginatus (Rüppell)
Chromis
  Chromis lepidolepis Bleeker
  Chromis elerae Fowler and Bean
  Chromis dimidiatus (Klunzinger)
  Chromis fumea (Tanaka)

Chromis notatus (Temminck and
  Schlegel)
Chromis chrysurus (Bliss)
Chromis ovatiformis Fowler
Chromis alleni Randall *et al.*
Chromis caeruleus (Cuvier and
  Valenciennes)
Chromis ternatensis (Bleeker)
Chromis xanthochir (Bleeker)
Chromis xanthurus (Bleeker)
Chromis analis (Cuvier)
Cheiloprion
  Cheiloprion labiatus (Day)
Pomacentrus
  Pomacentrus albifasciatus Schlegel
    and Müller
  Pomacentrus lividus (Bloch and
    Schneider)
  Pomacentrus jenkinsi Jordan and
    Evermann
  Pomacentrus nigricans (Lacépède)
  Pomacentrus violascens (Bleeker)
  Pomacentrus philippinus Evermann
    and Seale
  Pomacentrus melanopterus Bleeker
  Pomacentrus taeniurus Bleeker
  Pomacentrus perspicilliatus Cuvier
    and Valenciennes
  Pomacentrus prosopotaenia Bleeker
  Pomacentrus notophalmus Bleeker
  Pomacentrus moluccensis Bleeker
  Pomacentrus pavo (Bloch)
  Pomacentrus dorsalis Gill
  Pomacentrus tripunctus Cuvier and
    Valenciennes
Abudefduf
  Abudefduf dickii (Liénard)
  Abudefduf coeletinus (Cuvier and
    Valenciennes)
  Abudefduf curacao (Bloch)
  Abudefduf sordidus (Forsskål)
  Abudefduf vaigiensis (Quoy and
    Gaimard)
  Abudefduf septemfasciatus (Cuvier
    and Valenciennes)
  Abudefduf bengalensis (Bloch)
  Abudefduf lacrymatus (Quoy and

Gaimard)
 Abudefduf behni (Bleeker)
 Abudefduf leucogaster (Bleeker)
 Abudefduf bankieri (Richardson)
 Abudefduf thoracotaeniatus Fowler
  and Bean
 Abudefduf richardsoni Snyder
 Abudefduf anabatoides Bleeker
 Abudefduf glaucus (Cuvier and
  Valenciennes)
 Abudefduf cyaneus (Quoy and
  Gaimard)
 Abudefduf zonatus (Cuvier and
  Valenciennes)
 Abudefduf xanthozona (Bleeker)
 Abudefduf melas (Cuvier and
  Valenciennes)
 Abudefduf biocellatus (Quoy and
  Gaimard)
 Abudefduf uniocellatus (Quoy and
  Gaimard)
 Hemiglyphidodon
 Hemiglyphidodon plagiomandopon
  (Bleeker)
Cirrhitidae
 Cyprinocirrhites
 Cyprinocirrhites polyactis (Bleeker)
 Cirrhitus
 Cirrhitus pinnulatus (Bloch and
  Schneider)
 Paracirrhites
 Paracirrhites forsteri (Bloch and
  Schneider)
 Paracirrhites arcatus (Cuvier and
  Valenciennes)
 Amblycirrhitus
 Amblycirrhitus bimacula (Jenkins)
 Cirrhitichthys
 Cirrhitichthys aprinus (Cuvier and
  Valenciennes)
 Cirrhitichthys aureus (Temminck
  and Schlegel)
 Cirrhitichthys falco Randall
 Cirrhitichthys oxycephalus (Bleeker)
Aplodactylidae
 Goniistius
 Goniistius zonatus (Cuvier and
  Valenciennes)
 Goniistius quadricoris (Günther)
Bembropidae
 Bembrops
 Bembrops curvatura Okada and
  Suzuki
 Chrionema
 Chrionema chrysers Gilbert
Parapercidae
 Parapercis
 Parapercis quadrispinosus Weber
 Parapercis muronis Tanaka
 Parapercis aurantiaca Doerlein
 Parapercis hexophthalma (Cuvier
  and Valenciennes)
 Parapercis striolata (Weber)
 Parapercis tetracanthus (Lacépède)
 Parapercis xanthozona (Bleeker)
 Parapercis pulchella (Temminck
  and Schlegel)
 Parapercis scnyderi (Jordan and
  Starks)
 Parapercis cylindrica (Bloch)
 Parapercis ommatura (Jordan and
  Starks)
 Parapercis punctata (Cuvier and
  Valenciennes)
 Parapercis alboguttata (Günther)
Hemerocoetidae
 Acanthaphritis
 Acanthaphritis grandisquamis
  Günther
Trichonotidae
 Trichonotus
 Trichonotus setiger Bloch and
  Schneider
 Trichonotus filamentosus
  (Steindachner)
Owstonidae
 Owstonia
 Owstonia tosaensis Kamohara
Opisthognathidae
 Gnathypops
 Gnathypops evermanni Jordan and
  Snyder
Uranoscopidae
 Uranoscopus

Uranoscopus japonicus Houttuyn
Uranoscopus bicinctus Temminck and Schlegel
Uranoscopus oligolepis Bleeker
Zalescopus
  Zalescopus tosae Jordan and Hubbs
Ichthyoscopus
  Ichthyoscopus lebeck (Bloch and Schlegel)
Gnathagnus
  Gnathagnus elongatas (Temmink and Schlegal)
Champsodontidae
Champsodon
  Champsodon atridorsalis Ochiai and Nakamura
  Champsodon snyderi Franz
Tripterygidae
Tripterygion
  Tripterygion etheostoma Jordan and Snyder
  Tripterygion fuligicauda (Fowler)
Blenniidae
Aspidontus
  Aspidontus taeniatus Quoy and Gaimard
Dasson
  Dasson trossulus (Jordan and Snyder)
Omobranchus
  Omobranchus uekii (Katayama)
  Omobranchus kraussi (Klunzinger)
  Omobranchus japonicus (Bleeker)
  Omobranchus kallosoma (Bleeker)
Plagiotremus
  Plagiotremus spilistius Gill
Xiphasia
  Xiphasia setifer Swainson
Cirripectes
  Cirripectes variolosus (Cuvier and Valenciennes)
Ecsenius
  Ecsenius frontalis (Cuvier and Valenciennes)
Andamia
  Andamia pacifica Tomiyama
Alticus
  Alticus saliens (Forster)
Atrosalarias
  Atrosalarias fuscus (Rüppell)
Salarias
  Salarias fasciatus (Bloch)
  Salarias edentulus (Bloch and Schneider)
  Salarias periophthalmus (Cuvier and Valenciennes)
  Salarias guttatus (Cuvier and Valenciennes)
  Salarias dussumieri (Cuvier and Valenciennes)
  Salarias lineatus (Cuvier and Valenciennes)
  Salarias margaritatus (Kendall and Radcliffe)
Congrogadidae
Congrogadus
  Congrogadus subducens (Richardson)
Schindlerioidei
Schindleriidae
Schindleria
  Schindleria praematura (Schindler)
Ammodytoidei
Ammodytidae
Embolichthys
  Embolichthys mitsukurii (Jordan and Evermann)
Bleekeria
  Bleekeria anguilliviridis (Fowler)
Callionymoidei
Draconettidae
Draconetta
  Draconetta xenica Jordan and Fowler
  Draconetta margarostigma Cheng and Tain
Callionymidae
Diplogrammus
  Diplogrammus goramensis (Bleeker)
Callionymus
  Callionymus hainanensis Li
  Callionymus richardsoni Bleeker
  Callionymus marisinensis Fowler
  Callionymus altidorsalis

Wang and Ye
Callionymus flagris Jordan and Fowler
Callionymus schaapi Bleeker
Callionymus kaianus Günther
Callionymus monofilispinnus Li
Callionymus lunatus Temminck and Schlegel
Calliurichthys
Calliurichthys recurvispinnis Li
Calliurichthys filamentosus (Cuvier and Valenciennes)
Calliurichthys japonicus (Houttuyn)
Calliurichthys variegatus (Temminck and Schlegel)
Calliurichthys dorysus Jordan and Snyder
Snychiropus
Snychiropus ocellatus (Pallas)
Snychiropus altivelis (Temminck and Schlegel)
Snychiropus ornatus Fowler
Draculo
Draculo mirabilis Snyder
Dactylopus
Dactylopus dactylopus (Bennett)
Siganoidei
　Siganidae
　　Siganus
　　　Siganus vulpinus (Schlegel and Müller)
　　　Siganus corallinus (Cuvier and Valenciennes)
　　　Siganus puellus (Schlegel)
　　　Siganus virgatus (Cuvier and Valenciennes)
　　　Siganus javus (Linnaeus)
　　　Siganus chrysospilos (Bleeker)
　　　Siganus guttatus (Bloch)
　　　Siganus spinus (Linnaeus)
　　　Siganus rostratus (Cuvier and Valenciennes)
　　　Siganus oramin (Bloch and Schneider)
　　　Siganus fuscescens (Houttuyn)
Acanthuroidei
　Zanclidae

Zanclus
　Zanclus cornutus (Linnaeus)
Acanthuridae
　Ctenochaetus
　　Ctenochaetus striatus (Quoy and Gaimard)
　Zebrasoma
　　Zebrasoma veliferum (Bloch)
　　Zebrasoma scopas (Cuvier)
　　Zebrasoma flavescens (Bennett)
　Acanthurus
　　Acanthurus triostegus (Linnaeus)
　　Acanthurus olivaceus Bloch and Schneider
　　Acanthurus gahhm (Forsskål)
　　Acanthurus maculiceps (Ahl)
　　Acanthurus bariene Lesson
　　Acanthurus glaucopareius Cuvier
　　Acanthurus lineatus (Linnaeus)
　　Acanthurus xanthopterus Cuvier and Valenciennes
　　Acanthurus mota (Cuvier)
　　Acanthurus bleekeri Günther
　　Acanthurus dussumieri Cuvier and Valenciennes
　　Acanthurus thompsoni Fowler
　　Acanthurus nigrofuscus (Forsskål)
　　Acanthurus pyroferus Kittlitz
　Paracanthurus
　　Paracanthurus hepatus (Linnaeus)
　Prionurus
　　Prionurus scalprus Cuvier and Valenciennes
　Axinurus
　　Axinurus thynnoides Cuvier and Valenciennes
　Naso
　　Naso vlamingi (Cuvier and Valenciennes)
　　Naso brevirostrus (Cuvier and Valenciennes)
　　Naso herrei Smith
　　Naso annulatus (Quoy and Gaimard)
　　Naso unicornis (Forsskål)
　Callicanthus
　　Callicanthus hexacanthus (Bleeker)
　　Callicanthus lituratus (Bloch and

Schneider)
Trichiuroidei
　Trichiuridae
　　Tentoriceps
　　　Tentoriceps cristatus (Klunzinger)
　　Eupleurogrammus
　　　Eupleurogrammus muticus (Gray)
　　Lepturacanthus
　　　Lepturacanthus savala (Cuvier)
　　Trichiurus
　　　Trichiurus haumela (Forsskål)
　Gempylidae
　　Lepidocybium
　　　Lepidocybium flavobrunneum (Smith)
　　Ruvettus
　　　Ruvettus tydemani Weber
　　Thyrsitoides
　　　Thyrsitoides marleyi Fowler
　　Gempylus
　　　Gempylus serpens Cuvier and Valenciennes
　　Promethichthys
　　　Promethichthys prometheus (Cuvier and Valenciennes)
　　Rexea
　　　Rexea prometeoides (Bleeker)
Scombroidei
　Scombridae
　　Pneumatophorus
　　　Pneumatophorus japonicus (Houttuyn)
　　Rastrelliger
　　　Rastrelliger kanagura (Cuvier)
　Cybiidae
　　Grammatorcynus
　　　Grammatorcynus bicarinatus (Quoy and Gaimard)
　　Acanthocybium
　　　Acanthocybium solandi (Cuvier and Valenciennes)
　　Scombermorus
　　　Scombermorus commersoni (Lacépède)
　　　Scombermorus cavalla (Cuvier)
　　　Scombermorus niphonius (Cuvier)
　　　Scombermorus guttatus (Bloch and Schneider)
　Histiophoridae
　　Histiophorus
　　　Histiophorus orientalis Temminck and Schlegel
　　　Histiophorus gladius (Broussonet)
　　Tetrapturus
　　　Tetrapturus angustirostris Tanaka
　　Makaira
　　　Makaira marlina Jordan and Snyder
　　　Makaira mazara (Jordan and Snyder)
　　　Makaira formosana (Hirasaka and Nakamura)
　　　Makaira mitsukurii (Jordan and Snyder)
　Xiphiidae
　　Xiphias
　　　Xiphias gladius Linnaeus
Thunnioidei
　Thunnidae
　　Thunnus
　　　Thunnus thynnus (Linnaeus)
　　　Thunnus alalunga (Bonnaterre)
　　　Thunnus obesus Lowe
　　　Thunnus albacora (Lowe)
　　　Thunnus tonggol (Bleeker)
　　Sarda
　　　Sarda orientalis (Temminck and Schlegel)
　　Gymnosarda
　　　Gymnosarda unicolor (Rüppell)
　　Auxis
　　　Auxis tapeinosoma (Bleeker)
　　　Auxis thazard (Lacépède)
　　Katsuwonus
　　　Katsuwonus pelamis (Linnaeus)
　　Euthynnus
　　　Euthynnus yaito Kishinouye
Stromateoidei
　Ariommidae
　　Ariomma
　　　Ariomma indica (Day)
　　　Ariomma evermanni Jordan and Snyder
　Nomeidae
　　Psenes

Psenes pellucidus Lutken
Psenes arafurensis Günther
Nomeus
   Nomeus gronovii (Gmelin)
Stromateidae
Pampus
   Pampus chinensis (Euphrasen)
   Pampus nozawae (Ishikawa)
   Pampus argentatus (Euphrasen)
Centrolophidae
Psenopsis
   Psenopsis anomala (Temminck and Schlegel)
Hyperoglyphe
   Hyperoglyphe japonicus (Doderlein)
Schedophilus
   Schedophilus maculatus Günther
Gobioidei
 Eleotridae
  Bostrichthys
   Bostrichthys sinensis (Lacépède)
  Asterropteryx
   Asterropteryx semipunctatus Rüppell
  Eleotris
   Eleotris fortis Tanaka
   Eleotris fusca (Bloch and Schneider)
   Eleotris fasciatus Chen
   Eleotris oxycephala (Temminck and Schlegel)
   Eleotris melanosoma Bleeker
  Butis
   Butis butis (Hamilton)
  Prionobutis
   Prionobutis koilomatodon (Bleeker)
  Eviota
   Eviota abax (Jordan and Snyder)
  Ophiocara
   Ophiocara porocephala (Cuvier and Valenciennes)
   Ophiocara aporos (Bleeker)
  Eleotriodes
   Eleotriodes strigatus (Broussonet)
   Eleotriodes immaculatus Ni
   Eleotriodes muralis (Quoy and Gaimard)
   Eleotriodes longipinnis (Bennett)
  Oxymetopon

   Oxymetopon compressus Chan
  Ptereleotris
   Ptereleotris microlepis (Bleeker)
 Gobiidae
  Gobiodon
   Gobiodon erythrospilus Bleeker
   Gobiodon verticalis Alleyne and Macleay
   Gobiodon oculolineatus Wu
   Gobiodon quinquestrigatus (Cuvier and Valenciennes)
   Gobiodon multilineatus Wu
   Gobiodon okinawae Sawada
  Paragobiodon
   Paragobiodon echinocephalus (Rüppell)
   Paragobiodon melanosomus (Bleeker)
   Paragobiodon xanthosomus (Bleeker)
  Tridentiger
   Tridentiger obscurus (Temminck and Schlegel)
   Tridentiger trigonocephalus (Gill)
  Triaenopogon
   Triaenopogon barbatus (Günther)
  Bathygobius
   Bathygobius fuscus (Rüppell)
   Bathygobius hongkongensis Lam
  Mugilogobius
   Mugilogobius abei (Jordan and Snyder)
   Mugilogobius tagala (Herre)
  Glossogobius
   Glossogobius biocellatus (Cuvier and Valenciennes)
   Glossogobius olivaceus (Temminck and Schlegel)
   Glossogobius giurus (Hamilton)
  Awaous
   Awaous melanocephalus (Bleeker)
  Oplopomus
   Oplopomus caninoides (Bleeker)
  Callogobius
   Callogobius liolepis Koumans
   Callogobius sclateri (Steindachner)
  Zonogobius

Zonogobius semidoliatus (Cuvier
  and Valenciennes)
Quisquilius
  Quisquilius malayanus Herre
  Quisquilius eugenius Jordan and
    Evermann
Cryptocentrus
  Cryptocentrus gymnocephalus
    (Bleeker)
  Cryptocentrus yatsui Tomiyama
  Cryptocentrus pavoninoides
    (Bleeker)
  Cryptocentrus yangi Chen
  Cryptocentrus papuanus (Peters)
  Cryptocentrus filifer (Cuvier and
    Valenciennes)
  Cryptocentrus russus (Cantor)
Oxyurichthys
  Oxyurichthys tentacularis (Cuvier
    and Valenciennes)
  Oxyurichthys ophthalmonema
    (Bleeker)
  Oxyurichthys macrolepis Chu and
    Wu
  Oxyurichthys formosanus Nichols
  Oxyurichthys microlepis (Bleeker)
  Oxyurichthys papuensis (Cuvier and
    Valenciennes)
Stenogobius
  Stenogobius genivittatus (Cuvier and
    Valenciennes)
Oligolepis
  Oligolepis acutipinnis (Cuvier and
    Valenciennes)
  Oligolepis moloana (Herre)
Gnatholepis
  Gnatholepis otakii (Jordan and
    Snyder)
  Gnatholepis calliurus Jordan and
    Seale
Stigmatogobius
  Stigmatogobius javanicus (Bleeker)
  Stigmatogobius hoeveni (Bleeker)
Amblygobius
  Amblygobius bynoensis (Richardson)
  Amblygobius shatinensis Herre
  Amblygobius albimaculatus
    (Rüppell)
  Amblygobius sphynx (Cuvier and
    Valenciennes)
Acentrogobius
  Acentrogobius ornatus (Rüppell)
  Acentrogobius hoepplii (Wu)
  Acentrogobius triangularis (Weber)
  Acentrogobius bonti (Bleeker)
  Acentrogobius viridipunctatus
    (Cuvier and Valenciennes)
  Acentrogobius puntang (Bleeker)
  Acentrogobius cauerensis (Bleeker)
  Acentrogobius campbelli (Jordan
    and Snyder)
  Acentrogobius cyanomos (Bleeker)
  Acentrogobius caninus (Cuvier and
    Valenciennes)
  Acentrogobius hoshinonis (Tanaka)
  Acentrogobius chlorostigmatoides
    (Bleeker)
  Acentrogobius masoni (Bleeker)
Ctenogobius
  Ctenogobius brevirostris (Günther)
  Ctenogobius notophthalmus Bleeker
  Ctenogobius viganensis
    (Steindachner)
  Ctenogobius gymnauchen (Bleeker)
  Ctenogobius criniger (Cuvier and
    Valenciennes)
Synechogobius
  Synechogobius ommaturus
    (Richardson)
Parachaeturichthys
  Parachaeturichthys polynema
    (Bleeker)
Chaeturichthys
  Chaeturichthys stigmaturus
    Richardson
  Chaeturichthys hexanema Bleeker
Pseudapocryptes
  Pseudapocryptes lanceolatus (Bloch
    and Schneider)
Apocryptes
  Apocryptes bato (Hamilton)
Parapocryptes
  Parapocryptes serperaster
    (Richardson)

Parapocryptes macrolepis (Bleeker)
Apocryptichthys
  Apocryptichthys sericus Herre
Apocryptodon
  Apocryptodon madurensis (Bleeker)
  Apocryptodon malcolmi Smith
Periophthalmidae
  Periophthalmus
    Periophthalmus argentilineatus Cuvier and Valenciennes
    Periophthalmus cantonensis (Osbeck)
  Boleophthalmus
    Boleophthalmus maculatus (Oshima)
    Boleophthalmus pectinirostris (Linnaeus)
  Scartelaos
    Scartelaos viridis (Hamilton)
Taeniodidae
  Odontamblyopus
    Odontamblyopus rubicundus (Hamilton)
  Taenioides
    Taenioides cirratus (Blyth)
    Taenioides anguillaris (Linnaeus)
  Brachyamblyopus
    Brachyamblyopus brachysoma (Bleeker)
  Trypauchen
    Trypauchen vagina (Bloch and Schneider)
    Trypauchen taenia Koumans
  Ctenotrypauchen
    Ctenotrypauchen microcephalus (Bleeker)
  Amblytrypauchen
    Amblytrypauchen arctocephalus (Alcock)
Echeneoidei
  Echeneidae
    Echeneis
      Echeneis naucrates Linnaeus
    Remora
      Remora albescens (Temminck and Schlegel)
      Remora brachyptera (Lowe)
      Remora remora (Linnaeus)

Rhombochirus
  Rhombochirus osteochir (Cuvier)
Scorpaeniformes
  Scorpaenoidei
    Scorpaenidae
    Sebastiscus
      Sebastiscus marmoratus (Cuvier and Valenciennes)
      Sebastiscus albofasciatus (Lacépède)
      Sebastiscus armastus (Cuvier and Valenciennes)
    Scorpaenodes
      Scorpaenodes guamensis (Quoy and Gaimard)
      Scorpaenodes scabra (Ramsay and Ogilby)
    Sebastapistes
      Sebastapistes bynoensis Richardson
      Sebastapistes megalepis (Fowler)
      Sebastapistes vachelli (Richardson)
      Sebastapistes nuchalis Günther
    Scorpaena
      Scorpaena izensis Jordan and Snyder
      Scorpaena neglecta Temminck and Schlegel
      Scorpaena hatizyoensis Matsubara
    Parascorpaena
      Parascorpaena picta (Cuvier and Valenciennes)
    Scorpaenopsis
      Scorpaenopsis diabolus (Cuvier and Valenciennes)
      Scorpaenopsis cirrhosa (Thünberg)
      Scorpaenopsis gibbosa (Bloch and Schneider)
    Pterois
      Pterois russelli Bennett
      Pterois lunulata Temminck and Schlegel
      Pterois volitans Linnaeus
      Pterois radiata Cuvier and Valenciennes
      Pterois antennata (Bloch)
    Pteroidichthys
      Pteroidichthys amboinensis Bleeker
    Dendrochirus
      Dendrochirus bellus Jordan and

Hubbs
Dendrochirus zebra (Quoy and
  Gaimard)
Brachypterois
  Brachypterois serrulatus
    (Richardson)
Ebosia
  Ebosia bleekeri (Steindachner and
    Doderlein)
Parapterois
  Parapterois heterurus Bleeker
Setarches
  Setarches fidjiensis Günther
  Setarches longimanus (Alcock and
    McGilchrist)
Apistus
  Apistus carinatus Bloch and
    Schneider
Synanceiidae
Minous
  Minous monodactylus (Bloch and
    Schneider)
  Minous inermis Alcock
  Minous pusillus Temminck and
    Schlegel
Inimicus
  Inimicus japonicus (Cuvier and
    Valenciennes)
  Inimicus didactylus (Pallas)
  Inimicus cuvieri (Gray)
Choridactylus
  Choridactylus multibarbis
    Richardson
Erosa
  Erosa erosa (Langsdorf)
Synanceia
  Synanceia horrida Linnaeus
  Synanceia verrucosa Bloch and
    Schneider
Polycaulus
  Polycaulus uranoscopa (Bloch and
    Schneider)
Triglidae
Chelidonichthys
  Chelidonichthys kumu (Leason and
    Garnot)
Lepidotrigla

Lepidotrigla oglina Fowler
Lepidotrigla alata (Houttuyn)
Lepidotrigla marisinensis Fowler
Lepidotrigla punctipectoralis Fowler
Lepidotrigla spilopterus Günther
Lepidotrigla japonica (Bleeker)
Lepidotrigla lepidojugulata Li
Lepidotrigla longimana Li
Pterygotrigla
  Pterygotrigla hemisticta (Temminck
    and Schlegel)
  Pterygotrigla ryukyuensis Matsubara
    and Hiyama
Peristediidae
Gargariscus
  Gargariscus prinoncephalus
    (Dumeril)
Peristedion
  Peristedion nierstrasi Weber
Satyrichthys
  Satyrichthys piercei Fowler
  Satyrichthys welchi (Herre)
Congiopodidae
Centropogon
  Centropogon urostigma (Bleeker)
  Centropogon fuscovierens (Cuvier
    and Valenciennes)
Ocosia
  Ocosia vespa Jordan and Starks
Hypodytes
  Hypodytes longipinnis (Cuvier and
    Valenciennes)
  Hypodytes indicus (Day)
  Hypodytes rubripinnis (Temminck
    and Schlegel)
Tetraroge
  Tetraroge leucogaster (Richardson)
Erisphex
  Erisphex potti (Steindachner)
Amblyapistus
  Amblyapistus taenianotus (Cuvier
    and Valenciennes)
  Amblyapistus macracanthus Bleeker
Vespicula
  Vespicula sinensis (Bleeker)
  Vespicula trachinoides (Cuvier and
    Valenciennes)

Cottapistus
  Cottapistus cottoides (Linnaeus)
Acanthosphex
  Acanthosphex leurynnis (Jordan and Seale)
Apcoactis
  Apoactis aspera Richardson
Sthenopus
  Sthenopus mollis Richardson
Platycephaloidei
  Bembridae
    Bembras
      Bembras japonicus Cuvier and Valenciennes
  Platycephalidae
    Onigocia
      Onigocia macrolepis (Bleeker)
      Onigocia spinosus (Temminck and Schlegel)
      Onigocia tuberculatus (Cuvier and Valenciennes)
    Rugadius
      Rugadius asper (Cuvier and Valenciennes)
    Grammoplites
      Grammoplites scaber (Linnaeus)
    Suggrundus
      Suggrundus meerdervoorti (Bleeker)
      Suggrundus rodericensis Cuvier and Valenciennes
      Suggrundus macracanthus (Bleeker)
    Inegocia
      Inegocia japonicus (Tilesius)
      Inegocia guttatus (Cuvier and Valenciennes)
    Cociella
      Cociella crocodilus (Tilesius)
    Kumococius
      Kumococius detrusus (Jordan and Seale)
    Ratabulus
      Ratabulus megacephalus (Tanaka)
    Thysanophrys
      Thysanophrys bataviensis (Bleeker)
    Elates
      Elates ransonneti (Steindachner)
    Platycephalus
      Platycephalus indicus (Linnaeus)
    Cymbacephalus
      Cymbacephalus nematophthalmus Günther
Hoplichthyoidei
  Hoplichthyidae
    Hoplichthys
      Hoplichthys langsdorfi Cuvier and Valenciennes
      Hoplichthys regani Jordan and Richardson
      Hoplichthys gilberti Jordan and Richardson
Dactylopteroidei
  Dactylopteridae
    Dactyloptena
      Dactyloptena orientalis (Cuvier and Valenciennes)
      Dactyloptena gilberti (Snyder)
    Daicocus
      Daicocus peterseni (Nystrom)
Pleuronectiformes
  Psettodoidei
    Psettodidae
      Psettodes
        Psettodes erumei (Schneider)
  Pleuronectoidei
    Citharidae
      Citharides
        Citharides marcrolepidotus Hubbs
      Brachypleura
        Brachypleura novaezeelandiae Günther
      Lepidoblepharon
        Lepidoblepharon ophthalmolepis Weber
    Paralichthyidae
      Tephrinectes
        Tephrinectes sinensis (Lacépède)
      Paralichthys
        Paralichthys olivaceus (Temminck and Schlegel)
      Pseudorhombus
        Pseudorhombus dupliocellatus Regan
        Pseudorhombus malayanus Bleeker
        Pseudorhombus oligodon (Bleeker)

Pseudorhombus triocellatus (Schneider)
Pseudorhombus javanicus (Bleeker)
Pseudorhombus levisquamis (Oshima)
Pseudorhombus ctenosquamis (Oshima)
Psuedorhombus quinquocellatus Weber and Beaufort
Pseudorhombus elevatus Ogilby
Pseudorhombus cinnamomeus (Temminck and Schlegel)
Pseudorhombus neglectus Bleeker
Tarphops
  Tarphops oligolepis (Bleeker)
Bothidae
Psettina
  Psettina hainanensis (Wu and Tang)
  Psettina filimanus Li and Wang
Arnoglossus
  Arnoglossus tapeinosoma (Beeker)
  Arnoglossus aspilos (Bleeker)
  Arnoglossus tenuis Günther
  Arnoglossus polyspilus (Günther)
  Arnoglossus scapha (Schneider)
  Arnoglossus japonicus Hubbs
Neolaeops
  Neolaeops microphthalmus (Von Bonde)
Laeops
  Laeops parviceps Günther
  Laeops lanceolata Franz
Asterorhombus
  Asterorhombus intermedius (Bleeker)
Parabothus
  Parabothus coarctatus (Gilbert)
Crossorhombus
  Crossorhombus azureus (Alcock)
  Crossorhombus kanekonis (Tanaka)
  Crossorhombus valderostratus (Alcock)
  Crossorhombus kobensis (Jordan and Starks)
Engyprosopon
  Engyprosopon grandisquama (Temminck and Schlegel)
  Engyprosopon multisquama Amaoka
  Engyprosopon filipennis Wu and Tang
  Engyprosopon longipelvis Amaoka
  Engyprosopon mogki (Bleeker)
  Engyprosopon latifrons (Regan)
Bothus
  Bothus assimilis (Günther)
  Bothus myriaster (Temminck and Schlegel)
  Bothus mancus (Broussonet)
  Bothus pantherinus (Rüppell)
Grammatobothus
  Grammatobothus polyophthalmus (Bleeker)
Chascanopsetta
  Chascanopsetta lugubris Alcock
Kamoharia
  Kamoharia megastoma (Kamohara)
Pleuronectidae
Pleuronichthys
  Pleuronichthys cornutus (Temminck and Schlegel)
Poecilopsetta
  Poecilopsetta colorata Günther
  Poecilopsetta praelonga Alcock
  Peocilopsetta plinthus (Jordan and Starks)
  Peocilopsetta natalensis Norman
Samaris
  Samaris cristatus Gray
Samariscus
  Samariscus inornatus (Lloyd)
  Samariscus huysmani Weber
  Samariscus latus Matsubara and Takamuki
  Samariscus longimanus Norman
Plagiopsetta
  Plagiopsetta glossa Franz
  Plagiopsetta fasciatus (Fowler)
Soleoidei
Soleidae
Solea
  Solea ovata Richardson
Monochirus
  Monochirus trichodacrylus (Linnaeus)

Pardachirus
  Pardachirus pavoninus (Lacépède)
Aseraggodes
  Aseraggodes kobensis (Steindachner)
  Aseraggodes kaianus (Günther)
Liachirus
  Liachirus melanospilus (Bleeker)
Brachirus
  Brachirus orientalis (Schneider)
  Brachirus pan (Hamilton)
  Brachirus annularis Fowler
  Brachirus swinhonis (Steindachner)
Zebrias
  Zebrias quagga (Kaup)
  Zebrias japonicus (Bleeker)
  Zebrias crossolepis Cheng and Chang
  Zebrias zebra (Bloch)
Aesopia
  Aesopia cornuta Kaup
Cynoglossidae
 Paraplagusia
  Paraplagusia bilineata (Bloch)
  Paraplagusia blochi (Bleeker)
  Paraplagusia japonica (Temminck and Schlegel)
  Paraplagusia guttata Macleay
 Cynoglossus
  Cynoglossus robustus Günther
  Cynoglossus oligolepis (Bleeker)
  Cynoglossus arel (Schneider)
  Cynoglossus macrolepidotus (Bleeker)
  Cynoglossus melampetalus (Richardson)
  Cynoglossus monopus (Bleeker)
  Cynoglossus sibogae (Weber)
  Cynoglossus brachycephalus Bleeker
  Cynoglossus lineolatus Steindachner
  Cynoglossus lida (Bleeker)
  Cynoglossus puncticeps (Richardson)
  Cynoglossus sinicus Wu
  Cynoglossus bilineatus (Lacépède)
  Cynoglossus interruptus Günther
  Cynoglossus nigropinnatus Ochiai
  Cynoglossus joyneri Günther
  Cynoglossus lighti Norman
  Cynoglossus semilaevis Günther
  Cynoglossus roulei Wu
  Cynoglossus gracilis Günther
  Cynoglossus xiphoides Günther
  Cynoglossus trigrammus Günther
  Cynoglossus abbreviatus (Gray)
  Cynoglossus purpueomaculatus Regan
  Cynoglossus itinus (Snyder)
 Symphurus
  Symphurus orientalis (Bleeker)
Tetraodontiformes
 Balistoidei
  Triacanthodidae
   Triacanthodes
    Triacanthodes anomalus (Temminck and Schlegel)
   Paratriacanthodes
    Paratriacanthodes retrospinis Fowler
   Tydemania
    Tydemania navigatoris Weber
    Tydemania japonica Kamohara
   Halimichirurgus
    Halimichirurgus alcocki Weber
  Triacanthidae
   Triacanthus
    Triacanthus biaculeatus (Bloch)
    Triacanthus blochi Bleeker
    Triacanthus brevirostris Temminck and Schlegel
    Triacanthus nieuhofi Bleeker
   Pseudotriacanthus
    Pseudotriacanthus strigilifer (Cantor)
  Balistidae
   Odonus
    Odonus niger (Rüppell)
   Pseudobalistes
    Pseudobalistes fuscus (Bloch and Schneider)
    Pseudobalistes flavimarginatus (Rüppell)
   Abalistes
    Abalistes stellatus (Lacépède)

Melichthys
  Melichthys vidua (Solander)
  Melichthys niger (Bloch)
Balistes
  Balistes vetula Linnaeus
Balistoides
  Balistoides conspicillum (Bloch and Schneider)
  Balistoides viridescens (Bloch and Schneider)
Sufflamen
  Sufflamen fraenatus (Latreille)
  Sufflamen chrysopterus (Bloch and Schneider)
Balistapus
  Balistapus undulatus (Mungo Park)
Rhinecanthus
  Rhinecanthus echarpe (Lacépède)
  Rhinecanthus aculeatus (Linnaeus)
  Rhinecanthus verrucosus (Linnaeus)
Xanthichthys
  Xanthichthys lineopunctatus (Hollard)
Canthidermis
  Canthidermis maculatus (Bloch)
Aluteridae
Pervagor
  Pervagor melanocephalus (Bleeker)
  Pervagor tomentosus (Linnaeus)
  Pervagor nitens (Hollard)
Laputa
  Laputa kneri (Steindachner)
Paramonacanthus
  Paramonachanthus oblongus (Temminck and Schlegel)
  Paramonachanthus nipponensis (Kamohara)
Stephanolepis
  Stephanolepis cirrhifer (Temminck and Schlegel)
  Stephanolepis japonicus (Tilesius)
Chaetodermis
  Chaetodermis spinosissimus (Quoy and Gaimard)
Arotrolepis
  Arotrolepis sulcatus (Hollard)
Monacanthus
  Monacanthus chinensis (Osbeck)
Navodon
  Navodon septentrionalis (Günther)
  Navodon tessellatus (Günther)
Rudarius
  Rudarius ercodes Jordan and Fowler
Oxymonacanthus
  Oxymonacanthus longirostris (Bloch and Schneider)
Cantherhines
  Cantherines dumerilli (Hollard)
  Cantherines pardalis (Rüppell)
Alutera
  Alutera monoceros (Osbeck)
  Alutera scripta (Osbeck)
Psilocephalidae
Psilocephalus
  Psilocephalus barbatus (Gray)
Ostracioidei
Aracanidae
Aracana
  Aracana rosapinto (Smith)
Ostraciontidae
Rhinesomus
  Rhinesomus gibbosus Linnaeus
  Rhinesomus concatenatus Bloch and Schneider
Rhynchostracion
  Rhynchostracion nasus Bloch
  Rhynchostracion rhinorhynchus Bleeker
Ostracion
  Ostracion tuberculatus Linnaeus
  Ostracion solorensis Bleeker
Lactoria
  Lactoria cornutus (Linnaeus)
  Lactoria diaphanus (Bloch and Schneider)
Tetraodontoidei
Tetraodontidae
Liosaccus
  Liosaccus cutaneus (Günther)
Lagocephalus
  Lagocephalus inermis (Temminck and Schlegel)
  Lagocephalus oceanicus Jordan and Evermann

Gastrophysus
  Gastrophysus lunaris (Bloch and Schneider)
  Gastrophysus spadicens (Richardson)
Pleuranacanthus
  Pleuranacanthus sceleratus (Forster)
  Pleuranacanthus suezensis (Gohar)
Amblyrhynchotus
  Amblyrhynchotus hypselogens (Bleeker)
  Amblyrhynchotus rufopunctatus Li
  Amblyrhynchotus honckeni (Bloch)
  Amblyrhynchotus spinosissimus (Regan)
Fugu
  Fugu vermicularis (Temminck and Schlegel)
  Fugu ocellatus (Linnaeus)
  Fugu niphobles (Jordan and Snyder)
  Fugu xanthopterus (Temminck and Schlegel)
  Fugu bimaculatus (Richardson)
  Fugu alboplumbeus (Richardson)
  Fugu oblongus (Bloch)
Chelonodon
  Chelonodon patoca (Hamilton)
Boeaemanichthys
  Boeaemanichthys firmamentum (Temminck and Schlegel)
Canthigaster
  Canthigaster valentini (Bleeker)
  Canthigaster jactator (Jenkins)
  Canthigaster rivulatus (Temminck and Schlegel)
Arothron
  Arothron immaculatus (Bloch and Schneider)
  Arothron nigropunctatus (Bloch and Schneider)
  Arothron stellatus (Bloch and Schneider)
  Arothron hispidus (Linnaeus)
  Arothron melaegris (Lacépède)
Triodontidae
 Triodon
  Triodon bursarius Reinhardt
Diodontidae
 Diodon
  Diodon hystrix Linnaeus
  Diodon holacanthus Linnaeus
  Diodon novemmaculatus Cuvier
  Diodon bleekeri Günther
 Chilomycterus
  Chilomycterus echinatus (Gronow)
  Chilomycterus orbicularis (Bloch)
  Chilomycterus affinis Günther
Moloidei
Molidae
 Mola
  Mola mola (Linnaeus)
 Masturus
  Masturus lanceolatus (Lienard)
Pegasiformes
 Pegasidae
  Pegasus
   Pegasus volitans Cuvier
   Pegasus laternarius Cuvier
   Pegasus draconis Linnaeus
Lophiiformes
 Lophioidei
  Lophiidae
   Lophiomus
    Lophiomus setigerus (Vahl)
 Antennarioidei
  Antennaridae
   Histrio
    Histrio histrio (Linnaeus)
   Antennarius
    Antennarius dorehensis Bleeker
    Antennarius hispidus Bloch and Schneider
    Antennarius nummifer Cuvier
    Antennarius pinniceps Commerson
  Chaunacidae
   Chaunax
    Chaunax fimbriatus Hilgendorf
  Ogcocephalidae
   Malthopsis
    Malthopsis luteus Alcoco
   Halieutaea
    Halieutaea stellata (Vahl)

Halieutaea indica Annandale and Jenkins
Halieutaea fumosa Alcock
Halieutaea sinica Tchang and Chang

Halicmetus
Halicmetus reticulatus Smith and Radcliffe

FOULING
SESSION PAPERS

The Marine Biology of the South China Sea
(ed. B. Morton). Proceedings of the First
International Conference on the Marine
Biology of Hong Kong and the South China Sea,
Hong Kong, 28 October – 3 November 1990.
Hong Kong: Hong Kong University Press, 1993.

FOULING ORGANISMS AT DAYA BAY NUCLEAR POWER STATION, CHINA

Z.G. Huang, C.X. Zheng, S. Lin, C.Y. Li, J.J Wang and S.K. Yan

Third Institute of Oceanography, State Oceanic Administration,
P.O. Box 0570, Xiamen, China

ABSTRACT

In 1987, test panels were exposed at the materials pier of the Daya Bay nuclear power station in order to determine the fouling organisms. One hundred and sixty-two species were recorded. The dominant species were *Obelia bicuspidata*, *Bugula neritina*, *Sinupetraliella umbonatoidea*, *Cosciniopsis hongkonggensis*, *Schizoporella unicornis*, *Hydroides inornata*, *Pomatoleios kraussii*, *Dexiospira foraminosus*, *Musculus nanus*, *Ostrea* spp., *Balanus cirratus*, *Chthamalus sinensis*, *Symplegma oceania* and *Styela canopus*. Attachment occurred year round, with peaks from May to June and from October to November. Monthly seasonal, semi-annual and annual thicknesses, areas of cover and wet and dry weights were recorded. The average monthly, seasonal, semi-annual and annual wet weights on the cement panels were 52, 603, 1891 and 1959 $g \cdot m^{-2}$, respectively.

Fouling organisms of Daya Bay comprise mainly coastal, high-salinity, eurytopic, warm-water species.

INTRODUCTION

Daya Bay nuclear power station is situated on the southwestern shore of Daya Bay, Guangdong Province, China (Fig. 1). Its installed capacity is 2 x (9 x 10^5) kW. The flow of sea water used for cooling is 108 $m^3 \cdot sec^{-1}$. The power station will be fully operational in 1993. Between December 1986 and December 1987, a panel test for fouling organisms was carried out at the materials pier of the power station.

MATERIALS AND METHODS

The test site was in the port area on the inner side of the materials pier, with calm waters and subject to little wave action. The water depth was 5 m and the transparency was 3-5 m. The average monthly salinity was stable between 29.0-33.5‰; and the average monthly surface water temperature varied between 17.7-29.3°C.

Two sets of test panels were exposed simultaneously, each at three depths: surface (4.5 m from the bottom), middle (2.5 m from the bottom) and bottom (close to the bottom). Both PVC and cement panels were tested monthly, seasonally, semi-annually, annually and monthly, accumulatively. Two hundred and forty panels were recovered and analysed for biomass, species occurrence and diversity.

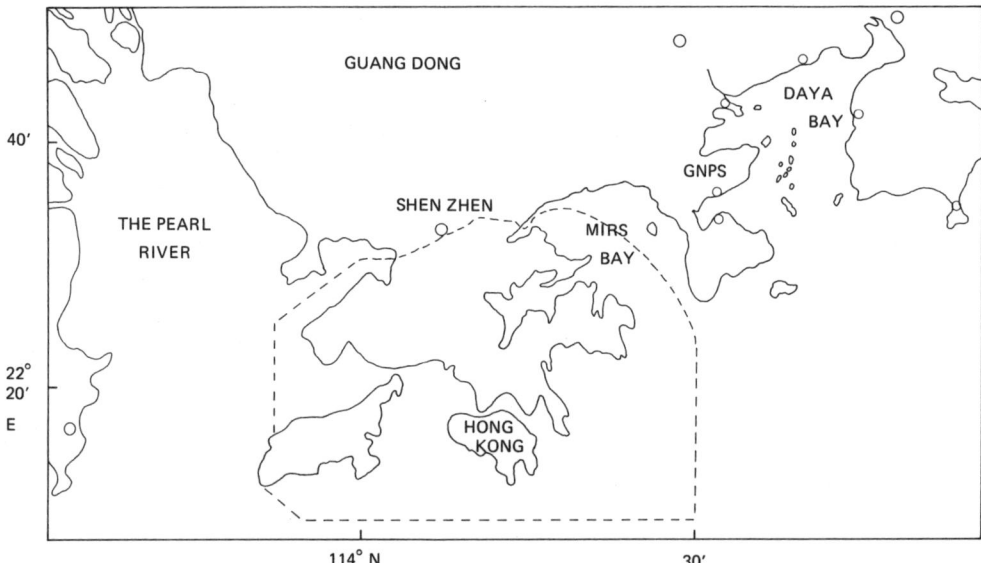

Fig. 1. A map showing the location of Daya Bay and the nuclear power station (GNPS).

RESULTS

Species

One hundred and sixty-two species were recorded: 13 were algae and 149 were animals (Table 3). Thirty-four species occurred 24 or more times on the 240 panels. The species present in greatest quantity and frequency of occurrence were: *Obelia bicuspidata*, *Bugula neritina*, *Sinupetraliella umbonatoidea*, *Cosciniopsis hongkongensis*, *Schizoporella unicornis*, *Hydroides inornata*, *Pomatoleios kraussii*, *Dexiospira foraminosus*, *Musculus nanus*, *Ostrea* spp., *Balanus cirratus*, *Chthamalus sinensis*, *Symplegma oceania* and *Styela canopus*.

Attachment periods

Attachment occurred in every month of the year, but there were differences in species and their numbers over the months. Generally, fewer species occurred in months with the lowest and highest water temperatures, i.e., February and August, respectively. Figure 2 illustrates the attachment periods of 24 species and the yearly variation in average monthly water temperature and salinity.

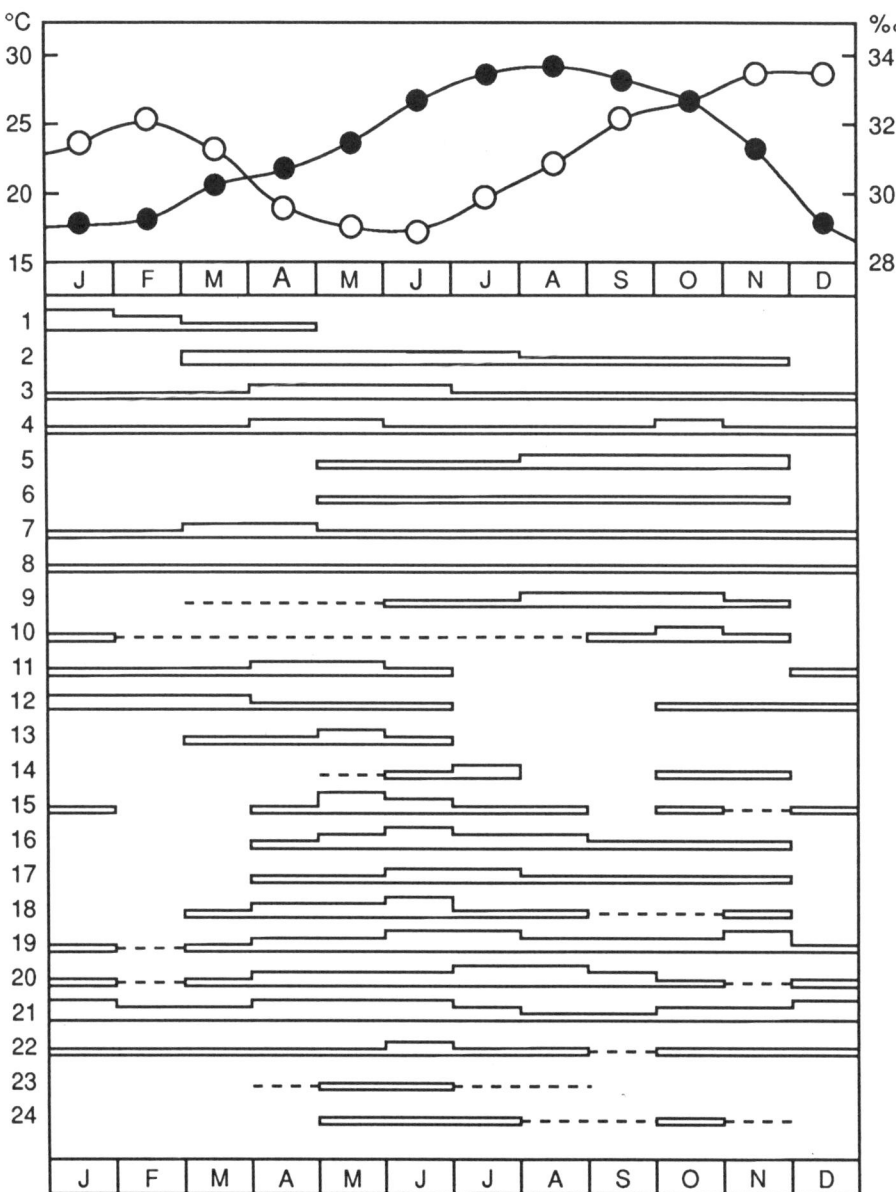

Fig. 2. Attachment periods of major biofoulers at Daya Bay nuclear power station materials pier (December 1986 – November 1987)

1, *Tubularia mesembryanthemum;* 2, *Obelia geniculata;* 3, *Hydroides* spp.; 4, *Serpula vermicularis;* 5, *Spirorbis* spp.; 6, *Pomatoleios kraussii;* 7, *Bugula neritina;* 8, *Sinupetraliella umbonatoidea;* 9, *Cosciniopsis hongkongensis;* 10, *Schizoporella unicornis;* 11, *Watersipora subovoidea;* 12, *Lichenopora imperialis;* 13, *L. radiata;* 14, *Brachidontes variabilis;* 15, *Saccostrea cucullata;* 16, *Alectryonella radix;* 17, *Dendostrea crenulifera;* 18, *Balanus trigonus;* 19. *B. reticulatus;* 20, *B. cirratus;* 21, *Chthamalus sinensis;* 22, *Symplegma oceania;* 23, *Botryllus schlosseri;* 24, *Styela canopus*

Biomass

Table 1 and 2 present the average biomass of fouling organisms at the three exposure depths and for each kind of panel. The results show two features: First, the biomass of fouling organisms was not large, with a maximum thickness of 6mm (annual panel) and an average monthly thickness of < 1 mm. None of the average areas of cover reached 100%. The heaviest wet weight was 2.4 kg·m^{-2} and the monthly and seasonal wet weights were all < 1 kg·m^{-2}. Second, the quantities of fouling organisms increased with the length of test time, that is in the sequence: monthly < seasonal < semiannual < annual (Plate I).

Table 1
Biomass of fouling organisms at the materials pier of Daya Bay nuclear power station (average for the three depths).

Period	Thickness (mm)		Area of cover (%)		Wet weight (g·m^{-2})	
	P	C	P	C	P	C
January	1.7	1.0	9.0	6.5	30.2	45.1
February	0.5	0.8	0.5	1.3	1.8	3.4
March	0.4	0.8	19.2	11.8	13.3	12.5
April	1.1	1.0	20.6	41.2	39.4	119.8
May	0.7	0.8	51.3	24.8	77.8	44.2
June	1.0	1.1	36.1	59.5	53.2	90.6
July	1.3	1.5	21.5	26.4	26.9	83.3
August	1.0	1.0	33.9	44.3	13.5	50.9
September	0.1	0.1	28.3	38.6	20.3	17.2
October	0.5	0.6	24.5	12.0	29.0	23.7
November	0.6	0.7	22.4	21.7	19.8	19.7
December	1.5	1.5	16.8	18.2	119.4	113.6
Mar-May	1.6	2.4	55.9	65.8	235.0	321.2
Jun-Aug	5.0	4.3	80.8	92.5	1875.9	1860.0
Sep-Nov	0.9	0.9	60.2	69.7	188.8	169.1
Dec-Feb	0.9	0.9	16.8	19.9	104.8	62.7
Dec-May	4.1	5.3	73.8	84.7	642.6	1210.9
Jun-Nov	4.4	5.8	92.5	78.3	1792.3	2571.2
Dec-Nov	5.9	6.0	98.2	98.2	2444.3	1959.4

P = PVC panel; C = cement panel.

Table 2
Average quantities of fouling organisms at Daya Bay nuclear power station, for different periods of the year.

Period	Thickness (mm)		Area of cover (%)		Wet weight (g·m^{-2})	
	P	C	P	C	P	C
Monthly	0.9	0.9	23.7	25.5	37.1	52.0
Seasonal	2.1	2.1	53.4	62.0	601.1	603.3
Semi-annual	4.3	5.6	83.2	81.5	1217.5	1891.1
Annual	5.9	6.0	98.2	98.2	2444.3	1959.4

P = PVC panel; C = cement panel.

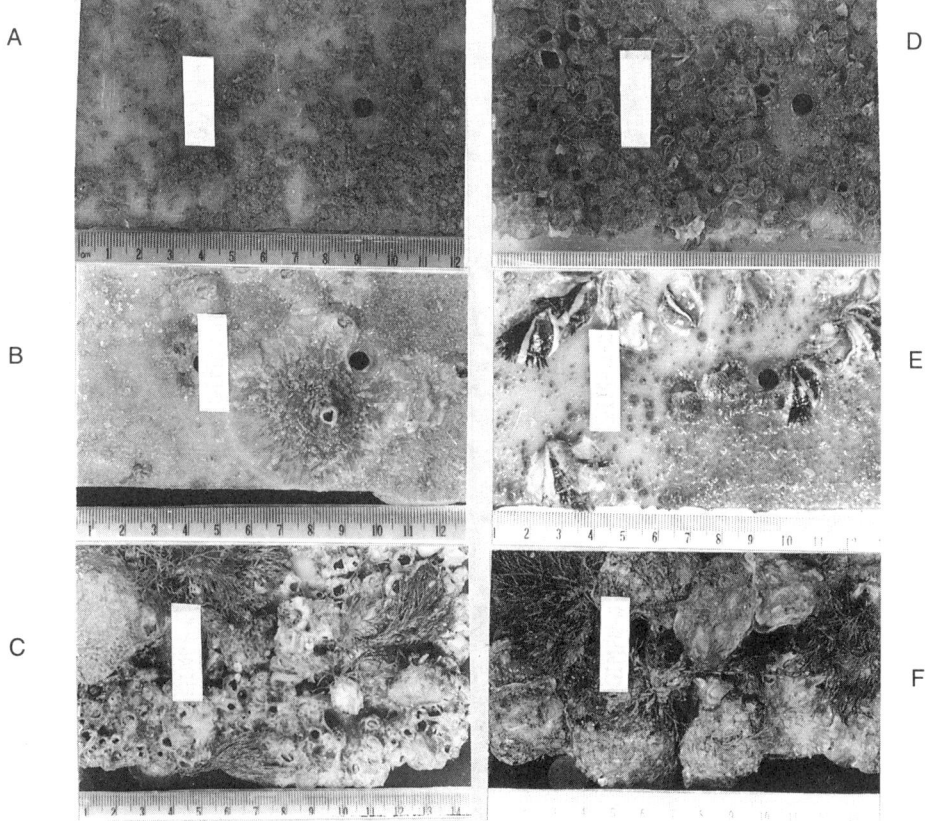

Plate 1. Fouling communities on panels (8 x 14 cm²) after different exposure periods
  A. 3 months (spring: March – May)
  B. 3 months (summer: June – August)
  C. 3 months (autumn: September – November)
  D. 3 months (winter: December – February)
  E. 6 months (semi-annual: June – December)
  F. 12 months (annual: June – May)

Table 3
Fouling organisms at the materials pier of Daya Bay nuclear power station and their occurrences on the 240 panels.

CYANOPHYTA

Microcoleus tenerrimus	1
Lyngbya semiplena	7

RHODOPHYTA

Scinaia tsinglanensis	2
Herposiphonia parca	2

PHAEOPHYTA

Ectocarpus sp.	9

CHLOROPHYTA

Ulothrix flacca	1
Enteromorpha clathrata	4
Enteromorpha sp.	1
Cladophora sp.	1
Microdictyon japonicum	3
Microdictyon pseudohapteron	1
Codium papillatum	1
C. repens	7

PORIFERA

Mycale adhaerens	20
Suberites carnosa	22
Scypha coronatum	21

CNIDARIA

Tubularia mesembryanthemum	25
Bougainvillia sp.	1
Clytia sp.	39
Obelia bicuspidata	29
Obelia geniculata	10
Synthecium campylocarpum	1
Lyntyecium nutting	4
Plumularia sp.	6
Actiniaria sp.	4

ECTOPROCTA (BRYOZOA)

Membranipora savartii	4
M. grandicella	6
M. lamellosa	3
M. tuberculata	1
Electra tenella	2
Beania mirabilis	1
Bugula neritina	46
B. californica	1
Scruporellaria unicornis	1
Sinupetraliella umbonatoidea	82
Hippopodina feegeensis	3
Cosciniopsis hongkongensis	79
Smittina projecta	36
S. trispirosa acuta	44
Cheiloporina haddoni	37
Vittaticella elegans	5
Watersipora subovoidea	43
Holoporella erectorostris	1
Crisia elongata	2
C. eburneo-denticulata	1
Crisia sp.	3
Tubulipora pulchra	6
Proboscinia coapta	11
Crisulipora occidentalis	5
Diaperoecia radicata	7
Lichenopora radiata	56
L. imperialis	56
Alcyonidium polyum	9
Amothia distans	1
Bowerbankia imbricata	2
Bryozoa spp.	18

ENTOPROCTA (KAMPTOZOA)

Barentsia sp.	

PLATYHELMINTHES

Stylochus ijimai	31
Pseudoceros exoptatus	5

NEMERTEA

Eubortasia sp.	7
Lineus sp. (1)	1
Lineus sp. (2)	1
Lineus sp. (3)	11

ANNELIDA
POLYCHAETA

Eumida sanguinea	2
Phyllodoce cf. madeirensis	2
Trypanosyllis taeniaformis	3
Syllis gracilis	2
Syllis sp.	1
Nereis multignatha	22
Perinereis cultrifera	11
Platynereis bicaliculata	1
Eunice antennata	2
Lysidice ninetta	2
Marphysa sanguinea	2
Terebella ehrenbergi	3
Demonax sp.	1
Sabellaria sp.	8

Table 3 (Continued)

Hydroides albiceps	11	*Pyrene bella*	1
H. elegans	15	*Viriola* sp.	2
H. exaltata	2	*Balcis* sp.	8
H. ezoensis	21	snail juvenile	13
H. inornata	32	Acteocinidae sp.	1
H. prisea	12	*Greilada* sp.	1
H. rhombulus	4	*Homiodoris japonica*	3
H. tambaagamensis	1	snail egg	7
Serpula vermicularia	14		
Pomatoleios kraussii	65	**ARTHROPODA**	
Spirobranchus semperi	6	**CRUSTACEA**	
S. cf. *polytrema*	1	**CIRRIPEDIA**	
Dexiospira foraminosus	91	*Balanus trigonus*	65
Spirorbis sp.	98	*B. reticulatus*	54
		B. cirratus	119
MOLLUSCA		*B. amphitrite amphitrite*	4
AMPHINEURA		*Chthamalus sinensis*	148
Lepidopleurus sp.	1	**MYSIDACEA**	
		Tenagomysis orientalis	41
BIVALVIA			
		TANAIDACEA	
Modiolus comptus	3		
Musculista senhausia	3	*Anatanais* sp.	18
M. nanus	20		
Brachidontes variabilis	24	**ISOPODA**	
Septifer bilocularis	1		
Isogomon legumen	11	*Sphaeroma walkeri*	35
Pinctada martensi	3	*Limnoria lignorum*	1
Spondylus nicobaricus	2		
Anomia chinensis	2	**AMPHIPODA**	
A. cyteum	1		
Saccostrea cucullata	113	*Caprella equilibra*	3
S. glomerata	2	*Caprella scaura*	1
S. echinata	2	*Corophium acheruscum*	40
Alectryonella radix	91	*Jassa falcata*	17
Dendostrea crenulifera	85	*Leucothoe alata*	36
Planostrea pestigris	48	*Stenothoe gallensis*	36
Chama dunkeri	1	*Podocerus brasiliensis*	12
Chama jukesi	19	Amphipoda	10
Bivalvia spp.	1		
		DECAPODA	
GASTROPODA			
		Leptochela pugnax	1
Notoacmea schrenckii	7	Hippolytidae	15
Patelloida pygmaea	5	*Metapenaeopsis barbatus*	1
Siphopatella walshi	1	*Alpheus bisincisus*	1
Serpulorbis sp.	6	*A. japonicus*	1
Thais luteostoma	7	*Galathea orientalis*	2
Cronia margariticola	2	*Pisidia serratifrons*	2
Latirus sp.	3	*Hyastenus pleione*	2
Zafra pumila	32	*Nanosesarma minutum*	8
Z. sinensis	7	Brachyura larva	3

Table 3 (Continued)

		Herdmania momus	8
Sphaerozius nitidus	3	VERTEBRATA	
INSECTA		PISCES	
insect larva	1	Dasson japonicus	1
ASCIDIA			
Symplegma oceania	53		
Botryllus schlosseri	22		
B. tuberatus	7		
Didemnum sp.	1		
Styela canopus	21		
Microcosmus exasperatus	3		
Molgula manhattensis	10		

DISCUSSION

Species

The basic characteristics of the fouling organisms of the materials pier at Daya Bay nuclear power station are characteristic of either inner-bay, high-salinity, eurytopic species or warm-water species. Estuarine low-salinity species, temperate-water species and oceanic species were absent. Inner-bay, high-salinity, eurytopic species such as *Bugula neritina* and *Hydroides elegans* are also distributed in high-salinity harbours along the coast of China and other high-salinity waters of the world, e.g., Nagasaki Harbour of Japan and the Suez Canal (Kawahara 1969; Huang and Mak 1980; Huang and Cai 1984; Whitehouse *et al.* 1985; Li, *et al.* 1990). Not recorded were: *Balanus uliginosus*, a low-salinity species abundant in other estuaries of China (Huang *et al.* 1981); *Balanus improvisus*, a temperate water species (Woods Hole Oceanographic Institution 1952; Li *et al.* 1990); and *Megabalanus tintinnabulum tintinnabulum* which occurs in large quantities in the open waters of the South China Sea (Huang *et al.* 1982).

Attachment periods

Attachment occurred year round in Daya Bay, but different species had different attachment periods and these can be divided into three groups:

  1. Year-round attachment. These species grew rapidly and had short maturation periods and short life cycles. For example, barnacles such as *Chthamalus sinensis*, *Balanus reticulatus* and *B. cirratus*, and bryozoans such as *Bugula neritina* and *Sinupetraliella umbonatoidea*.

  2. Biannual attachment. Such species as the bivalve *Perna viridis* attached in large numbers in spring, disappeared in summer and occurred again in autumn, but in fewer numbers.

  3. Yearly attachment. There were two kinds: (1) those attaching when the water

temperature was either rising or in the high-temperature season, e.g., *Lichenopora radiata*, *Pinctada martensii* and *Styela canopus*; (2) those attaching in the low-temperature season, e.g., algae such as *Enteromorpha* spp. and *Lyngbya semiplena*, and the hydroids *Tubularia mesembryanthemum* and *Obelia* spp.

The attachment period of fouling organism is a direct reflection of reproductive season. It is closely related to water temperature (Yasuda *et al.* 1981; Huang and Cai 1984), as well as to the physiological features of the fouling organisms themselves. Daya Bay is situated in the subtropics. The reproductive seasons of organisms occurring here, therefore, possess some characteristics of both temperate and tropical waters, but is more tropical.

Biomass

This test was conducted at the materials pier so as to simulate the biofouling condition of the equipment at the water inlet of the nuclear power station. For comparison, another two groups of panels were tested at a raft away from the water inlet, in waters with a flowing current and directly impacted by waves from the bay mouth (Huang *et al.* 1990).

The results showed that species numbers, thickness, area of cover and wet weight of the fouling organisms at the materials pier were far less than at the raft.

One hundred and ninety-eight species of fouling organisms were recorded from the raft, 36 more than at the pier. The average monthly, seasonal, semi-annual and annual wet weights at the raft were 1.4, 5.5, 4.7 and 4.1 times those at the pier, respectively. This indicates that current flow is advantageous to the attachment and growth of fouling organisms, because the two species numbers and monthly wet weights did not differ greatly while the seasonal, semi-annual and annual wet weights differed by more than four times

REFERENCES

Huang, Z.G. and Cai, R.X. 1984. *Marine biofouling and its prevention*. Beijing: China Ocean Press.
Huang, Z.G. and Mak, P.M.S. 1982. Studies on biofouling in Tolo Harbour. In *Proceedings of the First International Workshop on the Marine Flora and Fauna of Hong Kong and Southern China, Hong Kong, 1980* (ed. B. Morton and C.K. Tseng), 767-87. Hong Kong: Hong Kong University Press.
Huang, Z. G., Cai, R.X., Jiang, J.X., Cai, E.X. and Wu, Q.Q. 1982. Biofouling on the buoys off the Qiongzhou Channel and Leizhou Penisula coast, South China Sea. *Oceanologia et Limnologia Sinica* 13:259-66.
Huang, Z.G., Li, C.Y., Zhang, L.X., Li, F.R. and Zheng. C.X. 1981. The distribution of fouling organisms in Changhiang River Estuary. *Oceanologia et Limnologia Sinica* 12:531-7.
Huang, Z.G., Zheng, C.X., Li, C.Y., Wang, J.J., Lin, S., Yan, S.K., Zheng, D.Q. and Lin, N. 1990. Biofouling at the water inlet of Guangdong nuclear power station. *Collections of Papers on Marine Ecology in Daya Bay (II)*. Beijing: China Ocean Press.
Kawahara, T. 1969. Differences in the constitution of fouling communities according to localities at Nagasaki Harbour. *Report of the Faculty of Fisheries, Prefectural University of Mie* 6:109-26.
Li, C.Y., Huang, Z.G., Wang, J.J., Zheng, C.X. and Lin, S. 1990. An ecological study of fouling organisms in Yantai, China. *Acta Oceanologica Sinica* 12:107-14.

Whitehouse, J.W., Khalanski, M. and Jenner, H.A. 1985. *Marine fouling and power stations. A collaborative research working group report for use by station disigners and station managers*. CEGB EDF ENEL KEMA, 48.

Woods Hole Oceanographic Institution 1952. *Marine fouling and its prevention*. Annapolis: US Naval Institute.

Yasuda, T., Kawashiro, M. and Hibino, K. 1981. Studies on the effect on marine organisms of the warm water effluent from a nuclear power plant — relation between the distribution of the acorn barnacles and the warm water effluent in Uchiura Bay. *Marine Fouling* 3:71-80.

BIOFOULING OF SHIPS IN DAYA BAY, CHINA

S.K. Yan and Z.G. Huang

Third Institute of Oceanography, State Oceanic Administration,
P.O. Box 0570, Xiamen, China

ABSTRACT

Fouling organisms of ships in Daya Bay, South China Sea, were investigated and 78 species recorded, with *Balanus reticulatus* and *B. amphitrite amphitrite* dominant. Communities in which *B. reticulatus* was dominant had high wet weights (>10.0 kg·m^{-2}) and were complex, with *Bugula neritina*, *Hydroides elegans*, *Alectryonella radix*, *Dendostrea crenulifera*, *Styela plicata*, *S. canopus* and *Microcosmus exasperatus* abundant. Conversely, communities dominated by *B. amphitrite amphitrite* (> 90.0% of the wet weight) weighed less (< 4.5 kg·m^{-2}) and had simpler species compositions.

Area of cover was 75–100%, reaching 100% on three of the five ships surveyed. Fouling thickness varied between 12–26 mm and the greatest wet weight was 11.39 kg·m^{-2}.

Ship biofouling communities in Daya Bay are characterisitic of subtropical, coastal, inner-bay, high-salinity waters.

INTRODUCTION

Since 1960, more than 100 ships have been investigated for fouling organisms along the coast of China and their characteristics in various waters elucidated (Huang and Cai 1984). There is, however, no information about Daya Bay.

MATERIALS AND METHODS

Daya Bay (114°39'E; 22°40'N) is located in the northern part of the South China Sea. In 1987, eight samples (30 x 30 cm^2 each) of fouling organisms from five ships in the bay were collected and analysed. This paper discusses the biofouling characteristics of these ships.

RESULTS

Species

Seventy-eight species belonging to ten major taxonomic groups were recorded, i.e., Algae, Porifera, Coelenterata, Platyhelminthes, Nemertea, Bryozoa, Polychaeta, Bivalvia, Crustacea and Ascidia (Table 1). The dominant species were *Balanus reticulatus and B. amphitrite amphitrite*. Species with frequencies of occurrence > 60% were: *Bugula neritina, Hydroides elegans, Perna viridis, Chthamalus sinensis, Balanus trigonus* and *Styela canopus*.

Biomass and species composition

Table 2 shows the biomass and species composition of the ship fouling organisms in Daya Bay and indicates severe biofouling. The hulls of the five surveyed ships were 75–100% covered by fouling organisms; three of them with 100% cover. Wet weights ranged between 1.15–11.39 kg·m^{-2} and the thicknesses between 12–26 mm. Between 20–47 species were obtained from each ship. Barnacles were dominant in these communities, comprising between 39.2–97.7% of the wet weights. In the communities dominated by *Balanus reticulatus*, oysters, bryozoans and ascidians were also abundant. Conversely, *Balanus amphitrite amphitrite* dominated communities were simpler when this barnacle comprised > 90% of the wet weights.

DISCUSSION

Ship fouling organisms in Daya Bay were numerous and comprised three characteristic species groups: subtropical, high-salinity coastal bay and eurytopic.

Subtropical

The annual water temperature of Daya Bay is 18–31°C. The fouling organisms were dominated by subtropical, warm water species. Attachment occurred year round but intensity was distinctly seasonal. These features are reflected, to some degree, in the ship fouling organisms. For example, some common species such as *Mycale adhaerens, Sinupetraliella umbonatoidea, Hydroides inornata, Perna viridis, Brachidontes variabilis, Dendostrea crenulifera, Chthamalus sinensis* and *Styela plicata*, are warm water species (Huang and Mak 1982; Huang et al. 1988). Some dominant species, such as *Bugula neritina* and *Hydroides elegans*, attached during each month of the year, but flourished in the period from March to May (Yan and Huang 1990).

High-salinity coastal bay

There is no large freshwater runoff into Daya Bay so that the salinity lies between 30.0–33.8‰. Species typically abundant in the coastal estuarine waters of China, such as *Balanus uliginosus, Bougainvillia* sp. and *Membranipora lingdingensis* (Huang 1984; Huang and Cai 1984) are, therefore, absent from Daya Bay. This characterises the inner bay as a high-salinity area.

Table 1
Ship fouling organisms of Daya Bay and their frequencies of occurrence.

Species	Frequency (%)	Species	Frequency (%)
ALGAE		*Perna viridis*	62.5
		Brachidontes variabilis	37.5
Ectocarpus sp.	25.0	*Hormomya mutabilis*	12.5
Sargassum sp.	12.5	*Septifer keenae*	2.5
PORIFERA		*Modiolus comptus*	12.5
		Musculus nanus	25.0
Mycale adhaerens	37.5	*Xenostrobus atrata*	12.5
Suberites carnosa	12.5	*Hiatella orientalis*	12.5
		Isognomon legumen	12.5
COELENTERATA		*Dendostrea crenulifera*	25.0
Actiniaria	37.5	*Planostrea pestigris*	2.5
		Alectryonella radix	37.5
PLATYHELMINTHES		*Saccostrea cucullata*	25.0
Pseudoceros exoptatus	37.5	*Chama brassica*	12.5
Stylochus ijimai	37.5	*Irus macrophylla*	12.5
		Bivalvia spp.	2.5
NEMERTEA		**CRUSTACEA**	
Lineus sp.	12.5		
Eubortasia sp.	37.5	*Chthamalus sinensis*	87.5
BRYOZOA		*Balanus reticulatus*	00.0
		B. amphitrite amphitrite	50.0
Membranipora grandicella	12.5	*B. cirratus*	50.0
M. tuberculata	3.8	*B. trigonus*	75.0
Bugula neritina	87.5	*Megabalanus*	
Cosciniopsis hongkongensis	25.0	*tinntinabulum tinntinabulum*	12.5
Sinupetraliella umbonatoidea	12.5	*Sphaeroma walkeri*	62.5
Schizoporella unicornis	37.5	*Caprella equilibra*	2.5
POLYCHAETA		*Jassa falcata*	2.5
		Podocerus brasiliensis	25.0
Syllis gracilis	37.5	*Stenothoe gallensis*	2.5
Eulalia viridis	12.5	*Ampelisca* sp.	25.0
Halosydna brevisetosa	37.5	*Leucothe alata*	25.0
Lepidonotus cf. *tenuisetosus*	12.5	*Corophium acheruscum*	37.5
Leonnates dicipiens	12.5	Amphipoda spp.	12.5
Nereis multignatha	37.5	*Alpheus brevicristatus*	12.5
Perinereis cultrifera	75.0	*Charybdis hongkongensis*	12.5
Nectoneanthes multignatha	37.5	*Sphaerozius nitidus*	12.5
N. oxypoda	12.5	*Hexapus anfractus*	12.5
Lysidice ninneta	12.5	*Nanosesarma minutum*	25.0
Demonax microphthalmus	62.5	Brachyura larvae	12.5
Serpula vermicularis	50.0		
Hydroides dirampha	12.5	**ASCIDIA**	
H. elegans	62.5		
H. ezoensis	12.5	*Styela canopus*	87.5
H. inornata	25.0	*S. plicata*	50.0
Spirorbis sp.	50.0	*Microcosmus australis*	12.5
Spirobranchus semperi	12.5	*M. exasperatus*	12.5
		Polyclinum constellatum	12.5
BIVALVIA		*Didemnum* sp.	12.5
Barbatia virescens	25.0	*Botryllus schlosseri*	12.5

Table 2
Biomass and composition of ship fouling organisms in Daya Bay.

Ship	Species numbers	Thickness (mm)	Area of cover (%)	Wet wt. (kg·m⁻¹)	Balanus reticulatus	B. amphitrite amphitrite	Other barnacles	Oysters	Other bivalves	Bryozoans	Tubiculous polychaetes	Ascidians	Others
								Percentage wet weight (%)					
1	47	26	90	10.96	50.1	3.0	3.7	11.0	4.4	4.9	6.7	12.4	3.8
2	30	15	100	11.39	38.0	—	1.2	7.6	0.2	18.9	<0.1	28.6	6.4
3	20	12	75	1.15	0.7	96.6	0.4	<0.1	<0.1	0.4	0.1	0.1	1.6
4	24	20	100	4.37	1.1	90.3	0.5	4.1	2.8	<0.1	1.2	—	—
5	35	15	100	9.42	86.1	—	2.2	10.0	0.6	0.1	0.3	0.1	0.6

Eurytopic

Many species of the ship fouling organisms in Daya Bay are eurytopic. Common species such as *Bugula neritina*, *Schizoporella unicornis*, *Hydroides elegans*, *Balanus amphitrite amphitrite*, *B. trigonus* and *Botryllus schlosseri*, have a wide distribution along the cost of China and many other parts of the world (Woods Hole Oceanographic Institution 1952; Ghobashy 1980; Huang 1984). This is closely related to the geographic position of Daya Bay, situated, as it is, in the subtropics. Vessels play a significant role in carrying fouling organisms elsewhere, widening their distribution range (Allen 1953; Huang *et al.* 1979). Hong Kong is an international harbour into which nearly 10,000 ocean-going vessels (30–40 million tons) enter from various countries each year. Daya Bay is but 10 miles from Hong Kong waters and there are many ships plying between the two places. This may constitute an additional important reason for the diversity of the fouling organisms in Daya Bay.

ACKNOWLEDGEMENTS

We are grateful for the help of our colleagues, D.Q. Zheng, C.X. Zheng, C.Y. Li, J.J. Wang and S. Lin.

REFERENCES

Allen, F.E. 1953. Distribution of marine invertebrates by ships. *Australian Journal of Marine and Freshwater Research* 4:307–16.

Ghobashy, F.A. 1980. Fouling in the Suez Canal. In *Proceedings of the 5th International Congress on Marine Corrosion and Fouling*, 75–92.

Huang, Z.G. 1984. Ecological and biological studies of fouling organisms along the coast of China. *Proceedings of the 6th International Congress on Marine Corrosion and Fouling*. 23–37.

Huang, Z.G. and Cai, R.X. 1984. *Marine biofouling and its prevention*, Vol. I, 66–155. (In Chinese)

Huang, Z.G. and Mak, P.M.S. 1982. Studies on biofouling in Tolo harbour. *Proceedings of the First International Marine Biological Workshop: The Marine Flora and Fauna of Hong Kong and Southern China, Hong Kong, 1980* (ed. B. Morton and C. K. Tseng), 767–87. Hong Kong: Hong Kong University Press.

Huang, Z.G., Li, C.Y., Zhang, L.X. and Zhuang, S.D. 1988. Fouling organisms on vessels and ocean installations in waters from Hainan Island to the Xisha Islands, China. In *Proceedings of the Third Chinese Oceanological and Limnological Science Conference*, 267–72. (In Chinese)

Huang, X.M., Ni, W.Z., Lu, H.Q. and Cui, K.D. 1979. A study on the interrelation between service condition of ships and fouling organisms. *Oceanologia et Limnologia Sinica* 10:82–9. (In Chinese)

Woods Hole Oceanographic Institution. 1952. *Marine fouling and its prevention*. Annapolis: US Naval Institute.

Yan, S.K. and Huang, Z.G. 1990. Study of fouling organisms in Daya Bay, China. *Biofouling* 2:229–37.

A PRELIMINARY INVESTIGATION OF MARINE FUNGI IN THE SOUTH CHINA SEA

L.L.P. Vrijmoed* and C.S.W. Kueh+

Department of Applied Biology and Chemical Technology,
Hong Kong Polytechnic, Hong Kong.

and

H.Q. Shen, C.H. Cai and Y.P. Zhou

South China Sea Institute of Oceanology, 164 West Xingang Road,
Academia Sinica, Guangzhou, China

ABSTRACT

An investigation of marine fungi in seawater and on driftwood was carried out in the South China Sea between July and August 1988. Water samples were collected from 24 stations between 6°02'03"–11°00'11"N and 112°05'47"–118°24'55"E at the surface and at depths of 25 m and 100 m. Driftwood was retrieved from coral reefs between 8°55'00"–9°55'00"N and 115°30'00"–116°33'18"E, which is one part of the Spratly Islands. Marine fungi in seawater were enumerated by membrane filtration using Mycological Agar medium (pH 7). Driftwood samples were incubated at ambient temperature for fungal sporulation. The fungal counts (Colony Forming Units 100 mL^{-1}) decreased with increasing depth with average values of 196, 123 and 104 CFUs 100 mL^{-1} at the surface and at 25 m and 100 m, respectively. Yeasts dominated the mycota at each depth; filamentous forms were absent from approximately 50% of the stations at various depths. No attempt was made to identify the yeasts but filamentous forms were dominated by *Aspergillus* spp. and *Cladosporium* spp. The lignicolous mycota was not abundant; only 10 species were recorded from 51 samples, of which sixteen did not show any development of higher fungi even after incubation. The dominant species were *Antennospora quadricornuta* (Cribb and Cribb) T.W. Johnson (39%), *Halosphaeria salina* (Meyers) Kohlm (14%) and *Periconia prolifica* Anastasiou (10%). These results are compared with studies of the mycota on submerged wood in other tropical and subtropical waters.

---

* Department of Biology and Chemistry, City Polytechnic of Hong Kong, Tat Chee Avenue, Kowloon, Hong Kong.
+ Water Policy Group, Environmental Protection Department, Hong Kong.

INTRODUCTION

In the summer of 1988 between mid-July and mid-August, scientists from the South China Sea Institute of Oceanology, Academia Sinica, Guangzhou, made a scientific expedition on board the research vessel *Shi Yan No. 3* to the South China Sea, especially around the Spratly Islands. One of the surveys carried out was the monitoring of microbial levels (bacteria and fungi) in the seawater and a collection of driftwood from coral reefs for lignicolous marine fungi. The results of the mycological investigation are described below.

MATERIALS AND METHODS

The South China Sea, also known as 'Nanhai', is located on the western part of the Pacific Ocean. It is bounded by China to the north, the Indo-China and Malay Peninsulas to the west, the Philippines and Taiwan Islands to the east and the Island of Borneo to the south. It embraces an area of about 2.2 million km^2 and has an average depth of 1.1 km. Scattered along the south-eastern part are numerous coral reefs. The weather is tropical and largely controlled by monsoons. The continental shelf is heavily fished by the bordering Southeast Asian countries providing as much as 50% of the animal protein used by the populace of the region.

The area of survey for bacteria and fungi of the seawater ranged from 6°02'03"–11°00'03" N to 112°05'47"–118°24'55". Surface water samples were collected from 24 stations and also at depths of 25 m and 100 m by means of a Zobell bacterial sampler. The marine fungi were enumerated by membrane filtration using filters with pore size of 0.45 µm and Mycological Agar (pH 7) (Difco) supplemented with antibiotics (0.06% benzylpenicillin and 0.1% streptomycin sulphate) as the selective medium. Samples were filtered immediately after the collection of water samples on board the research vessel. The membranes were incubated at ambient temperature (*ca.* 28 ± 2°C) for five to seven days. Colonies were then counted but no attempts were made to identify these fungi.

Driftwood was collected from the coral reef region of the Spratly Islands. Fifty-one samples were retrieved from six coral reefs between 8°55'00"–9°55'00"N and 115°30'00"–116°33'18"E. Surface fouling organisms on the wood were gently scraped off, followed by removal of surface debris by means of several rinses with seawater. These samples were then placed in sealed polythene bags lined with sterile paper towels moistened with sterile seawater. This set-up is similar to that of a chamber which provides a humid environment for the development of sporulating structures of marine fungi (Floodgate and Jones 1987). The wood samples were incubated at room temperature (*ca.* 28 ± 2°C) on board the research vessel during the survey and were later returned to the laboratory for examination and identification.

RESULTS

Hydrographic data

During the survey, the temperature, salinity and pH of the seawater at the 24 stations, at the surface and at depths of 25 m and 100 m were measured. The values were fairly constant at the same depth for all stations and the results are summarised in Table 1. These data reveal that salinity, temperature and pH of the seawater in the upper 25 m were fairly homogenous. At 100 m below the surface, a drastic drop in temperature was recorded (a difference of nine degrees), but only a slight change in salinity and pH was observed.

Table 1
A summary of the hydrographical data recorded at 24 test stations in the South China Sea between mid-July and mid-August 1988.

Parameter	Depth (m)		
	0	25	100
Salinity (‰)	33.2	33.6	34.4
Temperature (°C)	29.2	29.1	20.3
pH	8.1	8.1	7.9

Marine fungi isolated from seawater

Fungi that developed on the membrane filters after incubation were mainly yeasts; very few filamentous forms were obtained. As there were considerable variations in numbers of CFUs for both filamentous and yeast forms among the stations, only the summarised results are given (Table 2). Yeast colonies were recorded from almost all of the stations and at all depths; the only exceptions were two stations at 100 m below the surface where they were absent. In general, the average yeast counts decreased with increasing depth, being 196 CFUs 100 mL^{-1} at the surface and 104 CFUs 100 mL^{-1} at 100 m. In comparison, filamentous forms were much lower in numbers. They were only recorded from 11 stations (45.8%), both from the surface waters and at a depth of 25 m, and from nine stations (37.5%) at 100 m. The highest number of CFUs recorded was 12, both at the surface and at 25 m. Only 1–4 CFUs were recorded at the rest of the stations at all depths.

No attempt was made to identify the fungi isolated on the membrane filters. However, random examination of the filamentous forms revealed the predominance of *Aspergillus* spp. and *Cladosporium* spp. among the sporulating colonies. Many isolates remained in the mycelial, non-sporulating state.

Table 2
Distribtution of filamentous fungi and yeast in seawater of 24 test stations in the South China Sea.

Depth (m)	Colony Forming Units 100·mL^{-1}			
	Filamentous		Yeast	
	mean	range	mean	range
0	1	1–12	196	71–479
25	2	1–12	123	27–435
100	1	1–3	104	12–367

Lignicolous marine fungi from driftwood

The majority of the wood samples collected were riddled with shipworm tubes and had remains of attached surface fouling organisms. Sixteen (31.4%) of the 51 wood samples did not yield sporulating fungi even after incubation for a period between four and eight weeks. The lignicolous marine fungi detected on the remaining samples and their percentage of occurrence are listed in Table 3. A total of ten species were recorded with the exception of one species (*Stachybotrys*-like sp.), which can be considered an obligate marine fungi. The most abundant species were *Antennospora quadricornuta* (39%), *Halosphaeria salina* (14%) and *Periconia prolifica* (12%). The occurrence of the remaining species varied between 2–8% only. The number of lignicolous fungi was low, both in terms of species diversity and abundance.

Table 3
Higher fungi recorded on driftwood collected from six coral reefs in the Spratly Islands.

Fungi	Occurrence no.	%
Antennospora quadricornuta (Cribb & Cribb) T W Johnson	20	39
Clavatospora bulbosa (Anastasiou) Nakagiri & Tubaki	2	4
Corollospora pulchella Kohlmeyer	1	2
Dictyosporium sp.	3	6
Halosphaeria salina (Meyers) Kohlmeyer	7	14
Humicola alopallonella Meyers & Moore	3	6
Monodictys sp.	2	4
Periconia prolifica Anastasiou	6	12
Stachybotrys-like sp.	2	4
Trichocladium achrasporum (Meyers & Moore) Dixon in Shearer & Crane	4	8

No. of wood samples examined = 51
No. of 'sterile' samples = 16 (31.4%)

DISCUSSION

The advantages and disadvantages of using the membrane filtration technique for the enumeration of fungi have been reviewd by Sherry and Qureshi (1986). It is well documented that the use of this technique results in a predominance of yeast colonies (Clesceri et al. 1989). Concentrations of yeast cells in ocean waters are generally low, varying from 1–10 CFUs·100 mL^{-1} (Meyers and Ahearn 1974). However, higher values are associated with either nutrient maxima at thermoclines or current boundaries, or with plankton blooms (Meyers and Ahearn 1974). The fairly high average values of yeast (100–200 CFUs·100 mL^{-1}) in our survey may be due to the proximity of some of the stations to the coral reefs where dissolved organics in the surrounding waters are higher than normal oceanic waters. However, no other reports of yeast counts recovered from waters collected near coral reefs are available for comparison. Filamentous forms such as *Aspergillus* and *Cladosporium* have frequently been isolated from seawater in similar investigations, e.g., Roth *et al.* (1964), Muntanola-Cvetkovic (1980), Miller and Whitney (1981). Fell (1967) suggested that the incidence of moulds in oceanic waters appeared to be partially dependent on the proximity of terrigenous materials. The low frequency of these filamentous forms in this survey agrees with this.

The driftwood lignicolous mycota is represented by typical tropical/subtropical species. The three dominant fungi, namely *Antennospora quadricornuta*, *Halosphaeria salina* and *Periconia prolifica* have been collected frequently in tropical/subtropical regions (Kohlmeyer 1984). *Corollospora pulchella* and its anamorph *Clavatospora bulbosa*, although occurring in low frequencies in this collection, belong to the same category. *H. alopallonella* and *T. achrasporum* are considered to be cosmopolitan species (Hughes 1974).

The presence of shipworms, tubes and remains of attached fouling organisms on the driftwood samples indicate these samples had been submerged for a considerable period of time. It was noted that some fungi such as *A. quadricornuta* and *H. salina* were associated with the calcareous tubes of shipworms as previously reported by Vrijmoed *et al.* (1986a). However, no experimental work has been carried out to establish whether these fungi decompose the calcium carbonate matrix (Kohlmeyer 1984).

This is the first report of lignicolous marine fungi on submerged driftwood collected from coral reefs. The only comparison that can be made of the mycota on submerged wood in the tropics and subtropics is that of baited blocks exposed in the coastal waters of Hong Kong (Vrijmoed *et al.* 1982), Indonesia (Suhirman and Jones 1983) and Kuwait (Zainal and Jones 1986). Table 4 shows the number of species, the total number of wood blocks examined, the period of submersion and the frequency occurrence of the dominant species at each of these sites with similar data from the present investigation. The number of species recorded was low considering the large number of panels examined and the lengthy period of submersion, especially for Kuwait. These low numbers are in sharp contrast with the large number of species recorded from driftwood collected in intertidal regions in mangrove communities, e.g., 82 species from 627 samples in Malaysia (Jones and Kuthubutheen 1989); 39 species from 150 samples in northern Sumatra (Hyde 1989a); 41 species from 188 samples (Tan *et al.* 1989); 17 species from 33 samples in Thailand (Koch 1986) and 43 species from 300 samples in non-mangrove areas in Brunei (Hyde 1989b). There are a number of factors, both abiotic and biotic, that can affect the colonisation of wood by fungi in the marine environment (Floodgate and Jones 1987). Some of the important abiotic factors include temperature and salinity of the water (Hughes 1986), the type of wood species (Vrijmoed *et al.* 1986b), the depth at which the substrata are either exposed or recovered (Floodgate and Jones 1987) which implies the possible effect of oxygen tension. Miller *et al.* (1985) have shown evidence of interference competition among fungi when colonizing wood and their field studies were supported by an *in vitro* assessment of the index of antagonism of the marine fungi involved.

The results in Table 4 apparently suggest that of the four species which were invariably found on the submerged panels in the tropical and subtropical waters, *A. quadricornuta* and *P. prolifica* appeared to be most frequent. Different wood species were employed in these exposure experiments and thus care has to be taken when interpreting such results. The low incidence/absence of *C. halima* in Indonesia and Kuwait may be due to the use of teak in the exposure experiments. In Hong Kong coastal waters, this fungus was abundant on submerged pine blocks but was absent on submerged teak panels (Vrijmoed et al. 1986b). Better field experiments have yet to be designed to study the interacting factors affecting colonisation of wood in the marine environment.

Table 4
A comparison of fungi recorded (% occurrence) in exposure experiments carried out in tropical/subtropical waters.

Fungi	Hong Kong	Kuwait	Indonesia	South China Sea
Antennospora quadricornuta	50	72	2	39
Ceriosporopsis halima	36	2	–	–
Halosphaeria salina	2	–	–	14
Periconia prolifica	77	3	16	12
No. of species recorded	28	7	23	10
No. of panels examined	212	50*	270	51
Period of submersion (months)	18	29	15	NR

– absent
* approximate number
NR no record, unable to trace

ACKNOWLEDGEMENTS

The authors would like to thank the Research Committee of The Hong Kong Polytechnic, Hong Kong, and the South China Sea Institute of Oceanology, Academia Sinica, Guangzhou, for sponsorship and financial support for the project and Mr George Lau for his technical assistance. The senior author is also grateful to Professor E.B. Gareth Jones of the University of Portsmouth, UK, for his encouragement in the preparation of this manuscript.

REFERENCES

Clesceri, L.S., Greenburg, A.E. and Trussell, R.R. 1989. *Standard methods for the examination of water and wastewater.* 17th ed. Washington, DC: American Public Health Association.
Fell, J.W. 1967. Distribution of yeasts in the Indian Ocean. *Bulletin of Marine Science* 17:454–70.
Floodgate, G.D. and Jones, E.B.G. 1987. Bacteria and fungi. In *Biological surveys of estuaries and coasts* (ed. J.M. Baker and W.J. Wolff), 238–79. Cambridge: Cambridge University Press.
Hughes, G.C. 1974. Geographical distribution of the higher marine fungi. *Veroffentlichungen des Instituts für Meeresforschung in Bremerhaven. Supplement* 5:419–41.

Hughes, G.C. 1986. Biogeography of marine fungi. In *The biology of marine fungi* (ed. S.T. Moss), 275–96. Cambridge: Cambridge University Press.

Hyde, K.D. 1989a. Intertidal mangrove fungi from north Sumatra. *Canadian Journal of Botany* 67:3078–82.

Hyde, K.D. 1989b. Ecology of tropical marine fungi. *Hydrobiologia* 178:199–208.

Jones, E.B.G. and Kuthubutheen, A.J. 1989. Malaysian mangrove fungi. *Sydowia* 41:160–9.

Koch, J. 1986. Some lignicolous marine fungi from Thailand, including two new species. *Nordic Journal of Botany* 6:497–99.

Kohlmeyer, J. 1984. Tropical marine fungi. *P.S.Z.N.I: Marine Ecology* 5:329–78.

Meyers, S.P. and Ahearn, D.G. 1974. Implication of yeasts and yeast-like fungi in marine processes. *Veroffentlichungen des Instituts für Meeresforschung in Bremerhaven. Supplement* 5:321–38.

Miller, J.D. and Whitney, N.J. 1981. Fungi from the Bay of Fundy II. Observations on fungi from living and cast seaweeds. *Botanica Marina* 24:405–11.

Miller, J.D., Jones, E.B.G., Moharir, Y.E. and Findlay, J. 1985. Colonization of wood blocks by marine fungi in Langstone Harbour. *Botanica Marina* 28:251–7.

Muntanola-Cvetkovic, M. 1980. A mycological survey of the South Adriatic Sea. *Journal of Experimental Marine Biology and Ecology* 43:193–206.

Roth, F.J., Orpurt, P.A. and Ahearn, D.G. 1964. Occurrence and distribution of fungi in a subtropical environment. *Canadian Journal of Botany* 42:375–83.

Sherry, J.P. and Qureshi, A.A. 1986. Isolation and enumeration of fungi using membrane filtration. In *Membrane filtration applications, techniques, and problems* (ed. B.J. Dutka), 189–218. New York: Marcel Dekker.

Suhirman and Jones, E.B.G. 1983. Preliminary observations on lignicolous marine fungi in the Java Sea, Indonesia. *Annales Bogorienses* 8:35–49.

Tan, T.K., Leong, W.F. and Jones, E.B.G. 1989. Succession of fungi on wood of *Avicennia alba* and *A. lanata* in Singapore. *Canadian Journal of Botany* 67:2686–91.

Vrijmoed, L.L.P., Hodgkiss, I.J. and Thrower, L.B. 1982. Factors affecting the distribution of lignicolous marine fungi in Hong Kong. *Hydrobiologia* 87:143–60.

Vrijmoed, L.L.P., Hodgkiss, I.J. and Thrower, L.B. 1986a. Effects of surface fouling organisms on the occurrence of fungi on submerged pine blocks in Hong Kong coastal waters. *Hydrobiologia* 135:123–30.

Vrijmoed, L.L.P., Hodgkiss, I.J. and Thrower, L.B. 1986b. Occurrence of fungi on submerged pine and teak blocks in Hong Kong coastal waters. *Hydrobiologia* 135:109–22.

Zanail, A. and Jones, E.B.G. 1986. Occurrence and distribution of lignicolous marine fungi in Kuwait coastal waters. In *Biodeterioration 6* (ed. S. Barry, D.R. Houghton, G.C. Llewellyn and C.E. O'Rear), 596–600. C.A.B. International Mycological Institute.

The Marine Biology of the South China Sea
(ed. B. Morton). Proceedings of the First
International Conference on the Marine
Biology of Hong Kong and the South China Sea,
Hong Kong, 28 October – 3 November 1990.
Hong Kong: Hong Kong University Press, 1993

CHOANOFLAGELLATES AS FOULING ORGANISMS

Seamus M. Jackson and E.B. Gareth Jones

School of Biological Sciences, Portsmouth University, King Henry Building,
King Henry I Street, Portsmouth, Hants. PO1 2DY, UK

ABSTRACT

There have been many studies on the formation of biofilms on various surfaces and the subject of biofilm development has been widely reviewed. Such studies have also reported the presence of attached protozoa. Their role and importance in biofilm development has, however, been largely ignored.

Test samples of glass, Thermanox, stainless steel, brass, copper and antifouling paints were exposed at three sites (Portsmouth and Poole in the United Kingdom and near Barcelona in Spain). Their colonisation was monitored with particular reference to the choanoflagellates present.

The results show that choanoflagellates are frequently a major component of developing and established biofilms. Both sessile and planktonic forms were collected, the latter being entrapped in the developing film. The species collected also showed variations in numbers depending on the exposure site and conditions and the nature of the surface. Thecate forms were apparently more tolerant of toxic systems (brass, copper and antifouling paints) than loricate forms.

INTRODUCTION

Surfaces placed in an aquatic environment are rapidly colonised by a range of micro-organisms. Much attention has been given to this and it has been termed, amongst other things, microfouling and biofilm development.

The area that has received the greatest attention is that of bacterial attachment (Marshall 1984, 1985) and bacterial biofilm development, physiology and composition (Characklis 1983; Characklis and Cooksey 1983; Savage and Fletcher 1985; Costerton *et al.* 1987; Hamilton 1987). Likewise, the microalgae, including cyanobacteria and diatoms have been examined extensively (Cooksey *et al.* 1984; Callow 1986a,b; Daniel *et al.* 1987). Also, rather than considering bacteria and microalgae separately, their close contact in biofilms and consequent interactions have been studied (Escher and Characklis 1982; Murray *et al.* 1986)

Many groups of protozoa that are constituents of natural biofilms have been neglected. Some studies on ciliates commonly found on surfaces have been carried out (Brown and Jones 1982; Brown *et al.* 1984, 1986). One group, the choanoflagellates, has been neglected. Choanoflagellates are typified by the presence of a protoplast with a single anterior flagellum. This flagellum is surrounded by a collar of tentacles or microvilli. The structure and diversity of these is clearly indicated by Leadbeater (1985).

The Choanoflagellida is divided into three families according to their basic morphology: Codonosigidae, Salpingoecidae, and Acanthoecidae. The most easily distinguishable of these are the Acanthoecidae due to the presence of a lorica. This is a basket-like structure composed of siliceous strips.

This paper indicates the abundance of choanoflagellates on various surfaces. Representatives of all three families were obtained from substrata exposed to seawater at various locations and under different conditions.

MATERIALS AND METHODS

A range of substrata (glass, Thermanox, stainless steel, brass, copper and antifouling paints) were used in this investigation. These were exposed to natural seawater at three locations, two in England (Portsmouth and Poole) and one in Spain (near Barcelona). All materials were exposed in Portsmouth, at the other sites glass, Thermanox and antifouling paints were exposed. In addition, observations were made on the colonisation of glass coverslips in the laboratory. These were exposed to a continual flow of natural seawater.

Samples from the three exposure sites were removed at intervals of between five or ten days for the first two months and at monthly intervals thereafter. Material from the laboratory was collected every two hours for the first 48 hours and every twelve hours thereafter up to a period of two weeks.

Fresh samples on transparent material were first examined using phase contrast and interference contrast microscopy. Thereafter, all material was fixed in 4% v/v glutaraldehyde in filtered (0.8 µm pore size) seawater. For light microscopy material was treated with one of several general stains. For electron microscopy material was either dehydrated in an ethanol series and critical point dried or freeze dried. After coating the material it was examined in a scanning electron microscope (JEOL T20).

RESULTS

Initial observations indicated that there was a wide diversity of choanoflagellates present on the exposed surfaces. The most rapid colonisation was seen in the laboratory, where choanoflagellates attached within twelve hours of exposure.

Representatives of all three families of choanoflagellates were examined. Within the Codonosigidae only one species was found, i.e., *Monosiga* sp., typified by a long stalk and protoplast lacking a distinct theca.

The most abundant choanoflagellates were various species Salpingoecidae. This group can be identified by the presence of a membrane (the theca) around the protoplast. Several forms were identified including *Choanoeca* spp. and *Salpingoeca* spp. The former genus is typified by the lack of a flagellum, the latter by possession of one One form was commonly obtained from material exposed in Portsmouth, and was considered to be a previously undescribed species. The other forms in this group were all attached to the surface via a short stalk. However, this species lacked a stalk and the protoplast adhered directly to the surface. Attachment was mediated by the production of large amounts of mucilage.

Though the most abundant family were the Salpingoecidae, the greatest diversity was found within the Acanthoecidae. Six species were present, attached to surfaces and entrapped within established biofilms. The former, sessile, forms included: *Acanthoeca spectabilis* Ellis, *Polyoeca dichotoma* Kent and *Stephanoeca campanula* Kent. Of these, *A. spectabilis* was the most abundant. The species entrapped within established biofilms had no obvious means of attachment and are generally regarded as planktonic and included: *Diplotheca costata* Volkanov, *Diaphanoeca grandis* Ellis and *Pleurasiga* sp.. In Spain, one unidentified loricate species was also collected.

On samples of glass exposed for 30 days in Portsmouth, the numbers of the four most abundant choanoflagellates were counted, using an electron microscope. The results are presented in Table 1. *Salpingoeca* sp. was the most abundant, and this was consistent on all the materials examined. The loricate choanoflagellate *A spectabilis* was the next most abundant species on three of the four coverslips examined. The unidentified species listed in Table 1 is the representative of the Salpingoecidae mentioned above. In most cases, there was a high standard deviation, indicating a large variation in the distribution of the choanoflagellates between the five areas counted. In comparison to the numbers of bacteria, the choanoflagellates were two orders of magnitude lower in abundance.

There were variations in the species obtained from the three sites. The nine species collected in Portsmouth are listed in Table 2 and compared to those at the other sites. In Poole, five of these species were collected and *D. costata* was the most abundant. Four of the species collected in Portsmouth were also collected in Spain. In addition to those species collected in Portsmouth two additional unidentified thecate choanoflagellates were collected in Poole. In Spain one additional loricate and one thecate species (both unidentified) were obtained.

Table 3 lists the variation in colonisation of different substrata exposed in Portsmouth. From this it can be seen that all species were collected from glass, Thermanox and stainless steel. On brass, the range was restricted and included only one loricate species. On copper and antifouling paints, no loricate species were collected. *Monosiga* sp. was not collected from brass, copper or the antifouling paints.

DISCUSSION

From the results, it is clear that a variety of choanoflagellates can be found colonising surfaces exposed in the marine environment. Most previous studies have only investigated planktonic species (Thomsen 1978; Leadbeater 1980; Fenchel 1982; Thomsen and Boonruang 1983a,b; Norris 1984). Their importance in planktonic food chains has also been noted (Buck and Garrison 1983; Tanouhe 1985a,b).

The only previous study that has considered the colonisation of surfaces was that of Marszalek *et al.* (1979), and that referred to the presence of *A. spectabilis*. This

Table 1
Numbers of choanoflagellates·mm^{-2} colonising glass slides exposed in Portsmouth for 30 days (SD = standard deviation). Each average was taken from five counts made on different areas of each coverslip. For bacteria, 50 fields of view were counted.

Coverslip 1

Species	numbers·mm^{-2}	(SD)
Salpingoeca sp.	680	(54)
Acanthoeca spectabilis	154	(40)
Choanoeca sp.	67	(29)
Unidentified sp.	38	(39)

Coverslip 2

Species	numbers·mm^{-2}	(SD)
Salpingoeca sp.	651	(43)
Acanthoeca spectabilis,	133	(49)
Choanoeca sp.	56	(21)
Unidentified sp.	36	(53)

Coverslip 3

Species	numbers·mm^{-2}	(SD)
Salpingoeca sp.	753	(142)
Acanthoeca spectabilis	82	(32)
Choanoeca sp.	87	(47)
Unidentified sp.	103	(23)

Average number of choanoflagellates   1026 mm^{-2}
Average number of bacteria   674000 mm^{-2}

Table 2
Distribution of choanoflagellates in relation to exposure site. At the site in Poole one species was far more abundant than all of the others, indicated by an *.
(+ indicates species present and – indicates species absent)

	Exposure site		
Choanoflagellate	Portsmouth	Poole	Spain
Monosiga sp.	+	–	–
Choanoeca sp.	+	+	+
Salpingoeca spp.	+	+	+
Acanthoeca spectabilis	+	+	+
Polyoeca dichotoma	+	–	–
Stephanoeca campanula	+	–	–
Diplotheca costata	+	+*	+
Diaphanoeca grandis	+	–	–
Pleurasiga sp.	+	+	–

Table 3
Variation in colonisation of different substrata (+ indicates species present and – indicates species absent).

Choanoflagellate	Surface		
	Glass, Thermanox and stainless steel	Brass	Copper and antifouling
Codonosigidae			
Monosiga sp.	+	–	–
Salpingoecidae			
Choanoeca spp.	+	+	+
Salpingoeca spp.	+	+	+
Acanthoecidae			
Acanthoeca spectabilis	+	+	–
Polyoeca dichotoma	+	–	–
Stephanoeca campanula	+	–	–
Diplotheca costata	+	–	–
Diaphanoeca grandis	+	–	–
Pleurasiga sp.	+	–	–

choanoflagellate species is readily identified due to the presence of a lorica. The larger numbers of reports of loricate species are undoubtedly due to their easier identification. However, this study indicated the presence of many more non-loricate than loricate choanoflagellates. Non-loricate species are difficult to pick out in established biofilms though in the experience of the authors they are nearly always present. This is undoubtedly due to their small size and the difficulty in distinguishing them from other organisms that are present.

The variation in species diversity with location probably relates to the number of samples examined from each site. More material was examined from Portsmouth than the other two sites, and this is reflected by the greater number of species recorded.

The abundance of planktonic species found in the biofilms would indicate their presence in the water column. The high numbers of *Diplotheca costata* in Poole would suggest that this is abundant in the water column at this site. Unfortunately, suitable plankton samples were not available for comparison. Such material gathered in Portsmouth had too much particulate material present and few choanoflagellates could be found. Stages in the division of planktonic species, while still trapped in the biofilm, were noted suggesting that these species may survive within a biofilm, as reported for *D. costata* (Jackson and Leadbeater 1991). However, their lack of an attachment mechanism suggests that they are not adapted for this mode of existence.

There was a clear substrate preference indicated in this study. Loricate species were absent from the toxic surfaces (copper and antifouling paints), with only one species on brass. The latter is slightly toxic, due to the copper present, and it would seem that *A. spectabilis* has a degree of tolerance towards copper. The study of Marszalek *et al.* (1979) also noted the presence of this species on a copper surface.

In conclusion, it is clear that choanoflagellates are an important component of developing and established biofilms. Since the completion of this study, material (glass) exposed in Norway, Denmark and Italy has also been examined. In all cases, choanoflagellates were among the first colonisers. Again, non-loricate species were more abundant than loricate species. The apparent absence of them on surfaces in previous reports is due, at least partly, to their small size and difficulty of identification.

ACKNOWLEDGEMENTS

The authors are indebted to Hempel A/S for financial support of this project and to Graham Bremer for assistance with scanning electron microscopy.

REFERENCES

Blunn, G. 1986. Biological fouling of copper and copper alloys. In *Biodeterioration 6* (ed. S. Barry, D.R. Houghton, G.C. Llewellyn and C.E. O'Rear), 567–76. Aberystwyth: Cambrian News Ltd.

Brock, T.D. and Clyne, J. 1984. Significance of algal excretory products for growth of epilimnetic bacteria. *Applied and Environmental Microbiology* 47:731–4.

Brown, I., Blunn, G. and Jones, E.B.G. 1984. Attachment of marine fouling protozoa. *Proceedings of the Sixth Congress on Marine Corrosion and Fouling*, 113–27.

Brown, I. and Jones, E.B.G 1982. An investigation into the microbial colonisation of the surface of titanium condenser tubes exposed to Thames River water. *International Biodeterioration Bulletin* 18:67–79.

Brown, I., Jones, E.B.G. and Moss, S.T. 1986. The settlement, attachment and growth of a sessile, fouling peritrich protozoan, *Carchesium polypinum*, under laboratory conditions. In *Biodeterioration 6* (ed. S. Barry, D.R. Houghton, G.C. Llewellyn and C.E. O'Rear), 576–84. Aberstwyth: Cambrian News Ltd.

Buck, K.R. and Garrison, D.L. 1983. Protists from the ice-edge region of the Weddel Sea (Antarctica). *Deep Sea Research Part A Oceanography Research Papers* 30:1261–78.

Callow, M.E. 1986a. Fouling algae from "in-service" ships. *Botanica marina* 24:351–7.

Callow, M.E. 1986b. A world-wide survey of slime formation on antifouling paints. In *Algal Fouling* (ed. L.V. Evans and K.D. Hoagland), 1–20. Amsterdam: Elsevier.

Characklis, W.G. 1981. Fouling biofilm development: a process analysis. *Biotechnology and Bioengineering* 23:1923–60.

Characklis, W.G. and Cooksey, K.E. 1983. Biofilms and microbial fouling. *Advances in Applied Microbiology* 29:93–138.

Cooksey, B., Cooksey, K.E., Miller, C.A., Paul, J.H., Rubin, R.W. and Webster, D. 1984. The attachment of microfouling diatoms. In *Marine Biodeterioration: An Interdisciplinary Study* (ed. J.D. Costlow and R.C. Tipper), 161–71. Annapolis: Naval Institute Press.

Costerton, J.W., Cheng, K.J., Geesey, G.C., Ladd, T.I., Nickel, J.C. Dasgupta, M. and Marrie, T.J. 1987. Bacterial biofilms in nature and disease. *Annual Review of Microbiology* 41:435–64.

Daniel, G.F., Chamberlain, A.H.L. and Jones, E.B.G. 1987. Cytochemical observations on the adhesive chemicals of marine fouling diatoms. *British Phycology Journal* 22:101–18.

Escher, A. and Characklis, W.G. 1982. Algal-bacterial interactions in aggregates. *Biotechnology and Bioengineering* 24:2283–90.

Fenchel, T. 1982. Ecology of heterotrophic microflagellates: 4. Quantitative occurrence and importance as bacterial consumers. *Marine Ecology Progress Series* 9:35–42.

Haack, T.K. and McFeters, G.A. 1982. Nutritional relationships among organisms in an epilithic biofilm community. *Microbial Ecology* 8:115–26.

Hamilton, W.A. 1987. Biofilms: Microbial interactions and metabolic activities. In *Ecology of Microbial Communities* (ed. M. Fletcher, T.R.G. Gray and J.G. Jones), 361–87. Society for

General Microbiology.

Jackson, S.M. and Leadbeater, B.S.C. 1991. Costal strip accumulation and Lorica assembly in the marine choanoflagellate *Diplotheca costata* Volkanov. *Journal of Protozoology* 38:97–104.

Leadbeater, B.S.C. 1980. Four new species of loricate choanoflagellates from South Britanny, France. *Cahiers de Biologie Marine* 21:345–53.

Leadbeater, B.S.C. 1985. Choanoflagellida. In *Illustrated Guide to the Protozoa* (ed. J.J. Lee, S.H. Hunter and E.C. Bovee), 106–16. Kansas: Society of Protozoologists.

Marshall, K.C. 1984. *Microbial Adhesion and Aggregation.* Berlin and New York: Springer Verlag.

Marshall, K.C. 1985. Mechanisms of bacterial adhesion at solid-water interfaces. In *Bacterial Adhesion: Mechanisms and Physiological Significance* (ed. D.C. Savage and M. Fletcher), 133–61. New York: Plenum.

Marszalek, D.S., Gerchakov, S.M. and Udey, L.R. 1979. Influence of substrate composition on marine microfouling. *Applied and Environmental Microbiology* 38:987–95.

Murray, R.E., Cooksey, K.E., and Priscu, J.C. 1986. Stimulation of bacterial DNA synthesis by algal exudates in attached algal-bacterial consortia. *Applied and Environmental Microbiology* 52:1177–82.

Norris, R.E. 1984. Phytoplankton, including nanoplankton, in the Enguela upwelling system as revealed by scanning electron microscopy. *Transactions of the Royal Society of South Africa* 45:139–68.

Savage, D.C. and Fletcher, M. 1985. *Bacterial Adhesion: Mechanisms and Physiological Significance.* New York: Plenum.

Tanouhe, E. 1985a. Organic composition of faecal pellet of the krill *Euphausia superba*: 1. Lipid composition. *Transactions of the Tokyo University of Fisheries* 10:125–34.

Tanouhe, E. 1985b. Organic composition of faecal pellet of the krill Euphausia superba: 1. Amino acid composition. *Transactions of the Tokyo University Fisheries* 10:135–8.

Thomsen, H.A. 1978. Nanoplankton from the Gulf of Elat (= Gulf of Aqaba), with particular emphasis on choanoflagellates. *Israeli Journal of Zoology* 27:34–44.

Thomsen, H.A. and Boonruang, P. 1983a. Ultrastructural observations on marine choanoflagellates (Choanoflagellida, Acanthoecidae)from the coast of Thailand: species of Apheloecion, new genus. *Journal of Planktonic Research* 5:739–44.

Thomsen, H.A. and Boonruang, P. 1983b. A microscopical study of marine collared flagellates (Choanoflagellida) from the Andaman Sea, Southwest Thailand: species of *Stephanacantha*, new genus and *Platypleura*, new genus. *Protistologica* 19:193–214.

BIOFOULING OF DEEP BAY BUOYS

Z.G. Huang and S. Lin

Third Institute of Oceanography, State Oceanic Administration,
P.O. Box 0570, Xiamen, China

ABSTRACT

Deep Bay is located on the eastern flank of the Pearl River where salinity ranges between 5–15‰ and 28–32‰ in the rainy season and dry seasons, respectively. The water is extremely turbid. Fouling organisms of seven buoys and three pairs (at Lau Fau Shan, Tsim Bei Tsui and Shekou) were investigated and 103 species recorded. A year-long study of the population structures of the dominant species was carried out. These included *Balanus reticulatus*, *Membranipora amoyensis*, *Crassostrea rivularis*, *Perna viridis*, *Irus irus*, *Trapezium sublaevigatum*, *Hiatella orientalis*, *Anomia chinensis*, *Hicksonella guishanensis* and *Nanosesarma minutum*.

The thickness of biofoulers on the buoys was between 26–51 mm, with a cover of 91–100%. Biofouling wet weights at the waterline, on the sides, bottom and in the endpipes of the buoys were 8, 13, 12 and 20 kg·m^{-2}, respectively. Biofouling communities on the Deep Bay buoys were dominated by low-salinity species and eurytropic species, occurring in large numbers but with high mortalities. Such features are characteristic of estuarine biofouling communities.

INTRODUCTION

Deep Bay (22°30'N; 114°02') is located on the eastern flank of the Pearl River Estuary, the South China Sea. On its southern (Hong Kong) mud flat is cultured *Crassostrea rivularis*; its northern bank comprises the industrial area and harbour of Shekou, Shenzhen, China. During the rainy season, it is affected by the freshwater of the Shenzhen River and the Pearl River. Salinity, therefore, falls to between 5–15‰ from April to July, and approaches freshwater during low tide periods, with high turbidity. In the dry season (October–January), the salinity rises to between 28–32‰.

MATERIALS AND METHODS

The seven buoys surveyed were located from the bay mouth to the inner bay (Fig. 1). They are replaced by new ones every May. In May 1984, when the buoys were lifted for servicing, fouling organisms were studied *in situ*. Thickness and coverage were measured at the waterline, on the sides, bottom and inside and outside the end-pipe. All the buoys were sampled at the above positions with a (30 x 30) cm^2 quadrant. Wet weights, densities and population structures of dominant species were measured in the laboratory. Forty-six samples were obtained and 1,005 specimens separated.

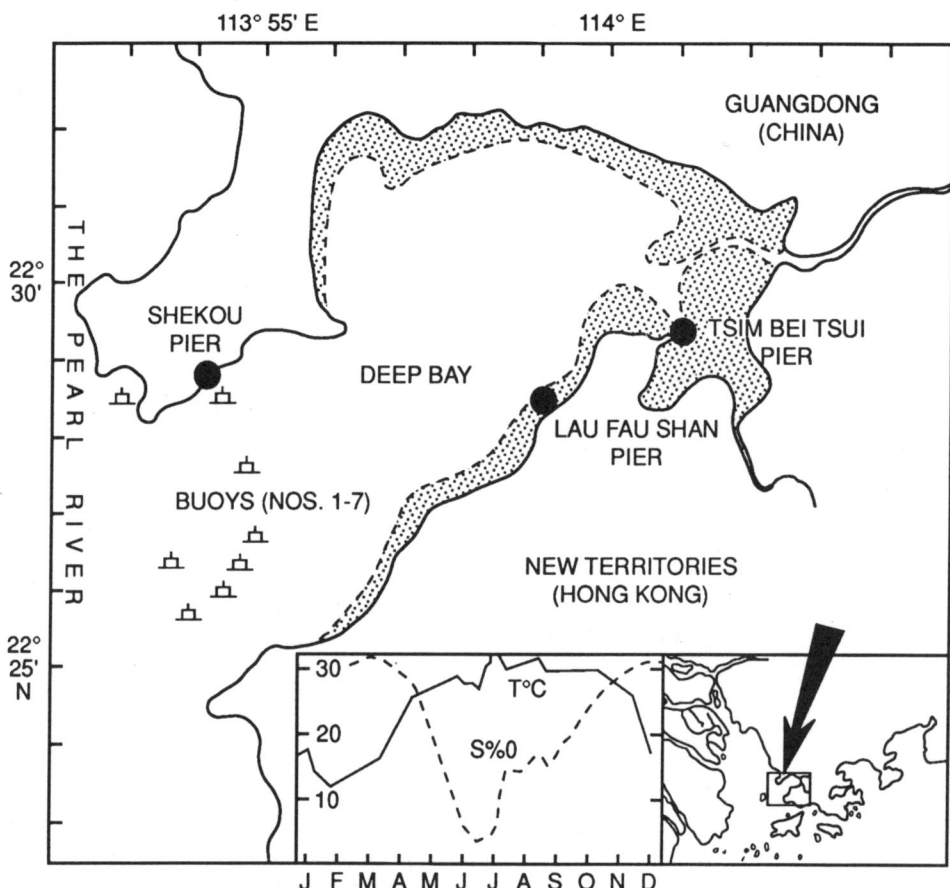

Fig. 1. Map of Deep Bay, showing the seven buoy sites, water temperatures and salinities.

RESULTS

Species

Forty species of diatoms and 103 species of large biofoulers were recorded. Diatoms were mainly distributed at the waterline of the buoys, with *Navicula ramosissima*,

Grammatophora marine, *Pleurosigma aestnarii* and *Synedra tabulata* var. *parva* dominant. The freshwater species *Nitzschia sigmoidea* and the salt-freshwater species *N. sigma* var. *sigmatella* also occurred frequently. The dominant species of large biofoulers were *Balanus reticulatus* (Cirripedia), *Membranipora amoyensis* (Bryozoa), *Crassostrea rivularis*, *Perna viridis*, *Irus irus*, *Trapezium sublaevigatum*, *Hiatella orientalis*, *Anomia chinensis* (Bivalvia), *Hicksonella guishanensis* (Alcyonacea) and *Nanosesarma minutum* (Decapoda).

There were differences in species among different positions of the buoys. At the waterline, besides *Balanus reticulatus*, there were algae and some upper or middle tide species such as *Euraphia withersi* and *Saccostrea echinata*. The sides were covered by *B. reticulatus* and their lower parts were covered by white *Membranipora amoyensis* on the barnacle shells. On the bottom and outside the end-pipe, the situations were similar to that on the lower parts of the sides. Inside the end-pipe, *Crassostrea rivularis* attached overlappingly (Plate 1).

Plate 1. A Deep Bay buoy (May 1983 – May 1984) fouled by *Balanus reticulatus* (dark) below the waterline and barnacle shells covered by *Membranipora amoyensis* (light) lower down.

Quantities

The average density of diatoms at the waterline was 62,273 individuals·cm^{-2}. Table 1 presents the average quantities of large biofoulers on six different positions of the seven buoys. The results show that wet weight was largest inside the end-pipe, least at the waterline and about the same, medium, on the other three positions (Fig. 2). The differences in wet weight among different positions were closely related to species differences. Though differences in wet weight existed among the seven buoys, these were random because the seven buoys lay in the same channel experiencing similar environmental conditions.

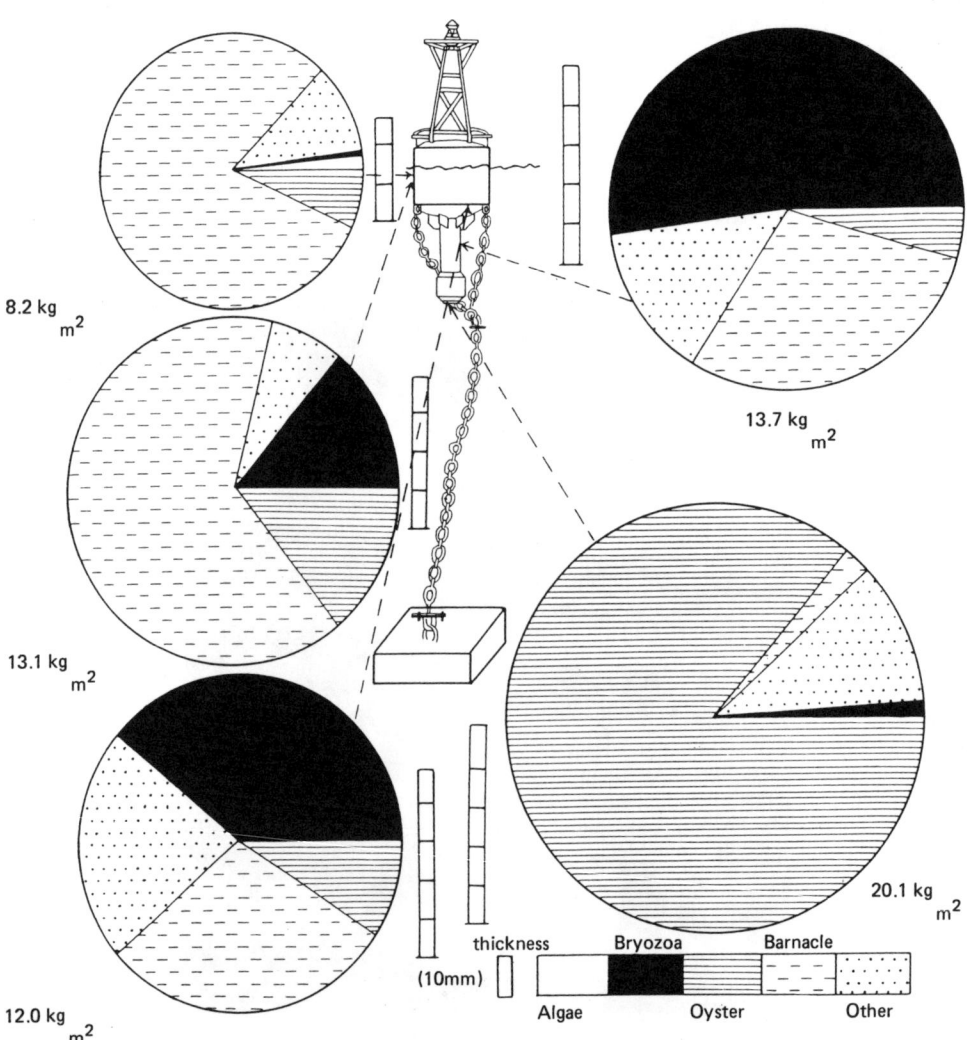

Fig. 2. Thickness, wet weight and composition of fouling organisms on different positions of the buoys in Deep Bay.

Table 1
Quantities of fouling organisms on Deep Bay buoys (May 1983 – May 1984).

Position	Species numbers	Thickness (mm)	Cover (%)	Wet wt. (kg·m^{-2})	Percentage wet weight (%)				
					Algae	*Membranipora amoyensis*	*Crassostrea rivularis*	Barnacles	Others
Waterline	52	26.4	91.4	8.15	1.89	0.16	7.00	79.88	11.07
Sides	50	39.3	100	13.11	—	14.16	14.64	64.18	7.02
Bottom	54	48.6	100	11.96	—	39.26	8.97	29.33	22.43
End-pipe (outside)	57	50.7	100	13.65	—	52.53	4.33	29.20	13.95
End-pipe (inside)	53	51.4	95.7	20.10	—	1.18	85.95	2.04	10.83
Anchor chain	27	45.0	98.8	—	—	—	—	—	—

Population characteristics of dominant species

The seven buoys were set in May, during the rainy season. Some of them might not have been fouled until July or August. For this reason, the following populations were formed within one year or less.

Balanus reticulatus. The population in an area of 450 cm² on buoy sides was measured. A total of 732 individuals were recorded, with living individuals comprising 33% of the total. The basal size (diameter) peaks of living and dead individuals were both between 7–12 mm. The living individuals basal size ranged between 3–17 mm and for dead individuals between 3–15 mm. 200 living individuals on the bottom were also measured. Their basal size range was 3–19 mm, with two peaks of between 5–7 mm and 13–15 mm, respectively. This indicates a difference in size structure between the sides and the bottom of the buoys (Fig. 3).

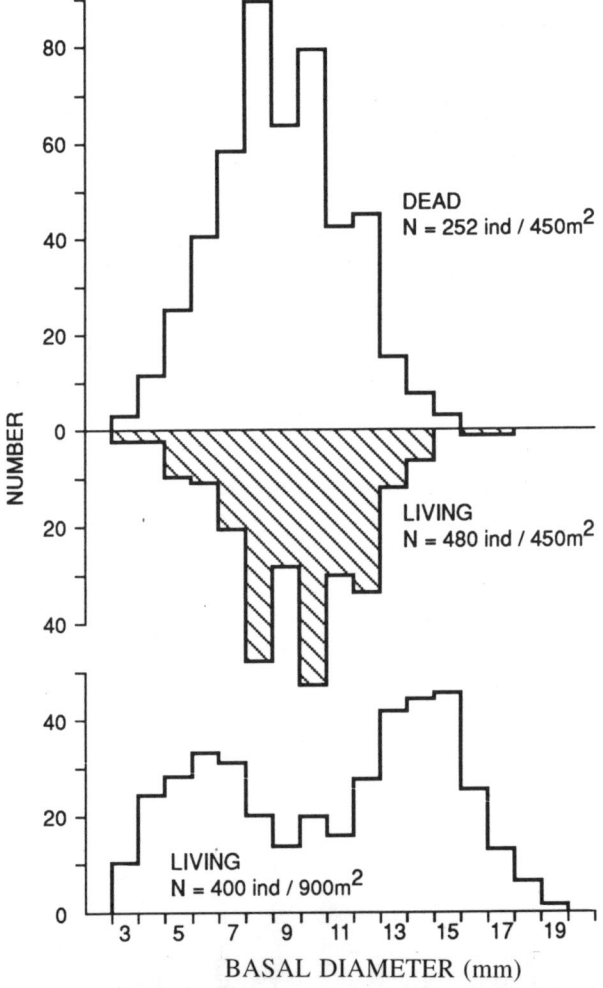

Fig. 3. Size distribution of *Balanus reticulatus* on the Deep Bay buoys.
Above: Population on the sides.
Below: Population on the bottom.

The wet weight of this barnacle did not differ greatly at the waterline, on the sides, bottom and outside the end-pipe, being between 3.9–5.7 kg·m^{-2}. It was, however, only 0.4 kg·m^{-2} inside the end-pipe.

Crassostrea rivularis. This species comprised two size groups, that is, the present year group and the previous year group. The previous year group comprised large quantities of large individuals, with shell lengths ranging between 21–120 mm and the peak between 56–90 mm. Conversely, the present year group comprised small quantities of small individuals, with shell lengths ranging between 21–35 mm (Fig. 4).

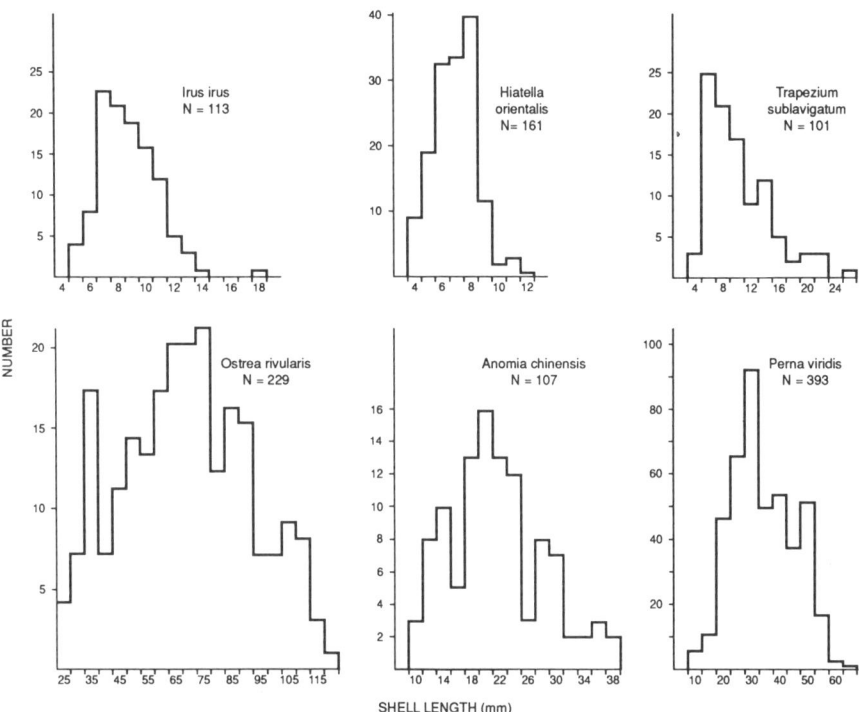

Fig. 4. Size distributions of six bivalves on the Deep Bay buoys.

The wet weight distribution of this species was opposite that of *B. reticulatus*, being as heavy as 17.2 kg·m^{-2} inside the end-pipe, but only between 1.0–3.4 kg·m^{-2} on the other four positions.

Perna viridis. The shell length composition of this species showed a normal distribution, with the range between 6–65 mm and a peak of between 21–30 mm. Such a length composition indicates a long reproductive period with larvae attaching every month of the year. The individuals of between 6–10 mm had attached in the present year. Figure 4 also shows the population structures of four small bivalves, i.e., *Irus irus*, *Hiatella orientalis*, *Trapezium sublaevigatum* and *Anomia chinensis*.

Nanosesarma minutum. This species occurred in large numbers. Female individuals comprised 74.3% of the population and males comprised 25.7%. Individual size composition showed a normal distribution, with a carapace width range of between 2.5–10.0 mm and a peak at between 5.0–6.0 mm (Fig. 5).

Hicksonella guishanensis. This white species of Alcyonacea (Coralliidae) was first recorded at Guishan in the Pearl River Estuary. It was numerous on the buoys. Individual length ranged between 11–150 mm, with a peak at between 26–60 mm. Most individuals were branched. The majority had 2–6 branches, the largest number being 12.

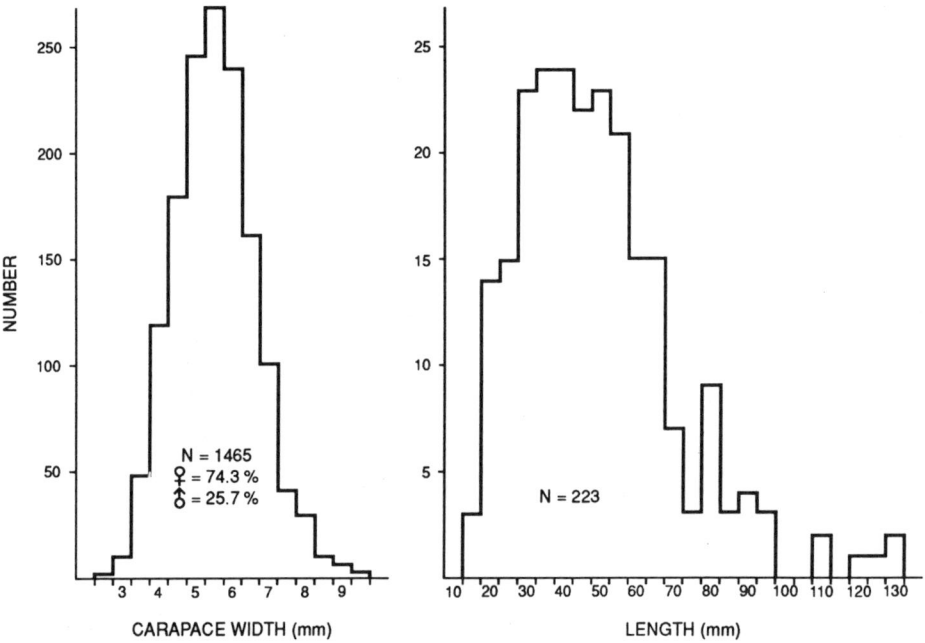

Fig. 5. Size distributions of *Nanosesarma minutum* (left) and *Hicksonella guishanensis* (right) on the Deep Bay buoys.

DISCUSSION

In Deep Bay, there is a great difference in salinity between the rainy season and the dry season. Therefore, some dominant, high-salinity, species, e.g., *Balanus reticulatus*, showed high mortalities. Many low-salinity, eurytopic, species, such as *Membranipora amoyensis* and *Crassostrea rivularis*, grow well here. The occurrence of large numbers of *Membranipora amoyensis* was the main characteristic of the buoy biofoulers in Deep Bay. This is different from the buoy biofoulers in high salinity waters of the South China Sea (Huang et al. 1982).

Balanus uliginosus is a dominant species of the fouling communities in coastal estuarine waters of China (Ren and Liu 1978). It was, however, less abundant in Deep Bay. *Limnoperna fortunei* is a freshwater biofouler common in Southern China (Lee and Morton 1983; Wang and Qi 1984) and occurs frequently in the Pearl River Estuary, in areas near freshwater. It was not, however, recorded from the Deep Bay buoys.

ACKNOWLEDGEMENTS

Our colleagues Chuanyan Li, Chengxing Zheng and Jianjun Wang helped identify some of the specimens. Liu Shicheng from Xiamen University identified the diatoms. Songkai Yan and Na Lin assisted in the arrangement of data. We hereby express our gratitude to them.

REFERENCES

Huang, Z.G. Cai, R.X., Jiang, J.X., Cai, E.X. and Wu, Q.Q. 1982. Biofouling on the buoys off the Qiongzhou Channel and Leizhou Penisula coast, South China Sea. *Oceanologia et Limnologia Sinica* 13:259–66. (In Chinese)

Lee, S.Y. and Morton, B. 1983. The Hong Kong Mytilidae. In *Proceedings of the Second International Workshop on the Malacofauna of Hong Kong and Southern China, Hong Kong, 1983.* (ed. B. Morton and D. Dudgeon), 49–76. Hong Kong: Hong Kong University Press

Ren, X.Q. and Liu, J.Y. 1978. Studies on Chinese Cirripedia (Crustacea). I. Genus *Balanus*: *Studia Marina Sinica* 13:119–96. (In Chinese)

Wang, Z.T. and Qi, Z.Y. 1984. Study on Chinese species of the family Mytilidae. *Studia Marina Sinica* 22:199–221. (In Chinese)

Appendix
Fouling organisms on Deep Bay buoys and their occurrences.*

Species	Occurrence
DIATOMS	
Achnanthes brevipes	
Achnanthes brevipes var. *angustata*	
Achnanthes brevipes var. *intermedium*	
Achnanthese javanica	
Amphora angusta	
Bacteriastrum hyalinum	
Biddulphia arundleri	
Biddulphia obtusa	
Biddulphia veticulata	
Cocconeis dirupta	
Cocconeis sp.	
Cyclotella striata	
Cyclotella stylorum	
Diploneis bombus	
Grammatophora marina	
Hemidiscus ovalis	
Licmophora californica	
Licmophora tenuis	
Mastogloia decipiens	
Mastogloia sp.	
Melosira moniliformis	
Navicula pupula var. *elliptica*	
Navicula ramosissima	
Navicula sp.	
Nitzschia fasciculata	
Nitzschia obtusa var. *scalpelliformis*	
Nitzschia sigmoidea	
Nitzschia sigma var. *sigmatella*	
Nitzchia sp.	
Pleurosigma aestuarii	
Pleurosigma intermedium var. *dongshanese*	
Pleurosigma rigidum	
Rhopalodia gibberula	
Skeletonema costatum	
Stauroneis constricta	
Striatella unipunctata	
Synedra tabulata	
Synedra tabulata var. *parva*	
Triceratium favus	
Tryblioptychus cocconeiformis	
PHAEOPHYTA	
Ectocarpus sp.	3

* The total sample number was 46.

Appendix (continued)

Species	Occurrence
CHLOROPHYTA	
Enteromorpha tubulosa	8
E. flexuosa	5
Ulva lactuca	1
U. fasciata	3
U. conglobata	3
Cladophora sp.	3
PORIFERA	
Mycale adhaerens	1
COELENTERATA	
Bougainvillia sp.	19
Obelia geniculata	1
Nephthea sp.	2
Hicksonella guishanensis	20
Telesto sp.	3
Oulangia stokesiana	9
Actinaria	37
NEMERTEA	
Lineus sp.	3
POLYCHAETA	
Halosydna brevisetosa	2
Parahalosydna pleiolepis	1
Harmothoe sp.	1
Trypanosyllis sp.	1
Platynereis bicanaliculata	1
Leonnates decipiens	1
Nereis multignatha	1
Nereis neoneanthes	1
Nereis persica	1
Neanthes succinea	1
Nectoneanthes oxypoda	2
Ceratonereis hircinicola	1
Perinereis camiguinoides	1
Perinereis cultrifera	2
Perinereis nuntia	3
Marphysa sanguinea	1
Lysidice ninetta	1
Dorvillea sp.	1
Loimia medusa	1
Sabellastarte zebuensis	1
Sabellastarte sp.	1
Pomatoleios kraussii	2

Appendix (continued)

Species	Occurrences
Spirobranchus tricornis	1
S. semperi var. *acroceros*	1
Hydroides elegans	35

SIPUNCULA

Phascolosoma scolops	1

BRYOZOA

Membranipora savartii	17
Membranipora amoyensis	34
Membranipora grandicella	14
Conopeum reticulum	7
Electra pseudopilosa	1
Bugula neritina	1
Cosciniopsis hongkongensis	2

MOLLUSCA
GASTROPODA

Cellana grata	2
Crepidula onyx	5
Crepidula sp.	1
Amathina tricarinata	1
Thais gradata	2
Pyrene bicincta	1
Cirsotrema sp.	1
Polynices macrostoma	1

BIVALVIA

Crassostrea rivularis	24
Saccostrea pestigris	5
S. echinata	11
S. cucullata	13
Perna viridis	33
Brachidontes variabilis	22
Xenostrobus atrata	16
Musculista senhausia	8
Modiolus comptus	15
Modiolus philippinarum	1
Pteria conturnix	2
Barbatia virescens	15
Barbatia signata	1
Scapharca satowi	1
Irus irus	17
Trapezium sublaevigatum	20
Hiatella orientalis	25
Anomia chinensis	20
Martesia striata	1

Appendix (continued)

Species	Occurrences
Kellia porculus	13
Tapes philippinarum	1
ARTHROPODA	
CRUSTACEA	
CIRRIPEDIA	
Balanus reticulatus	39
Balanus amphitrite amphitrite	2
Balanus albicostatus	1
Balanus uliginosus	8
Balanus cirratus	2
Balanus trigonus	11
Chirona amaryllis	1
Euraphia withersi	1
ISOPODA	
Sphaeroma walkeri	10
Gnorimosphaeroma cf. *oregonensis*	1
Ligia exotica	1
AMPHIPODA	
Caprella equilibra	8
C. penantis	1
C. scaura typica	1
Corophium lamellatum	1
Elasmopus pectenicrus	1
Ericthonius pugnax	1
DECAPODA	
Alpheus bisincisus	1
Alpheus sp.	1
Pisidia serratifrons	2
Charybdis japonica	1
Cleistostoma dilatatum	7
Sphaerozius nitidus	3
Pilumnopeus makiana	10
Nanosesarma minutum	35
Metapograpsus quadridentatus	2
ECHINODERMATA	
Amphimetra sp.	1
Temnopleurus toreumaticus	2
Ophiactis savignyi	1
PISCES	
Prionobutis koilomatodons	1
Triaenopogon barbatus	1

The Marine Biology of the South China Sea
(ed. B. Morton). Proceedings of the First
International Conference on the Marine
Biology of Hong Kong and the South China Sea,
Hong Kong, 28 October – 3 November 1990.
Hong Kong: Hong Kong University Press, 1993.

AN ECOLOGICAL STUDY OF FOULING ORGANISMS IN BEIHAI HARBOUR, BEIBU BAY, CHINA

J.J. Wang, Z.G. Huang, S. Lin, C.Y. Li and C.X. Zheng

Third Institute of Oceanography, State Oceanic Administration,
P.O. Box 0570, Xiamen, China

ABSTRACT

From June 1987 to May 1988, a yearly biofouling panel test was carried out in Beihai Harbour in Beibu Bay of the South China Sea. Ninety-four species of foulers were recorded (on ships, wharfs and buoys). The dominant species were *Balanus reticulatus, Balanus cirratus, Dendostrea crenulifera, Pomatoleios kraussii, Cosciniopsis hongkongensis* and *Obelia bicuspidata*. Attachment occurred year round, with a peak period from June to October. The average monthly wet weight of the foulers was 1.2 kg·m^{-2} with an average biomass thickness of 3 mm.

Some warm-water species, absent from the northern and middle parts of the China coast, were recorded. The monthly average salinity ranged between 29–30‰ but could fall to less than 16‰ in the rainy season. The fouling organisms were different from those in high-salinity waters such as Mirs Bay, Lushun Harbour (China) and Nagasaki Harbour (Japan) and in river-mouth waters such as the Pearl River and Changjiang River estuaries. Compared with other ports along the China coast, less fouling organisms occurred in Beihai Harbour.

INTRODUCTION

Beihai Harbour (21°30'N, 109°05'E; Fig. 1) is the largest harbour in Beibu Bay and is one of the most southern harbours along the coast of China. This is a study of the fouling communities of Beihai Harbour.

MATERIALS AND METHODS

From June 1987 to May 1988, a 12-month panel test was conducted at Dijiao wharf and surveys carried out of fouling organisms on wharfs and ships in the harbour. Based on the survey data, a preliminary study was undertaken of the species present, their attaching season and the abundance of fouling organisms in Beihai Harbour.

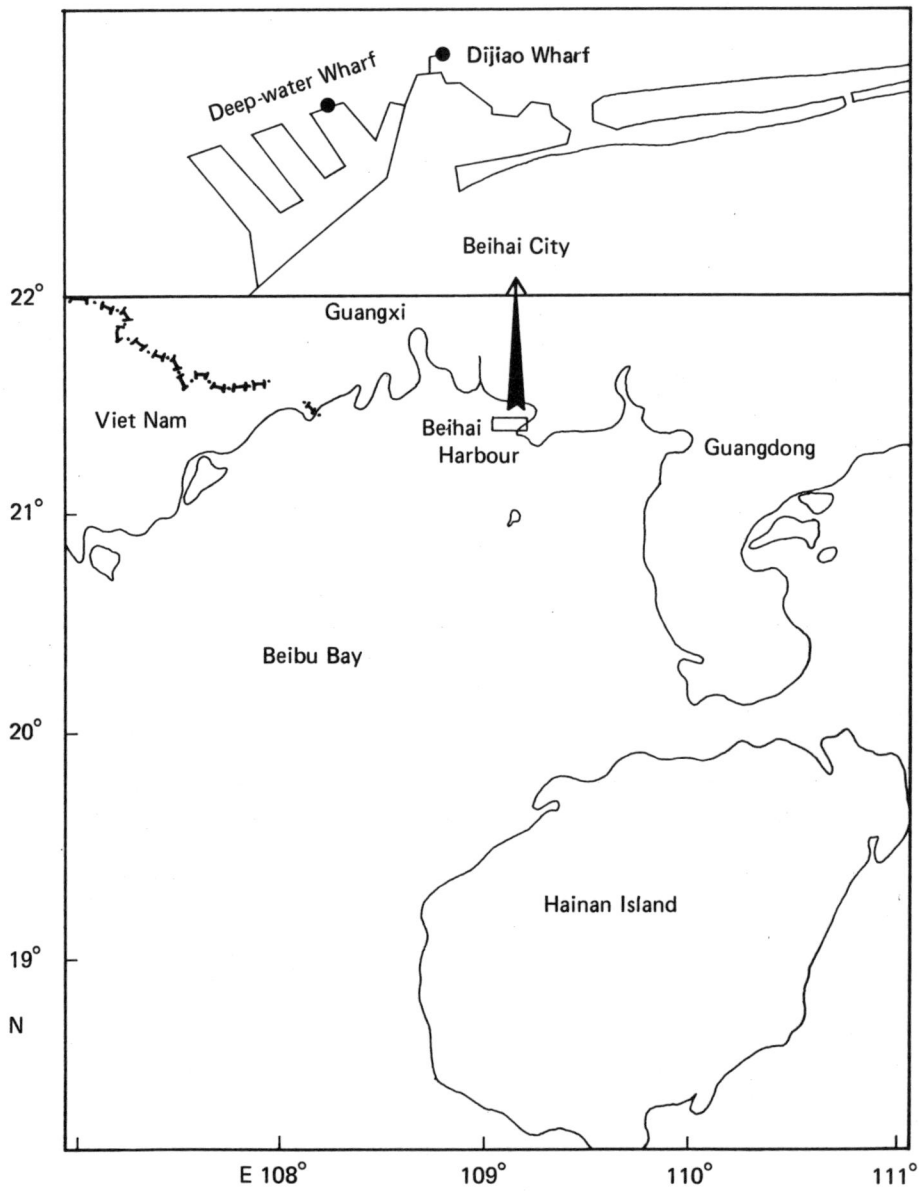

Fig. 1. Test sites for the fouling study in Beihai Harbour.

RESULTS

Fouling organisms on panels

A total of 73 panels were recovered. Sixty-five species of animals were recorded (Table 1). Most are tropical and subtropical species. Some species, such as *Hydroides elegans* and *Bugula neritina*, are widely distributed. The major species were *Obelia bicuspidata*, *Clytia* sp., *Cosciniopsis hongkongensis*, *Balanus reticulatus*, *B. cirratus* and

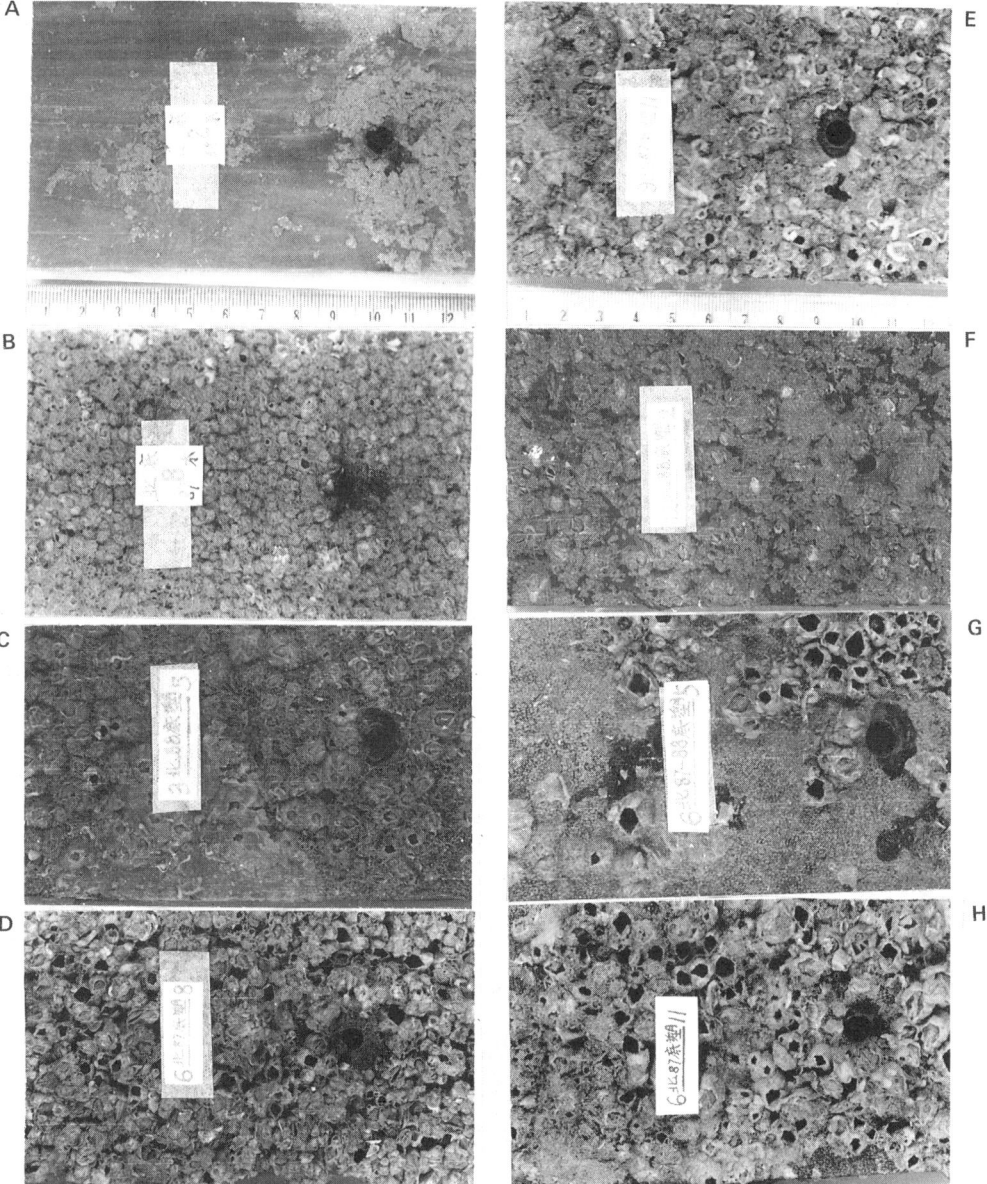

Plate 1. Fouling communities on panels (8 x 14 cm²) exposed for different periods.
 A. 1 month (February).
 B. 1 month (August).
 C. 3 months (Spring: March – May).
 D. 3 months (Summer: June – August).
 E. 3 months Autumn: September – November).
 F. 3 months (Winter: December – February).
 G. 6 months (Semiannual: June – November).
 H. 12 months (Annual: June – May).

Table 1
Fouling organisms at Beihai Harbour and their frequencies of occurrence (%).

Species	Numbers of samples		
	ships 13	wharfs 10	panels 73
ALGAE			
Lyngbya semiplema		20.0	
Gelidium divaricatum		10.0	
Herposiphonia sp.	7.7		
Enteromorpha sp.	23.1		
E. compressa	15.4		
E. tubulosa	7.7		
Cladophora sp.	15.4		
Anadyomene wrightii		10.0	
PORIFERA			
Gellius toxius			1.4
COELENTERATA			
Halocordyle disticha			4.1
Bougainvillia sp.			12.3
Obelia bicuspidata			38.4
Clytia sp.			45.2
Anthopleura sp.			39.7
Actinaria sp.	7.7	30.0	5.4
BRYOZOA			
Membranipora amoyensis	7.7		
M. grandicella			5.4
M. tuberculata	7.7		
M. savartii			1.4
Electra tenella	15.4		
Bugula neritina			19.2
B. californica			12.3
Cosciniopsis hongkongensis			32.9
Thalamoporella gothica	7.7		
PLATYHELMINTHES			
Stylochus sp.	7.7	10.0	41.1
Pseudoceros sp.			1.4
NEMERTEA			
Eubortasia sp.			1.4
Lineus sp.		10.0	20.5
POLYCHAETA			
Syllis gracilis	7.7	20.0	
Genetyllis castanea		10.0	
Leonnates decipiens			2.7
Platynereis bicanaliculata			2.7
Nereis multignatha			5.4
N. persica			1.4
Perinereis camiguinoides		10.0	
P. cultrifera		30.0	1.4
Marphysa sanguinea			1.4
Hydroides elegans	30.8	10.0	1.4
H. albiceps	7.7		
H. dirampha	15.4		
H. inornata	23.1		
Serpula vermicularis	23.1		4.1

Table 1 (continued)

Species			
Pomatoleios kraussii		30.0	16.4
Dexiospira foraminosus			2.7
SIPUNCULA			
Phascolosoma scolops	30.0	1.4	
MOLLUSCA			
Liolophura japonica		10.0	1.4
Cellana toreuma		10.0	1.4
Littoraria articulata		50.0	2.7
Thais clavigera		10.0	
Planaxis sulcatus		10.0	
Peasiella lutulenta		10.0	
Cerberilla sp.			2.7
Saccostrea cucullata		30.0	
Dendostrea crenulifera	30.8	30.0	37.0
Saccostrea echinata		60.0	1.4
Alectryonella radix			2.7
Ostrea sp.	7.7		
Brachidontes varialis		60.0	1.4
Hormomya mutabilis		10.0	
Modiolus comptus		20.0	1.4
Musculus sp.			1.4
Musculus nanus			1.4
Xenostrobus atrata		40.0	1.4
Botula siliculata		10.0	
Lithophaga malaccana		10.0	
Lithophaga curta		20.0	1.4
Mytilopsis sallei	7.7	10.0	
Martesia striata		10.0	1.4
Hiatella orentalis			1.4
Trapezium sublaevigatum		20.0	1.4
Barbatia virescens		20.0	1.4
B. yamamotoi			5.4
Irus irus		10.0	1.4
Isognomon acutirostris		60.0	2.7
Chama dunkeri		10.0	1.4
CRUSTACEA			
Euraphia withersi		20.0	1.4
Chthamalus sinensis	7.7	20.0	
Balanus amphitrite amphitrite	69.2	30.0	1.4
Balanus cirratus	30.8	10.0	50.7
Balanus reticulatus	100	70.0	93.2
Balanus trigonus	7.7		1.4
Sphaeroma walkeri	7.7	20.0	2.7
Ligia exotica		10.0	1.4
Caprella equilibra			19.2
Corophium ueoni	15.4	20.0	75.3
Palaemon serrifer			4.1
Petrolisthes japonicus		10.0	
Sphaerozius nitidus		10.0	9.6
Pilumnopeus makiana			1.4
Paracleisioma crassipilum		10.0	1.4
Nanosesarma minutun		40.0	21.9
ASCIDIA			
Symplegma oceania			11.0
Styela canopus			2.7
Microcosmus exasperatus			1.4

Corophium sp. The frequencies of occurrence of *Balanus reticulatus* and *Corophium* sp. were as high as 93.2% and 75.3%, respectively. The density of *Balanus reticulatus* reached 8.6×10^4 individuals·m^{-2} and a wet weight of 7.2 kg·m^{-2} (on the summer panel). The density of *Corophium* sp. reached 3.2×10^5 individuals·m^{-2} and a wet weight of 1.2 kg·m^{-2} (on the winter panel). These were the dominant species of fouling organisms in Beihai Harbour. There was year round attachment in the harbour, the peak period being recorded from June to October when the temperatures were high (27–31°C). The seasons for attachment of the major foulers and their relationship to temperature and salinity are shown in Figure 2.

The average fouling thickness of the monthly panels was 3 mm (range:1–6 mm) and the average monthly wet weight was 1.2 kg·m^{-2}. From January to March, small numbers of *Balanus reticulatus* and *Corophium ueoni* attached at a wet weight of < 0.1 kg·m^{-2}

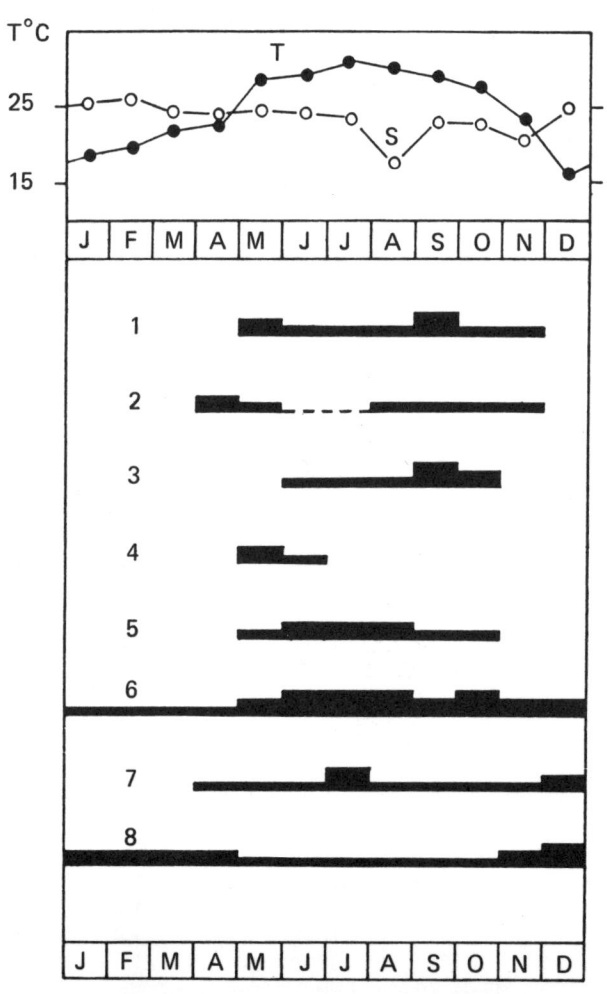

1. *Obelia bicuspidata*
2. *Clytia* sp.
3. *Cosciniopsis hongkongensis*
4. *Pomatoleios kraussii*
5. *Dendostrea crenulifera*
6. *Balanus reticulatus*
7. *Balanus cirratus*
8. *Corophium ueoni*

Fig. 2. Attachment season of the major foulers in Beihai Harbour in relation to temperature and salinity.

and a percentage cover of < 20%. From April, the abundance of fouling organisms began to increase. The greatest abundance occurred in October (Table 2). Barnacles were dominant on monthly panels. The percentage wet weights of all the groups were: hydroids, 4.1%; bryozoans, 0.9%; polychaetes, < 0.1%; bivalves, 0.4%; barnacles, 89.0%; amphipods, 5.2%; ascidians, < 0.1% and other groups, 0.2%.

On the four seasonal panels, coverages were all 100%. The average wet weight was 4.1 kg·m^{-2}, the greatest value being recorded in summer, followed by autumn, winter and spring. The average seasonal thickness was 7 mm (range: 5–10 mm), the greatest value being recorded in summer. Except for the winter panel, the species numbers of the other three seasonal panels were > 15, *Balanus reticulatus* being dominant, followed by *Corophium ueoni*.

On the semiannual and annual panels, the dominant *Balanus reticulatus* died and detached in great masses. The wet weights were, therefore, less than those of the seasonal panels. For example, the wet weights of the first and second semiannual panels were half those of the summer and winter panels, respectively. The wet weight on the annual panel was but one-third of the summer wet weight.

Fouling organisms on ships

Surveys on fouling organisms were undertaken on three ships. Guiyou 091 was most heavily fouled as compared with two other lighters (Table 3). *Balanus amphitrite amphitrite* was the major species on the waterline of the ships. *Balanus reticulatus* was the most dominant on the sides and the bottoms. The wet weights and densities of the major species on ships are shown in Tables 4, 5 and 6.

Fouling organisms on wharfs

Beihai Harbour has a regular diurnal tide, the greatest tidal difference being 5.7 m. Surveys of fouling organisms were conducted on Dijiao wharf and the Deepwater wharf. Forty-eight species of animals were recorded. Barnacles and oysters were the most dominant and were most abundant on Dijiao wharf. The wet weight at a tidal height of 1.8 m was 57.5 kg·m^{-2} with a thickness of 40 mm (Table 7). According to the vertical distribution of its foulers, Dijiao wharf can be divided into three bio-zones (Fig. 3).

(1) *Euraphia withersi* zone. This mainly occupied the high tidal area, +2.9 – +3.9 m. The density of *E. withersi* was 4.4 x 10^4 individuals·m^{-2}, with a wet weight of 538 g·m^{-2}. *Littoraria articulata* also occurred in this zone.

(2) *Saccostrea* spp. zone. *Saccostrea cucullata* and *S. echinata* were dominant. The density of the former was 3.7 x 10^3 individuals·m^{-2} with a wet weight of 16.3 kg·m^{-2}. The density of the latter was 5.0 x 10^3 individuals·m^{-2} with a wet weight of 55.0 kg·m^{-2}. Some major species such as *Barbatia virescens*, *Balanus reticulatus* and *Pomatoleios kraussii*, were also distributed in this zone.

(3) *Balanus reticulatus-Dendostrea crenulifera* zone. *Balanus reticulatus* was dominant, followed by *Dendostrea crenulifera*. The density of *B. reticulatus* was 5.3 x 10^3 individuals·m^{-2} with a wet weight of 2.4 kg·m^{-2}. The density of *Dendostrea crenulifera* was 489 individuals·m^{-2} with a wet weight of 1.4 kg·m^{-2}. In this zone, there were *Isognomon acutirostris* and *Pomatoleios kraussii*. On the Deepwater wharf, the vertical distribution of foulers was different from Dijiao wharf. It could, however, also be

Table 2
Abundance and composition of fouling organisms on panels submerged in Beihai Harbour (June 1987–May 1988).

Period	Numbers of species	Thickness (mm)	Cover (%)	Wet wt. (g·m⁻²)	Percentage wet weight (%)							
					Hydroids	Bryozoans	Polychaetes	Bivalves	Barnacles	Amphipods	Ascidians	Others
June	9	4	97	1597	0.1	1.6	0.1	1.3	97.1	0.1	–	0.1
July	7	4	91	2180	0.9	0.1	–	0.1	98.9	0.1	–	0.1
August	13	5	100	3502	0.4	0.1	0.1	0.5	98.9	0.1	–	0.2
September	14	3	100	1087	27.0	6.3	0.4	63.9	2.0	–	0.4	–
October	13	6	100	4008	0.1	0.7	0.2	98.4	0.2	–	–	0.3
November	8	2	75	299	19.1	0.1	–	–	69.0	11.6	–	0.2
December	5	3	100	904	0.2	–	–	–	45.9	53.9	–	–
January	2	1	16	72	–	–	–	–	0.7	99.3	–	–
February	2	1	8	35	–	–	–	–	0.3	99.7	–	–
March	2	1	9	44	–	–	–	–	0.3	99.7	–	–
April	7	2	73	139	31.4	7.6	0.4	–	31.9	28.7	–	–
May	11	3	100	485	31.6	0.1	2.3	0.1	62.8	1.5	1.5	0.4
Summer (6–8)	15	10	100	7611	0.6	0.6	0.1	4.1	94.3	–	–	0.4
Autumn (9–11)	15	7	100	4247	2.2	1.8	0.6	–	83.9	11.1	–	0.4
Winter (12–2)	6	6	100	3015	0.1	0.1	–	0.1	60.2	39.6	–	0.1
Spring (3–5)	19	5	100	1644	5.9	6.9	1.8	–	79.2	5.2	0.9	0.9
First Semi-annual (6–11)	24	9	100	4426	5.6	0.6	0.1	1.9	89.2	1.6	0.1	0.1
Second Semi-annual (12–5)	13	5	100	1512	18.0	0.1	0.1	0.1	79.7	1.7	0.3	0.1
Annual (6–5)	13	6	100	2419	13.7	0.1	0.1	0.3	76.4	1.4	–	8.2

Table 2

Quantity and composition of fouling organisms on panels submerged in Beihai Harbour (June 1987–May 1988).

Period	Numbers of species	Thickness (mm)	Cover (%)	Wet wt. (g·m^{-2})	Hydroids	Bryozoans	Polychaetes	Bivalves	Barnacles	Amphipods	Ascidians	Others
January	2	1.1	16	72	–	–	–	–	0.7	99.3	–	–
February	2	1.0	8	35	–	–	–	–	0.3	99.7	–	–
March	2	0.5	9	44	–	–	–	–	0.3	99.7	–	–
April	7	2.0	73	139	31.4	7.6	0.4	–	31.9	28.7	–	–
May	11	2.8	100	485	31.6	0.1	2.3	0.1	62.8	1.5	1.5	–
June	9	3.7	97	1597	0.1	1.6	0.1	1.3	97.1	0.1	–	0.1
July	7	4.3	91	2180	0.9	0.1	–	0.1	98.9	0.1	–	0.1
August	13	5.0	100	3502	0.4	0.1	0.1	0.5	98.9	0.1	–	0.2
September	14	2.8	100	1087	27.0	6.3	–	0.4	63.9	2.0	–	0.4
October	13	5.8	100	4008	0.1	0.7	–	0.2	98.4	0.2	–	0.3
November	8	2.3	75	299	19.1	0.1	–	–	69.0	11.6	–	0.2
December	5	3.0	100	904	0.2	–	–	–	45.9	53.9	–	–
Summer	15	10.3	100	7611	0.6	0.6	0.1	4.1	94.3	–	–	0.4
Autumn	15	6.8	100	4247	2.2	1.8	0.6	–	83.9	11.1	–	0.4
Winter	6	5.5	100	3015	0.1	0.1	0.1	–	60.2	39.6	–	–
Spring	19	4.5	100	1644	5.9	6.9	1.8	–	79.2	5.2	0.9	0.1
First Semi-annual (6–11)	24	8.5	100	4426	5.6	0.6	0.1	1.9	89.2	1.6	0.1	0.9
Second Semi-annual (12–5)	13	5.3	100	1512	18.0	0.1	0.1	0.1	79.7	1.7	0.3	0.1
Annual (6–5)	13	6.0	100	2419	13.7	0.1	0.1	0.3	76.4	1.4	–	8.2

divided into three zones.

(1) *Euraphia withersi* zone. This zone ranged from +2 – 4.5 m. The density of *E. withersi* was 4.4 x 10^4 individuals·m^{-2} with a wet weight of 955 g·m^{-2}. In this zone, there were *Littoraria articulata* and *Balanus amphitrite amphitrite*.

(2) *Saccostrea echinata* zone. The density of *S. echinata* was 3.5 x 10^3

Table 3
Abundance of fouling organisms on ships in Beihai Harbour.

		Numbers of species	Cover (%)	Thickness (mm)	Wet wt. (kg·m^{-2})	Dominant species
Zhuhai 03207	Waterline	5	60	2	0.1	*Enteromorpha* spp., *Balanus reticulatus*, *B. amphitrite amphitrite*
	Side	2	40	3	0.1	*Balanus reticulatus*, *B. amphitrite amphitrite*
	Bottom	2	70	5	0.3	*Balanus reticulatus*, *Barbatia virescens*
Guiyou 091	Waterline	5	100	4	1.7	*Balanus reticulatus*, *B. cirratus*
	Side	8	100	4	2.4	*Balanus reticulatus*, *B. cirratus*
	Bottom	8	100	7	2.1	*Balanus reticulatus*, *Dendostrea crenulifera*
Guiyou 467	Waterline	4	95	2	0.3	*B. amphitrite amphitrite*
	Side	5	90	3	0.5	*Balanus reticulatus B. amphitrite amphitrite*, *B. reticulatus*
	Bottom	9	95	2	0.5	*B. amphitrite amphitrite*, *Hydroides elegans*, *Dendostrea crenulifera*

Table 4
Wet weights and densities of major species on Zhuhai 03207.

	Species	Wet wt. (g·m^{-2})	Density (individuals·m^{-2})
Waterline	*Enteromorpha* spp.,	91	–
	Balanus reticulatus,	23	189
	B. amphitrite amphitrite	18	233
Side	*B. reticulatus*,	56	389
	B. amphitrite amphitrite	9	122
Bottom	*B. reticulatus*	310	1.2 x 10^3

Table 5
Wet weights and densities of dominant species on Guiyou 091.

	Species	Wet wt. (g·m^{-2})	Density (individuals·m^{-2})
Waterline	Balanus reticulatus,	1.3 x 10^3	2.9 x 10^4
	Balanus cirratus,	419	4.4 x 10^3
	Balanus reticulatus	2.0 x 10^3	3.8 x 10^4
Side	B. cirratus,	346	7.4 x 10^3
	Balanus reticulatus	1.7 x 10^3	2.6 x 10^4
Bottom	Dendostrea crenulifera	262	222

Table 6
Wet weights and densities of major species on Guiyou 467.

Part	Species	Wet wt. (g·m^{-2})	Density (individuals·m^{-2})
Waterline	Balanus amphitrite amphitrite,	257	6.7 x 10^3
	Balanus reticulatus	333	1.1 x 10^4
Side	B. amphitrite amphitrite,	111	5.8 x 10^3
	Balanus reticulatus	294	1.1 x 104
Bottom	B. amphitrite amphitrite,	111	3.9 x 10^3
	Hydroides elegans	56	3.3 x 10^3

Table 7
Abundance of fouling organisms on wharfs in Beihai Harbour.

Site	Tidal height (m)	Numbers of species	Cover (%)	Thickness (mm)	Wet weight (kg·m^{-2})	Dominant species
Dijiao wharf	3.0	10	80	15	19.4	Saccostrea cucullata, Barbatia virescens, Euraphia withersi
	1.8	25	100	40	57.5	Saccostrea echinata, S. cucullata, Barbatia virescens
	0.4	14	100	12	4.1	Balanus reticulatus, Dendostrea crenulifera
Deepwater wharf	4.0	4	95	4	1.0	Euraphia withersi
	2.0	11	100	10	8.5	Saccostrea echinata, Balanus reticulatus
	0.5	18	100	15	15.7	Dendostrea crenulifera, Balanus reticulatus

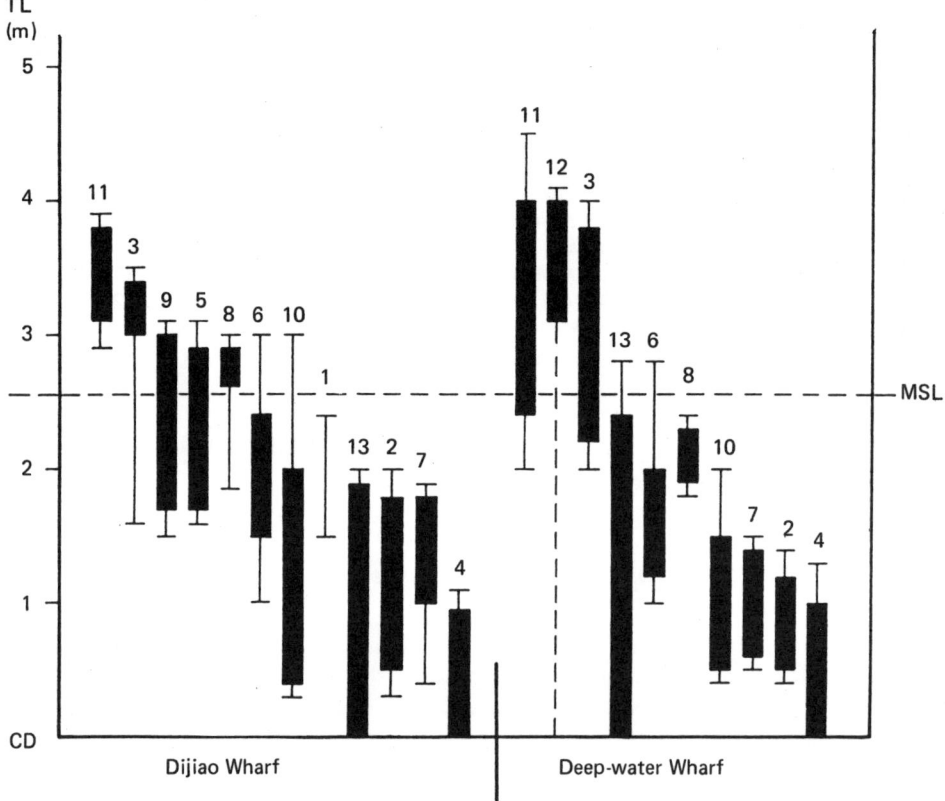

Fig. 3. Vertical distribution of the major foulers on wharfs in Beihai Harbour.
1. *Gelidium divaricatum.*
2. *Pomatoleios kraussii.*
3. *Littoraria articulata.*
4. *Dendostrea crenulifera.*
5. *Saccostrea cucullata.*
6. *Saccostrea echinata.*
7. *Brachidontes variabilis.*
8. *Xenostrobus atrata.*
9. *Barbatia virescens.*
10. *Isognomon acutirostris.*
11. *Euraphia withersi.*
12. *Balanus amphitrite amphitrite.*
13. *Balanus reticulatus.*

individuals·m^{-2} with a wet weight of 4.9 kg·m^{-2}. *Balanus reticulatus* was also dominant in this zone at a density of 7.6 x 10^3 individuals·m^{-2} and a wet weight of 3.5 kg·m^{-2}. In this zone, *Brachidontes varibilis* and *Isognomon acutirostris* also occurred.

(3) *Dendostrea crenulifera* zone. *D. crenulifera* was dominant, its density being 8.3 x 10^3 individuals·m^{-2} with a wet weight of 13.5 kg·m^{-2}. *Balanus reticulatus* was distributed from the *Saccostrea echinata* zone to this zone, its density being 3.5 x 10^3 individuals·m^{-2} with a wet weight of 1.9 kg·m^{-2}.

DISCUSSION

Beihai Harbour is an inner harbour in Beibu Bay. The salinity ranges between 29–30‰ but can fall to 16‰ in the rainy season in August. The fouling organisms here were characterized by widely distributed and warm-water species. The major species were *Obelia bicuspidata*, *Clytia* sp., *Cosciniopsis hongkongensis*, *Pomatoleios kraussii*, *Euraphia withersi*, *Balanus reticulatus*, *B. cirratus*, *B. amphitrite amphitrite*, *Corophium* sp., *Saccostrea cucullata*, *Saccostrea echinata* and *Dendostrea crenulifera*. Low salinity species occurring densely in the Pearl River and Changjiang River estuaries (Huang *et al.* 1981, 1984), such as *Balanus uliginousus* and *Crassostrea rivularis* were absent from Beihai Harbour. *Hydroides elegans* and *Bugula neritina* were similarly not as numerous as in Mirs Bay, Lushu Harbour (Li *et al.* 1982) and Nagaski Harbour (Kawahara 1969). Some warm-water species, such as *Balanus reticulatus*, *Euraphia withersi* and *Dendostrea crenulifera* are distributed only to the south of the Changjiang River esturary.

The monthly average water temperatures in Beihai Harbour are all > 16°C. Bio-attachment occurred year round. The average monthly wet weight was 1.2 kg·m^{-2} being more than Hong Kong Harbour (Greene and Morton 1976) but far less than in Lusiyang (Zhang 1981) and Quanzhou Bay, and close to that recorded for Zhanjiang Harbour and Yangpu Harbour. According to summer wet weights, Huang (1984) divided the fouling organisms of the China coast into five quantitative grades. The wet weight on the summer panel in Beihai Harbour was 7.6 kg·m^{-2}, making it a member of the greater grade.

Balanus reticulatus is a major fouler, widely distributed in tropical and subtropical waters. It is a dominant species of the fouling community in Beihai Harbour. This is similar to the situation in Zhanjiang Harbour and Yangpu Harbour, showing a general characteristic of subtropical inner harbours. The reproduction and attachment of *Balanus reticulatus* was reduced when the water temperature in Beihai Harbour was < 20°C. A water temperature of 20°C is clearly advantageous to the reproduction and attachment of *Balanus reticulatus*. For example, in August, density amounted to 7.4 x 10^4 individuals·m^{-2} with a wet weight of 3.5 kg·m^{-2}. The fluctuations in salinity in August affected the reproduction of *Balanus reticulatus*, so that its biomass in September was greatly reduced to 4.3 x 10^4 individuals·m^{-2} and a wet weight of 0.7 kg·m^{-2}, respectively half and one-fifth of the August values.

According to the vertical distribution of fouling organisms, the Beihai wharfs can be divided into three bio-zones: a *Euraphia withersi* zone; a *Saccostrea echinata* zone and a *Dendostrea crenulifera* zone. *Saccostrea cucullata* and *Balanus reticulatus* were also dominant species in the wharf fouling community.

REFERENCES

Cai, R.X. and Huang, Z.G. 1981. Studies on the biology of *Balanus reticulatus* Utinomi in Xiamen Harbour. I. Breeding, attachment and growth. *Acta Zoologica Sinica* 27:274–80. (In Chinese)

Greene, G.W. and Morton, B. 1976. Preliminary fouling and corrosion studies of painted metals in Hong Kong Harbour. *Proceedings of the Fourth International Congress on Marine Corrosion and Fouling*, 225–36.

Huang, Z.G. and Cai, R.X. 1984. *Marine biofouling and its prevention*. Beijing: China Ocean Press. (In Chinese)

Huang, Z.G. and Li, C.Y. 1981. The distribution of fouling organisms in Changjiang River estuary. *Oceanologia et Limnologia Sinica* 12:531–7. (In Chinese)

Kawahara, T. 1969. Studies on the marine fouling community IV. Difference in the constitute of fouling communities according to localities (Nagasaki Harbour). *Report of the Faculty of Fisheries of the Prefectural University of Mie* 6:109–25.

Li, C.Y. and Huang, Z.G. 1982. Studies on the ecology of fouling organisms in Lushun Harbour. *Acta Ecologica Sinica* 2:59–65.

Zhang, L.X. and Huang, Z.G. 1981. On the ecology of marine fouling and boring organisms in Lusiyang, China. *Acta Oceanologica Sinica* 3:139–48.

CONSERVATION
PLENARY PAPER

The Marine Biology of the South China Sea
(ed. B. Morton). Proceedings of the First
International Conference on the Marine
Biology of Hong Kong and the South China Sea,
Hong Kong, 28 October – 3November 1990.
Hong Kong: Hong Kong University Press, 1993.

RESEARCH UPON AND CONSERVATION OF CORALS AND CORAL REEFS IN CHINA

Zou Renlin and Wang Zhihao

South China Sea Institute of Oceanology, Academia Sinica,
164 West Xingang Road, Guangzhou, China

ABSTRACT

The history of research upon the corals of China is summarized. The scleractinian fauna, growth rates and zoogeography of reef-building corals in the South China Sea are also reported upon. Information about ecology, damage, conservation and the rebuilding of coral reefs is given.

INTRODUCTION

The earliest recognition and record of corals and coral reefs in China was made at the beginning of the third century, in the Three Kingdoms period. Kang Tai from the Wu Kingdom made such a record in his work *Funan zhuan*. After research and translation into modern Chinese, the record states 'There are coral reef islands in the South China Sea; the bottom is flat and on which corals grow'.

The earliest records of the practical use of corals, especially for medical purposes can be found in the *Newly Revised Canon of Materia Medica* published in A.D. 659 by Li Ji and in the famous work of Li Shizhen *Compendium of Materia Medica* published in A.D. 1578. After research, it is concluded that *Acropora sp.*, *Galaxea* sp., *Corallium* sp. and *Subergorgia* sp. were identified in these works. Here, we provide an outline of modern coral and coral reef research undertaken in China over the past one hundred years.

RESEARCH UPON MODERN CORALS AND CORAL REEFS

Modern corals are classified ecologically into two groups. The first is when there is a symbiosis with zooxanthellae, *Symbiodinium microadriaticum*. Such corals occur in warm, shallow, waters from –10 to –40 m or –60 m depth, and the majority of species of which are colonial. Such reef-building corals are called 'hermatypic' and are the most important components of coral reefs. Another group of corals, without symbiotic zooxanthellae, are distributed in cold, deep, waters worldwide, from the Arctic to Antarctica. The deepest distribution record for a representative of this group is 6,000 m. The majority of this group of corals are solitary, non-reef-building, and are called 'ahermatypic'.

Bassett-Smith (1890) reported upon the reef corals of the Zhenghe Islands and Zhongsha Islands, South China Sea. The specimens collected are kept in The Natural History Museum, London. In the late 1930s. T.Y.H. Ma (1937) published a paper 'On the growth rate of reef corals and its relation to sea water temperature', in which he dealt with 72 species of corals from the Dongsha Islands and 9 species from Hainan Island. He did not, however, report upon any species of *Acropora*. Most of Ma's specimens are scattered in museums and collections in Japan, although some are kept in the Beijing Natural History Museum. Yan (1956) and Naymov *et al.* (1960), following a joint Chinese and USSR marine biological survey, published general descriptions of stony corals and a simple report about coral reef ecology. Guo (1948) in his paper 'Geomorphology of the Tizard Bank and Reefs, Nan-sha Islands, China' provided a list of stony corals, identified by S. Kawaguti.

In Taiwan, Japanese scientists carried out the earliest work on stony coral classification. Kawaguti (1953) published a paper on the 'Coral fauna from Botel Tobago, Formosa, with a list of corals from the Formosa waters'. Jones *et al.* (1972) also provided a list of corals when they carried out 'A marine biological survey of southern Taiwan with emphasis on corals and fishes'. T.Y.H. Ma (1959), published his work 'Effect of water temperature on growth rate of reef corals' which represented the culmination of a lifetime's work but was not widely read beacause of its specialist subject area. Today, Professor Ma's colleagues and students, R.H. Randall, Y.M. Cheng, R.T. Yang and C.F. Dai are continuing his work and are engaged in coral reef research in Taiwan.

In the 1960s, coral reef geomorphology and coral ecology research groups were establised at the South China Sea Institute of Oceanology, Academia Sinica. Since then, the research groups have carried out systematic surveys and research into coral and coral reef geomorphology and ecology on Hainan Island and offshore from Guangdong and Guangxi provinces and published a number of research papers and reports. In addition, the Institute of Geology, Academia Sinica; the Department of Marine Geology, Tongji University, Shanghai; and the Institute of Geomorphology and the Geography Department, South China Normal University have also contributed much to the field of coral reef geomorphology. The Institute of Oceanology, Academia Sinica, has also undertaken some work in the field of coral ecology.

In the 1970s and 1980s, the South China Sea Institute of Oceanology, Academia Sinica, undertook research on coral biology and ecology and have surveyed the deep geomorphology of the Xisha Islands. All of the islands and submerged reefs of the Xisha Islands were covered in our surveys. Now we are carrying out an integrated, systematic, survey and research into coral ecology of the Nansha Islands. A series of formal reports will be published soon.

Because of well-known reasons, we do not known much about the corals and coral reefs of the Dongsha Islands, Penghu Islands and Taiwan. We hope that scientists in Taiwan will research these inadequately known areas.

In Hong Kong, there are 49 species of hermatypic corals. The earliest report of these was by A.E. Verrill (1902). In the past few years M. Cope, P.J.B. Scott, B. Morton, J.E.N. Veron and R.L. Zou have undertaken coral research in Hong Kong.

Based on the surveys and research data noted above we can summarise information about South China Sea corals as follows:

SCLERACTINIAN FAUNA

There are 21 genera and 45 species of shallow water reef-building corals found offshore in Guangdong and Guangxi Provinces; 21 genera and 49 species occur in Hong Kong (Veron 1982), 34 genera and 110 species and subspecies occur on Hainan Island, 38 genera and 127 species and subspecies occur on the Xisha Islands, 19 genera and 46 species occur on Huangyan Island, 27 genera and 72 species on the Dongsha Islands (Ma 1937) and 40 genera and 129 species occur in Taiwan. The Nansha Islands are being surveyed, although the identified specimens show that there are about 50 genera and 200 species of reef-building corals which is similar to the Philippines' 67 genera and 200 species. The ahermatypic corals of the South China Sea have been identified and are represented by 21 genera and 40 species; other specimens are, however, being identified.

THE GROWTH RATE OF REEF-BUILDING CORALS

Research using X-rays has shown that the growth rate of stony corals is closely related to latitude (Nie 1987). Generally speaking, those in low latitudes grow faster than those in high latitudes. The most important parameter is water temperature. The growth rate of stony corals also has a negative correlation with depth. For example, the growth rate of *Porites lutea* in southern Hainan Island, at 5 m depth, is between 7.2–7.4 mm·year^{-1}; in the Xisha islands at 8 m depth it is 6 mm·year^{-1} while in Zenmu Ansha at 17.5 m depth it is 5.5 mm·year^{-1}. This agrees with the work of Dustan (1975) from Jamaica using the living coral dyeing method, at depths of between 10–47 m.

ZOOGEOGRAPHY OF REEF-BUILDING CORALS IN THE SOUTH CHINA SEA

After many years of research, we have discovered that the distributions of *Stylophora* spp. and *Seriatopora* spp. are limited to the Islands of the South China Sea and Taiwan. They have not been recorded from Hainan Island. The most northerly distribution of *Pocillopora* spp. is Hainan Island. They have not been discovered in the Leizhou Peninsula opposite Hainan Island, across the Qiongzhou Channel. *Fungia* spp. also have a tendency to be more abundant at southern latitudes. *Turbinaria* spp. have the opposite tendency. Such observations tell us that different stony corals are adapted to different water temperatures which, in turn, determines their zoogeographic distributions. Modern reef-building corals from offshore mainland China and Hainan Island originated from the South China Sea islands. The ancient species of *Pocillopora* and *Fungia* are thus not distributed along the mainland coastline.

CORAL REEF ECOLOGY

In the 1970s, our researches on corals and coral reefs were mainly qualitative and comprised descriptive surveys to determine the distribution of coral communities and to understand the coral reefs of Hainan Island and the Xisha Islands. The former reef has a reef flat and seaward slope, with a pattern of zonation outwards from the shore as follows: *Goniastrea* zone; *Montipora* zone and *Acropora* zone (Zou et al. 1966). On the latter, on the northeastern reef flat, hermatypic corals grow luxuriantly, while on the southwest reef flat, they are rarely found. The other reef animals and plants have a similar distribution and the ecological characteristics of such reefs are, therefore, distinctive, in comparison to the well known Indo-Pacific reef coral fauna (Zou 1978). In order to solve arguments about coral classification, we have also studied the micro-structure of coral skeletons (Ni 1982) and initiated numerical taxonomic studies (Zou 1982; Zhang 1984), which complement traditional taxonomic methods. We have also investigated deeper water coral ecology (Zou et al. 1983; Zou 1988).

We have used a computer to construct a mathematical model of the coral community in the Xisha Islands. This employs multiple linear regression using a stepwise technique to generate a sub-model of the coral reef ecosystem. In this mode, the total biomass of corals on a particular reef is predicted at a statistically significant level from the component biomasses of a subset of the coral species. Regression equations were established for Zhongjian and Zhaoshu Island of the Xisha Islands as follows (Zou 1982):

Zhongjian = $1.11 + 0.931 X_1 + 0.997 X_{12} + 0.658 X_{14} + 2.80 X_{15} + 0.212 X_{23} + 0.257 X_{24} + 4.37 X_{26} + 16.2 X_{31} + 9.79 X_{33}$

Zhaoshu = $0.207 + 0.918 X_1 + 1.06 X_8 + 0.747 X_{11} + 1.12 X_{12} + 2.27 X_{21} + 2.29 X_{23} + 1.64 X_{24} + 1.35 X_{25} + 1.68 X_{31}$

We are also building a computer data base of the coral genus *Porites* (Wang 1989). Based on the results of a numerical analysis, we have established a computer data bank which has 5 functions, as follows: (1), classification; (2), distribution; (3), species descriptions; (4), lists of synonyms and (5), determinants of valid species.

Regarding the ecological characteristics of the ahermatypic corals of the South China Sea, our investigations prove that deep-sea corals are flourishing at depths of between 50–200 m. On the geological time scale, such 'living fossil corals' that have existed since the Plio-Pleistocene era account for 42.86% of the fauna. Sanders' stability-time hypothesis may again be proved by the deep-water coral fauna of the South China Sea. Meanwhile it is suggested that species evolution in a stable deep-sea environment differs from that in a rapidly changing one (Zou 1988).

DAMAGE, CONSERVATION AND REBUILDING OF CORAL REEFS

With economic development and open-door policies being initiated along the coast of China, the building industry has grown and tourism flourishes in China. This has seriously threatened the coral reefs of Hainan Island. It is said that the living corals of Hainan Island have been reduced by about 95%. During the past few years, the writers have made surveys along the coast of Hainan and found that coral rocks are used as building materials and burned for lime. Living corals are also collected for souvenirs. Human activities have damaged the coral's ecological balance so much that adverse consequences have resulted. For example, in the village of Bangtan, Wenchang County, because a large quantity of coral rocks were excavated, the coastline has been pushed back about 200 m. Over 200 coconut trees have been destroyed by waves and sea water has flooded the village. The safety of the villagers and their properties were imperilled. In the algae-culture fields of Qionghai County, because of coral excavation, the production of *Eucheuma gelatinae* which grows on corals, has been reduced from 300 t·year^{-1} in the 1980s to 100 t·year^{-1} today. The field is almost bankrupt and the question of whether or not to move the farm has been asked.

On the coast of Sanya City, people excavated coral to obtain lime. This brought them little money, but the coast road was subsequently seriously damaged. Through natural punishment, people have begun to understand the problems of coral reef damage and begun to devote more attention to protection. City governments have enacted local laws to protect coral reefs and forbid coral collecting. Lingao County has built a coral natural protection area, as has Sanya City, Dadonghai, Luhuitou and Bangtan villages to allow the coral ecosystem to reform naturally. The State Oceanic Administration and Department of Environmental Protection have formally enacted laws to protect coral reefs. Recently (7 October 1990), The State Council of The People's Republic of China has given official approval to establish coral reef areas. Also, because stony corals are collected and sold as souvenirs, the Endangered Species Scientific Commission of The People's Republic of China has moved corals into the second class of endangered species.

Scientists engaged in coral and coral reef research, through various methods, have emphasised the importance of coral reef protection and have a duty to obtain financial support to have coral reefs rebuilt. Now we are trying our best to obtain funding to establish a coral ecosystem rebuilding experiment in Hainan Island. We are also preparing a research programme to speed up coral ecosystem reformation by man-made transplantation of living corals, and thus to form a climax community more quickly.

ACKNOWLEDGEMENT

We would like to thank Prof. Brian Morton for his correction of the English manuscript of this paper.

A BIBLIOGRAPHY OF PUBLICATIONS ON THE CORALS OF THE SOUTH CHINA SEA

Bassett-Smith, P.W. 1980. Report on the corals from Tizard and Maccelesfied Banks. *Annals and Magazine of Natural History* 6th ser., 6:353–74; 443–58, pls. 12–14.
Ching, Y.M. 1971. On some recent commensal solitary corals from Anping Taiwan. *Taiwan Oceanography Sinica* 10: 1–6.
Cope, M. 1982. Interspecific coral interactions in Hong Kong. *Proceedings of the 4th Coral Reef Symposium Manila* 2:357–62.
Cope, M. 1982. A *Lithophyllon* dominated coral community at Hoi Ha Wan, Hong Kong. In *Pro-*

ceedings of the First International Marine Biological Workshop: The Marine Flora and Fauna of Hong Kong and Southern China, Hong Kong, 1980 (ed. B. Morton and C.K. Tseng), 587–94. Hong Kong: Hong Kong University Press.

Cope, M. 1986. Seasonal, diel and tidal hydrographic patterns, with particular reference to dissolved oxygen, above a coral community at Hoi Ha Wan, Hong Kong. *Asian Marine Biology* 3:59–74.

Cope, M. and Morton, B. 1988. The scleractinian coral community at Hoi Ha Wan, Hong Kong. *Asian Marine Biology* 5:41-52.

Dustan, P. 1975. Growth and form in the building coral *Montastrea annularis*. *Marine Biology* 33:101–7.

Guo, L.C. 1948. Geomorphology of the Tizard Bank and Reefs, Nan-sha Islands, China. *Acta Geologica Taiwanica* 2:45–54.

Jones, O.A. *et al.* 1972. A marine biological survey of southern Taiwan with emphasis on corals and fishes. *Institute of Oceanography, College of Natural Science Taiwan University, Special Publication* 1:1–93.

Kawaguti, S. 1953. Coral fauna from Botel Tobago, Formosa, with a list of corals from the Formosa waters. *Biology, Okayama University* 1:185–201.

Ma, T.Y.H. 1937. On the growth rate of reef corals and its relation to sea water temperature. *Memoirs of the National Institute, Academia Sinica, Zoology* 1:1–226, pls. 1–100.

Ma, T.Y.H. 1959. Effect of water temperature on growth rate of reef corals. *Oceanographia Sinica, Special Report* 1:1–116, pls. 1–321, figs. 1–12.

Morton, B. and Morton, J. 1983. *The Seashore Ecology of Hong Kong*. Hong Kong: Hong Kong University Press.

Naymov, D.V., Yan, J.S. and Huang, M.X. 1960. On the coral reefs of Hainan Island. *Oceanologia et Limnologia Sinica* 3:157–76. (In Chinese with a Russian Abstract)

Nie, B.F. 1982. Preliminary observations on the fine structure of faviids from Hainan Island. *Nanhai Studia Marina Sinica* 3:23–36. (In Chinese with an English Abstract)

Nie, B.F. 1987. Approach to the relationship between growth rate of some reef corals and surface water temperature in central and northern parts of the South China Sea. *Proceedings of the China-Australia Quaternary Studies*, 224-32. Beijing: Science Press. (In Chinese with an English abstract)

Randall, R.H. and Cheng, Y.M. 1977. Recent corals of Taiwan. Part 1. Description of reefs and coral environments. *Acta Geologica Taiwanica* 19:1–102.

Randall, R.H. and Cheng, Y.M. 1979. Recent corals of Taiwan. Part 2. Description of reefs and coral environments. *Acta Geologica Taiwanica* 20:1–32.

Randall, R.H. and Cheng, Y.M. 1984. Recent corals of Taiwan. Part 3. Shallow water hydrozoan corals. *Acta Geologica Taiwanica* 22:35–99.

Scott, P.J.B. 1984. *Corals of Hong Kong*. Hong Kong: Hong Kong University Press.

Scott, P.J.B. and Cope, M. 1982. The distribution of scleractinian corals at six sites within Tolo Harbour and Channel. In *Proceedings of the First International Marine Biological Workshop: The Marine Flora and Fauna of Hong Kong and Southern China, Hong Kong, 1980* (ed. B. Morton and C.K. Tseng), 575–86. Hong Kong: Hong Kong University Press.

Scott, P.J.B. and Cope, M. 1988. Tolo revisited: a survey of the corals in Tolo Harbour and Channel six years and half a million people later. In *Proceedings of the Second International Marine Biological Workshop: The Marine Flora and Fauna of Hong Kong and Southern China, Hong Kong, 1986* (ed. B. Morton), 1203-20. Hong Kong: Hong Kong University Press.

Thompson, G.B. and Cope, M. 1982. Estimation of coral abundance by underwater photography. In *Proceedings of the First International Marine Biological Workshop: The Marine Flora and Fauna of Hong Kong and Southern China, Hong Kong, 1982* (ed. B. Morton and C.K. Tseng), 557-73. Hong Kong: Hong Kong University Press.

Veron, J.E.N. 1982. Hermatypic Scleractinia of Hong Kong, an annotated list of species. In *Proceedings of the First International Marine Biological Workshop: The Marine Flora and Fauna of Hong Kong and Southern China, Hong Kong, 1980* (ed. B. Morton and C.K. Tseng), 111–25. Hong Kong: Hong Kong University Press.

Verrill, A.E. 1902. Notes on corals of the genus *Acropora (Madrepora* Lam.*)* with new descriptions and figures of types and of several new species. *Transactions of the Connecticut Academy of Arts and Sciences* 11:207–66, pls. 36–36F.

Wang, S.H. 1989. A fuzzy clustering analysis of genus *Porites* and its data bank. *Tropic Oceanology* 8:30–8 pls. 1–2. (In Chinese with an English Abstract)
Yan, J.S. 1956. Stony corals. *Biology Bulletin* 2:23–7. (In Chinese)
Yang, R.T. 1985. Coral communities in Nan-wan Bay, Taiwan. *Proceedings of the 5th International Coral Reef Congress, Tahiti.* 6:273–8.
Zhang, Y.L. 1984. A study on numerical taxonomy of *Tubastraea*. *Tropic Oceanology* 3:56–62, pls. 1–2. (In Chinese with an English Abstract)
Zhang, Y.L. and Zou, R.L. 1987. Community structure of shallow water stony corals in Daya Bay. *Tropic Oceanology* 6:12–8. (In Chinese with an English Abstract)
Zou, R.L. 1975. Studies on the corals of the Xisha Islands, Guangdong Province, China. A new genus and two new species of Siderastreidae. *Studia Marina Sinica* 10:61–4. (In Chinese with an English Abstract)
Zou, R.L. 1976 *The genus Millepora, with the description of a new species*, 85-90. Beijing: Science Press. (In Chinese with an English Abstract)
Zou, R.L. 1978. *An illustrated catalogue of Scleractinia, Hydrocorallina, Heliporina and Tubiporina*, 91-112, pls. 1-12. Beijing: Science Press. (In Chinese with an English Abstract)
Zou, R.L. 1978. *A preliminary analysis of community structure of the hermatypic corals of the Xisha Islands, Guangdong Province, China*, 125-32. Beijing: Science Press. (In Chinese with an English Abstract)
Zou, R.L. 1979. Further analysis on the community structure of the hermatypic corals of the Xisha Islands, Guangdong Province, China. *Oceanic Selections* 2:113–29 (In English) or *Acta Oceanologica Sinica* 2:98–110 (In Chinese)
Zou, R.L. 1980. Two new hermatypic scleractinian corals. *Nanhai Studia Marina Sinica* 1:113–8. (In Chinese with an English Abstract)
Zou, R.L. 1984. The deep-water *Acropora* with a description of a new species. *Tropic Oceanology* 3:52–5, pls. 1–3. (In Chinese with an English Abstract)
Zou, R.L. 1981. A mathematical model of the hermatypic coral community of the Xisha Islands, Guangdong Province, China. *Proceedings of the Fourth International Coral Reef Symposium Manila* 2:329–31.
Zou, R.L. 1982. A numerical taxonomic study of *Turbinaria* (Scleractinia) from Hong Kong. In *Proceedings of the First International Marine Biological Workshop: The Marine Flora and Fauna of Hong Kong and Southern China, Hong Kong, 1980* (ed. B. Morton and C.K. Tseng),127–34. Hong Kong: Hong Kong University Press.
Zou, R.L. 1984. Studies on the deep-water Scleractinia from South China Sea I. A *nomen novum* and a new species of *Caryophyllia*. *Tropic Oceanology* 3:51–4, pls. 1–5. (In Chinese with an English Abstract)
Zou, R.L. 1988. Studies on the deep water Scleractinia from South China Sea. II. Record and narration of species as well as time-spatial distributional characteristics. *Tropic Oceanology* 7:74–83, pls. 1–5. (In Chinese with an English Abstract)
Zou, R.L. and Chen Y.S. 1983. Preliminary study on the geographical distribution of shallow-water scleractinian corals from China. *Nanhai Studia Marina Sinica* 4:89–96. (In Chinese with an English Abstract)
Zou, R.L., Ma, J.H. and Song, S.W. 1966. A preliminary study on the vertical zonation of the coral reef of Hainan Island. *Oceanologia et Limnologia Sinica* 8:153–61. (In Chinese with an English Abstract)
Zou, R.L., Meng Z.M. and Guan X.L. 1983. Ecological analyses of ahermatypic corals from the northern shelf of South China Sea. *Tropic Oceanology* 2:1–6. (In Chinese with an English Abstract), or 1988. *Proceedings on Marine Biology of the South China Sea*, 193-9. Beijing: Ocean Press. (In English)
Zou, R.L., Song, S.W. and Ma, J.H. 1975. *The shallow-water scleractinian corals of Hainan Island*, 1-66, pls. 1-15. Beijing: Science Press. (In Chinese)
Zou, R.L., Zhang Y.L. and Xie Y.K. 1988. An ecological study of reef corals around Weizhou Island. *Proceedings on Marine Biology of the South China Sea*, 201-11. Beijing: China Ocean Press. (In English with a Chinese Abstract)
Zou, R.L., Zhang, Y.L. and Zhou J.M. 1987. *Scleractinians and antipatharians from Zengmu Ansha waters*, 203-5. Beijing: Science Press. (In Chinese)

CONSERVATION
SESSION PAPERS

The Marine Biology of the South China Sea
(ed. B. Morton). Proceedings of the First
International Conference on the Marine
Biology of Hong Kong and the South China Sea,
Hong Kong, 28 October – 3 November 1990.
Hong Kong: Hong Kong University Press, 1993.

SCIENCE AND THE MANAGEMENT OF MANGROVES IN ASIA AND THE PACIFIC

C.D. Field

City Polytechnic of Hong Kong, 83 Tat Chee Avenue, Kowloon, Hong Kong

ABSTRACT

There is a general expectation that a scientific understanding of mangrove ecosystems will automatically lead to a capacity for their management. Such an expectation is false. It is argued that basic studies of pristine systems are unlikely to satisfy the needs of management. On the contrary, the present uses of the mangrove environment are such that many other kinds of scientific, technological and economic expertise will have to be marshalled if tropical intertidal environments are to be utilised wisely for sustainable development.

INTRODUCTION

Mangroves are encountered almost inadvertently by visitors to the tropics because they occupy all but the most exposed and rocky shorelines. In sheltered estuaries and lagoons, they are usually extensive and may even form a community up to several kilometers wide with a gradual transition to terrestrial vegetation (Tomlinson 1986). Traditionally, mangroves have been a forgotten ecosystem (Vannucci 1989), considered as unpleasant and dangerous swamps, undervalued by governments and destroyed by developers. Indeed, the very sites occupied by the mangroves have had special attraction for port development, marinas, real estate, and agriculture and mariculture projects (Hamilton and Snedaker 1984). However, scientists have long been intrigued by these bizzare plants and modern tropical ecologists (Hutchings and Saenger 1987) find them fascinating because they represent an interphase between two contrasting types of commnity: terrestrial, as represented by lowland forests of various kinds, and marine, as represented by distinctive littoral ecosystems, notably seagrass meadows and coral reefs. In the early seventies, the scientific interest in mangroves began to intensify in part because of the recognition that mangroves were becoming endangered in some parts of the world and in part because funds became available through international agencies such as UNESCO, the World Bank and FAO for research activities. Rollet (1981) published a bibliography of the mangrove literature that cited 6,000 references to research reports and journal articles for the period 1600–1975. Since 1975 the number of research reports, journal articles and books on mangroves has undergone an explosion so that it would be safe to say that more has been published on mangroves since 1975 than prior to that date. There is now an unmanageable literature on the mangal.

One positive outcome of all this scientific activity was that governments, planners, developers and the general public became aware that mangrove ecosystems should be approached with more respect as they are highly productive ecosystems with economic potential. The indiscriminate destruction of mangrove forests became perceived as unacceptable throughout many countries of Asia and the Pacific.

THE SCIENTIFIC PERSPECTIVE

There is a general expectation that a scientific understanding of mangrove ecosystems will lead automatically to a capacity for their management. In recent years, there have been detailed studies of the fauna, flora, ecology, hydrology, physiology and productivity of many different mangrove ecosystems, most of them pristine (Clough 1984). This information, though of intrinsic value, is difficult to synthesise and interpret because of the varying techniques and conditions employed. The discrete nature of much of the scientific data makes identification of the principal factors responsible for overall productivity of mangroves very difficult to identify. The lack of knowledge of complete systems also makes it very difficult to understand the dynamics of particular systems. The conclusion must be that despite an enormous expenditure of scientific effort there is no acceptable model, simple or complex, as to how mangrove ecosystems function or how their productivity is controlled. This situation is perhaps not surprising given the complexity and heterogeneity of mangrove ecosystems. Indeed, the possibility of constructing a single model of the dynamics of a mangrove system which can be applied world-wide must be precluded. The expectation that more and more scientific information on increasingly obscure parts of specific pristine mangrove forests will lead to a capacity for management of the system would seem to be false.

THE NEED FOR MANAGEMENT

In the case of pristine mangrove forests that are free from external interference there should be no need for management. Indeed, management might be considered an unnecessary interference. The justification for management comes from the presence of an intrusion into the system or the need for deliberate manipulation. In both cases, a knowledge of the system alone would be inadequate to derive a management strategy.

There is an increasing realisation that there is an urgent need to manage mangrove ecosystems as multiple use systems for high and sustainable yield. This implies perturbation of the ecosystem without loss of productivity. The purpose of this approach is to try and preserve the natural productivity of the system while at the same time exploiting the system for compatible purposes.

To optimise compatible use of a mangrove forest may require radically different approaches and knowledge than that applicable to a natural system. In the extreme case of deliberate manipulation of a mangrove forest to convert it to a number of other uses while at the same time conserving important aspects of it, knowledge of the new system will be much more important than that of the pristine system. The extent to which basic scientific knowledge, and in particular the ecology of pristine systems, will assist the management of the perturbated system must be seen as limited.

USES OF MANGROVES

The uses of mangroves have been described fully in the scientific literature (Saenger *et al.* 1983; Field and Dartnall 1985) and for the present purpose it is sufficient to consider the uses in broad categories.

Category 1. Sustainable uses: consumables (timber, fish and Crustacea, chemicals), land stabilisation, conservation and recreation.

Category 2. Non-sustainable uses: land reclamation for urban development, extensive aquaculture, agriculture and mining.

It is clearly possible to have forms of mixed usage.

MANAGEMENT STRATEGIES

If one travels through the mangrove forests of the Asian and Pacific region one will see many examples of exploitation that have ended in disaster. Clear felled forests that will never recover, fish pond ventures that have created wastelands, mining areas that support no life, unchecked collection of foliage for fodder and fuel and rice paddy that produces low yield. In addition, urban development has removed vast areas of mangrove forest, often devastating far more land than was required and affecting the lives of subsistence coastal dwellers quite unnecessarily.

It is equally disturbing to witness the efforts of local people trying to rehabilitate effected mangrove lands in order to restore their productivity, without any basic agronomic knowledge. Their efforts often end in failure for lack of some very simple guidelines on how, where and when to plant mangrove propagules for maximum chance of success.

The needs of management in these instances are essentially those of forestry or animal husbandry, though of a specialised kind. The essential requirement is for knowledge of the processes essential to developing and supporting the productivity of the system rather than for understanding the system in all its parts. If there is to be intensive and selective use of mangrove forests then specialist knowledge needs to be acquired for plants and animals in areas such as genetics, nutrition, stocking procedures, disease control and harvesting. In turn, this knowledge needs to be supported by appropriate technology and suitable legislation.

So far very little effort has gone into the type of activity required for rational management. It can be argued that without the ecological studies, the significance of the mangrove forests would have remained obscure and there clearly continues to be scientific justification to continue pursuing a more complete understanding of mangrove ecosystems. Indeed, it is possible that practically relevant information will emerge from such studies in time. However, it is certain that basic studies of pristine systems will not satisfy the immediate needs of management.

The problems become even more complex when the strategies for combining sustainable and non-sustainable uses are considered. In cases such as these decisions are required on social and economic issues, as well as engineering and biological outcomes. The only viable management approach is to create a team of specialists preferably with overlapping expertise to advise on the best solutions. Unfortunately, the number of such specialists is extremely limited and such advice can rarely be obtained even if it is requested.

A PARTIAL SOLUTION

Mangrove forests continue to be abused, degraded and removed. There is an understanding on the part of the impoverished coastal dwellers throughout Asia and the Pacific that their existence is being threatened by these processes. There is also a willingness on the part of the people to try and reverse the process of destruction. A body of knowledge exists based partly on forestry practices in mangroves, known fisheries practice, and some practical findings that have emerged from ecological studies that could be synthesised into simple guidelines to enable coastal dwellers to rehabilitate their own environment with minimal cost and maximum chance of success.

For example, the regeneration of deforested areas can be achieved by the hand planting of seedlings at 1 m intervals of an appropriate mangrove species such as *Rhizophora apiculata*. Information also exists on the age at which a stand should be thinned, the organisation of the forest for harvesting and the utilisation of the forest for different purposes such as charcoal production and firewood production. The management strategies have been designed for sustained production of the end product.

Information also exists on the management of the fisheries and fauna of mangrove forests. It has been shown that it is important to protect the mangrove vegetation along the banks of creeks to protect the habitat and nursery functions of the mangroves. It has also been claimed that the introduction of culture methods to villages to fatten crabs caught by the fishermen could increase the value of the resource. The non-destructive use of the mangrove ecosystem for aquaculture should be encouraged in order to avoid the severe difficulties that have been encountered when mangroves are cleared for fishponds.

Mangrove forests are sensitive to changes in their hydrological environment. They are open systems, interacting with and influenced by both tidal processes and riverine and other freshwater sources from the land. This fact is often not appreciated by coastal planners and developers. Unnecessary damage to mangrove forests frequently occurs because of careless development.

As far as I am aware, no literature exists that presents such information in an easily accessible manner and perhaps it is time for dedicated ecologists to lift their heads out of the mud and to translate some of the existing knowledge into a form that will be useful to the poor people who dwell in the mangroves. There is also a need to continue to educate the local population on the importance of mangroves and to urge local authorities to enact legislation to control the use of the mangrove forests. It is possible that tighter control of the use of the mangrove forests would be more beneficial to local people than the study of mangrove ecology.

REFERENCES

Clough, B.F. 1984. *Mangrove ecosystems in Australia. Structure, function and management.* Canberra: Australian National University Press.

Field, C.D. and Dartnall, A.J. 1985. *Mangrove ecosystems of Asia and the Pacific: status, exploitation and management.* Queensland: Australia Institute of Marine Science.

Hamilton, L.S. and Snedaker, S.C. 1984. *Handbook of Mangrove Area Management. Division of Marine Science, UNESCO, Paris.* (East-West Centre, IUCN, UNESCO, UNEP).

Hutchings, P. and Saenger, P. 1987. *Ecology of Mangroves.* Australia: University of Queensland Press.

Saenger, P., Hegerl, E.J. and Davie, J.D.S. 1983. Global status of mangrove ecosystems. IUCN Commission on Ecology Papers No.3. Gland, Switzerland.

Rollet, B. 1981. *Bibliography on Mangrove Research 1600–1975.* Paris: UNESCO.

Tomlinson, P.B. 1986. *The Botany of Mangroves.* Cambridge: Cambridge University Press.

Vannucci, M. 1989. *The Mangroves and Us.* New Dehli: Indian Association for the Advancement of Science.

The Marine Biology of the South China Sea
(ed. B. Morton). Proceedings of the First
International Conference on the Marine
Biology of Hong Kong and the South China Sea,
Hong Kong, 28 October – 3 November 1990.
Hong Kong: Hong Kong University Press, 1993.

INVERTEBRATE SPECIES NEW TO SCIENCE RECORDED FROM THE MAI PO MARSHES, HONG KONG

S.Y. Lee

Department of Zoology and The Swire Marine Laboratory,
The University of Hong Kong, Hong Kong

ABSTRACT

A survey was made of the invertebrate community (excluding insects) at the Mai Po Marshes Nature Reserve, Hong Kong. Of the 81 species recorded, 13 (16.0%) have been found to be undescribed. Most of these new invertebrate species are important structural and functional components of the mangrove-dominated nature reserve. While the need to protect these wetland habitats for the preservation of biological diversity is apparent, many practical problems may render the rich diversity to be lost even before it is known to science. This is particular urgent for most southeast Asian wetlands where their conservation and management are severely hampered by: (1), a serious lack of local taxonomic expertise on the biota; (2), extremely high rates of rapid habitat destruction; and (3), lack of research on basic wetland ecology and the importance of endemic species to ecosystem maintenance and function.

INTRODUCTION

Recently, rapid loss of natural habitats has become an important issue in global conservation (Warren and Goldsmith 1983). Gilpin and Soule (1986) discussed the possible implications of such 'major habitat loss' for driving species extinction, that populations surviving in the habitat may be subject to immediate extinction or be increasingly vulnerable to stochastic extinction. Myers (1988) estimated that the present widespread global habitat destruction, particularly of the tropical forests, is eliminating from the biosphere every year about 15000 invertebrate or plant species, many of which are yet to be described. Consequently, habitats with a high frequency of new and endemic organisms are often accorded high conservation value.

In the habitat destruction scenario, wetlands seem to suffer particularly heavy losses (Abernethy and Turner 1987; Ewel 1990). Wilson (1988) estimated that human influence results in species extinction rates 1000 to 10,000 times higher in tropical forests when compared with pre-human times. Similarly, human intervention is one major cause of species extinction in wetlands. Destruction of coastal wetlands is mainly related to the various uses of the habitats for fishery production, the collection of raw materials for domestic uses (Chan 1987; Saenger 1987), or the conversion of the landscape into other forms to facilitate exploitation, e.g., tidal fish and shrimp ponds, paddy fields and freshwater ponds (de la Cruz 1984; Nor 1984; Choudhury 1987; Lahmann et al. 1987; Naamin 1987). This prevalence of consumptive land uses (Ewel 1990) is particularly evident in mangrove forests in tropical Asia and the Pacific, where traditional exploitation of the mangrove resource in various countries have resulted in large scale damage of the mangals (see various chapters in Field and Dartnall [1987] and Umali et al. [1987]).

This study argues for urgent conservation of wetlands in developing countries, from the view point of an important non-consumptive use — the conservation of biological diversity. Particular reference is made to the example of a mangrove-dominated wetland, the Mai Po Marshes Nature Reserve in Hong Kong.

MATERIALS AND METHODS

The Study Site

The Mai Po Marshes is an estuarine mangrove-dominated wetland located in northwest Hong Kong. The total area of about 300 ha comprises two different landscape features: about 80 ha of relatively undisturbed mangroves and 200 ha of tidal and freshwater ponds excavated from the native mangal for shrimp and fish cultivation. The marshes, with the extensive mudflat in Deep Bay (112 km^2) form an ecosystem frequented by about 250 species of resident and migratory birds (Fig. 1) (Irving and Morton 1988). Consequently, the Mai Po Marshes were accorded the status of nature reserve by the Hong Kong Government in 1976, with restricted entry to the general public. The integrity of the reserve is, however, jeopardized by the large number of urban and industrial developments around the area (Irving and Morton 1988; Lee 1988).

Sampling of the invertebrate fauna was initiated in July 1985, and covered the various habitat types within the system. Replicate samples of the benthic community on open mudflats were collected bi-monthly using an Ekman grab (225 cm^2). The fauna on the mangrove forest floor was collected by hand, as were animals on the mangrove canopy. Pelagic invertebrates were collected by sluice gate catches from the tidal ponds. Depending on the sampling method, quantitative measurement of abundance was possible for some of the habitats. Additional information on invertebrate abundance and occurrence was obtained from other recently published works (Soh 1978; Erséus 1990; Gibson 1990; Tong 1990).

Where quantitative sampling was possible, dry weights of small invertebrates were measured to 0.01 mg to give an estimate of the standing biomass. The invertebrates collected were all identified as far as possible. Prospective new species were sent to relevant experts for the respective groups. Observations were also made on the habit and any other biological factors of interest.

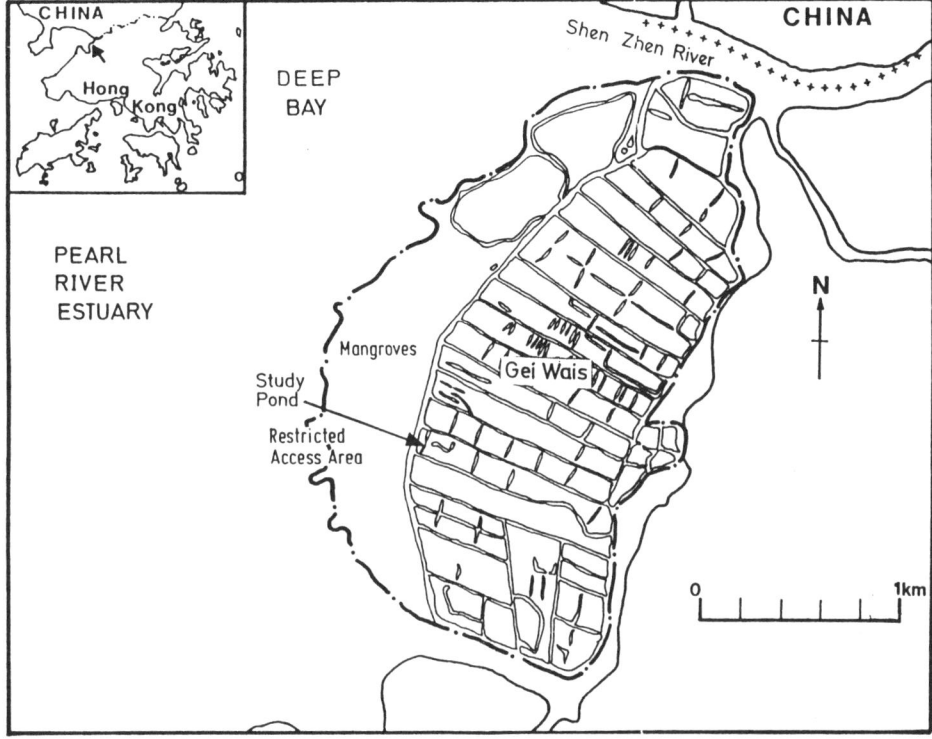

Fig. 1. A map of the Mai Po Marshes Nature Reserve and the location of the tidal pond and the mangrove mudflat where benthic samples were collected.

RESULTS

The invertebrate community at Mai Po

A total of 81 invertebrate species (excluding birds and the insects) were collected from the Mai Po Marshes during the study period (Table 1). The list is far from exhaustive but includes the more conspicuous components of the invertebrate community. Most of these species are quite well known in Asian mangals. Of these, 13 (16.0%) of all species recorded have been identified as undescribed species (Table 2). Arthropod crustaceans were best represented in the list of new species, particularly the Amphipoda.

The new species and their ecological importance

Most of the new invertebrate species recorded from Mai Po are important numerical components of the ecosystem, occurring at high densities or biomass in various microhabitats (Table 3).

Particular reference is made to the sesarminae crab *Chiromanthes maipoensis* Soh. This crab grows to about 4 cm carapace width for large males and is a conspicuous component of the mangrove floor community. This crab has never been reported from mangroves outside Mai Po but nevertheless acts as an important agent effecting man-

Table 1
List of invertebrates recorded from the Mai Po Marshes as of November 1990.
Relative abundance classes: C - common; O - occasional; R - rare; S - seasonal.

Phylum/Class	Species	Abundance
Nermetea		
Heteronemertea	*Dendrorhynchus sinensis*	C
	Procephalothrix orientalis sp. nov.	O
Annelida		
Oligochaeta	*Limnodriloides biforis* sp. nov.	C
	L. fraternus	C
	Tectidrilus achaetus	C
	Doliodrilus tener	C
	Rhizodrilus russus	C
Hirudinea	Unidentified leech	R
Polychaeta	*Dendronereis pinnaticirrus*	C
	Laonome sp. A	C
	Laonome sp. B	C
	Ceratonereis sp.	R
	Ceratonereies cf. *burmensis*	R
	Aglaophamus sp.	R
	Polydora sp.	C
	Neanthes sp.	R
	Namalycastis aibiuma	R
	Capitellid indet.	R
Mollusca		
Gastropoda	*Sermyla tornatella*	C
	Dostia violacea	C
	Cerithideopsilla cingulata	R
	Assiminea sp. 1	C
	Assiminea sp. 2	C
	Iravadia (Iravadia) ornata	R
	I. (Fairbankia) bombayana	R
	Stenothyra sp.1	R
	Stenothyra sp. 2	R
	Clenchiella sp.	R
	Salinator fragilis	R
	Salinator sp.	R
	Ellobium politum	R
	Ellobium sp.	R
	Melanoides tuberculata	O
	Littorina melanostoma	C
	Littoraria ardouiniana	C
Bivalvia	*Pseudopythina maipoensis* sp. nov.	O
	Musculista senhausia	R
	Glauconome chinesis	C
	Placuna placenta	C

Table 1 (continued)

Phylum/Class	Species	Abundance
	Crassostrea gigas	C
	Mytilopsis sallei	R
Arthropoda		
Crustacea		
Decapoda	*Metapenaeus ensis*	C
	M. affinis	O
	Penaeus monodon	R
	P. merguiensis	C
	P. penicillatus	C
	Macrobrachium nipponense	C
	Exopalaemon cf. *styliferus*	C
	Coutierella tonkinensis	C
	Caridina nilotica gracilipes	C
	Alpheus sp.	R
	Scylla serrata	R
	Chiromanthes maipoensis	O
	C. bidens	C
	Parasesarma affinis	C
	Sesarma tangi	R
	S. sinensis	R
	S. dehaani	O
	Metaplax longipes	C
	M. takahasii	C
	Varuna litterata	C
	Helice tridens	C
	Cleistocoeloma merguiensis	R
	Paracleistosoma depressum	R
	Ilyoplax ningpoensis	C
	I. serrata	C
	I. tansuiensis	C
	Uca arcuata	C
	Uca acuta	C
	U. chlorophthalmus	R
	U. dusummieri	O
	Macrophthalmus convexus	C
	Chasmagnathus convexum	R
Amphipoda	*Talorchestia* sp. nov.	C
	Grandidierella sp. nov.	C
	Kamaka sp. nov.	C
	Melita sp. nov.	C
	Victoriopisa sp. nov.	C
Tanaidacea	*Discapseudes* sp. nov.	C
Arthropoda		
Acarina	*Dometorina rostrata* sp. nov.	S
	Amblysius sp.	O

Table 2
List of new species with either Mai Po or Deep Bay as the type locality.

Arthropoda		
Crustacea		
Decapoda		
Sesarminae		*Chiromanthes maipoensis* Soh 1978
Amphipoda		
Aoridae		*Grandidierella* sp. nov.
Corophidae		*Kamaka* sp. nov.
Melitidae		*Melita* sp. nov.
		Victoriopisa sp. nov.
Talitridae		*Talorchestia* sp. nov.
Tanaidacea		
Apseudidae		*Discapseudes* sp. nov.
Arachnida		
Acarina		
Scheloribatidae		*Dometorina rostrata* Luxton 1993
Annelida		
Oligochaeta		*Limnodriloides biforis* Erséus 1990
		L. fraternus Erséus 1990
		Rhizodrilus russus Erséus 1990
Mollusca		
Bivalvia		*Pseudopythina maipoensis* Morton & Scott 1989
Nemertea		*Procephalothrix orientalis* Gibson 1990

grove litter turnover at Mai Po (Lee 1989; Poovachiranon 1990). Together with *Parasesarma affinis* and *C. bidens*, *C. maipoensis* can consume > 50% of the daily litter production in landward mangroves. This crab is therefore an important functional component of the mangal ecosystem at Mai Po.

In contrast to *C. maipoensis* which is a large and conspicuous species discovered early in the study on the invertebrate community at Mai Po, the mite *Dometorina rostrata* Luxton was discovered only recently. This minute mite has an adult body size up to 1 mm. Despite its small size, the mite is involved in massive defoliation of one of the dominant mangroves at Mai Po, *Avicennia marina*. The mites occur at densities up to 30 individuals per leaf during the first stage of the defoliation event, which typically takes place in April. Densities subsequently fall to lower values during the second half of the defoliation, when a pyralid moth larva completes the consumption of virtually all leaf tissue of *A. marina*. Like *C. maipoensis*, the mite is thus responsible for important ecological processes shaping the ecology of the Mai Po Marshes.

Table 3
Distribution and abundance of some of the more important new species found at Mai Po. Density and biomass figures are mean ± 1S.D. unless otherwise stated. n.d.: no data.

Species	Microhabitat/ feeding habit	Density ($\#\cdot m^{-2}$)	Biomass (g dry wt·m^{-2})
Discapseudes sp. nov.	Shallow mud burrows, detritivorous	3094 ± 2982	3.52 ± 3.39
Pseudopythina maipoensis	Shallow mud burrows, probably a commensal of Discapseudes, probably deposit-feeding	20.4 ± 41.5	0.024 ± 0.049
Talorchestia sp. nov.	Infrequently inundated mangrove floor, detritivorous	ca. 50–100	n.d.
Dometorina rostrata	Seasonal outbreak on Avicennia marina associated with massive defoliation, fungivorous	0 – 13.1 per leaf	n.d.
Limnodriloides biforis & L. fraternus	deposit-feeder	4419 ± 3964	n.d.
Melita sp. nov.	deposit-feeder	1986 ± 1786	0.825 ± 0.733

In addition to the grazers on fresh and senescent mangrove leaves, new invertebrate species are also involved in the turnover of vascular plant detritus in the benthic system. The tanaid *Discapseudes* sp. nov. occurs at high densities (3000·m^{-2}) in the muddy substrate at Mai Po, and is the numerically dominant species in most samples. Their burrowing behaviour probably also increase nutrient flux and aeration within the muddy substrate. It has been observed that the new bivalve *Pseudopythina maipoensis* sp. nov. probably leads a commensal relationship with *Discapseudes* inside its burrows (Morton and Scott 1989).

The amphipods *Grandidierella* sp. nov., *Victoriopisa* sp. nov., *Kamaka* sp. nov. and *Melita* sp. nov. are commonly found on the mudflat, although their functional importance still awaits further investigation. *Melita* sp. nov. achieves a density of nearly 2000 individuals·m^{-2}. The drier floor of the landward mangroves is colonised by the large amphipod *Talorchestia* sp. nov. Again, this species is an important component of the litter fauna at these sites.

DISCUSSION

Conservation of coastal wetland systems in developing countries faces a number of practical problems. While the general public in these countries are beginning to appreciate the importance of the non-consumptive uses (such as shoreline protection and conservation of biodiversity) of these environments, traditional dependence on the same environment for consumptive exploitation is still usually given higher priorities. This is particularly true in tropical southeast Asia, where some traditional uses such as *tambak* aquaculture have been practiced for centuries (Schuster 1952) and is still a flourishing landscape feature on southeast Asian shores (de la Cruz 1984; Singh 1987; Fortes 1988). The preponderance of these traditional uses and urbanization pressure both contribute to large scale destruction of coastal wetland systems throughout Asia (Fortes 1988), and their operation is generally incompatible to wildlife conservation (Lee 1992). Our inventory on the biological diversity of these vulnerable habitats is, however, much less well developed. Freeman (1989) suggested that while the tropics only make up 35% of all identified species, the actual contribution to total species present may be as high as 86%. Without proper taxonomic investigations, most species surviving in southeast Asian mangroves probably face extinction before they are even known to science. In the present study on the invertebrate community at the Mai Po Marshes, it is found that about 20% of all invertebrate taxa recorded are probably new. In addition to their zoological interests, many of these species are important structural and functional components of the local mangrove ecosystem. With the present level of intense development going on in the vicinity of Mai Po (Irving and Morton 1988), I hold a pessimistic view on the possibility that these new species will ever be studied in any detail before they become rare or even extinct. While scientists continue to argue for conservation value of a habitat on the basis of preservation of biological diversity, environmental values of wildlife are often difficult to specify or quantify. Kellert (1984) documented that the general public is usually biased towards according higher priority to factors measurable in dollars and those related to relatively critical human needs such as energy and jobs. Even when species are to be protected, priorities are often given to species 'useful' to man, e.g., food crops, or species with high potential for domestication (MacKinnon *et al.* 1986). In developing countries where economic return is often given precedence, will the government administrators consider seemingly unworthy marine invertebrates as important animals to save? Often the less spectacular organisms, by virtue of the ecosystem function they serve, are more important to the human future than the publicised endangered species (Ehrlich 1988). Evaluation of the conservation value of a habitat therefore strongly depends on the availability of ecological information at the species level to include, in particular, the less 'appealing' species.

Another potential facing scientists who try to promote conservation by the diversity approach is that it is very difficult to accurately estimate diversity losses. Lugo (1988) documented wide variations in recent estimates on tropical forest species loss, although all agree that the loss must be substantial. The lack of reliable and sufficient 'ground data' on diversity of various habitats just makes it impossible to arrive at realistic estimates. In order to have better estimates of diversity loss associated with destruction of a particular habitat type, data on species richness associated with the habitat is of primary importance. In the present study, a small mangrove wetland in Hong Kong provides home for over 81 species of invertebrates, reflecting the rich faunal communities typical of tropical wetland systems.

The present study also exposed a second practical problem while trying to argue for conservation value based on the preservation of biological diversity. Of the 13 invertebrate species suggested to be 'new' by the taxonomic experts, only seven have been described to date. These undescribed species reside in gray areas in ecological and biological literature: it is difficult to communicate a study on an animal when others do not know what species exactly one is working on! Taxonomists are probably overloaded with requests for help coming in from every corner of the world everyday. While preserved materials can wait in the museums to be studied, animals in habitats facing rapid development cannot afford to wait to be described. The delay caused by the sheer load the taxonomists have to clear may thus mean a loss of some species forever. This then points to the need to train more taxonomists to assist in the global conservation endeavour. Regrettably, the number of taxonomists is on the decline for various reasons, greatly hindering conservation efforts (Wilson 1988). This need applies especially to the developing countries, such as those in southeast Asia. Conservation efforts will be greatly hampered until these countries can provide enough local taxonomic expertise and the required supporting infrastructures such as museum collections.

Irving and Morton (1988) reviewed urban development projects in the vicinity of the Mai Po Marshes. Apart from being an important wetland habitat for over 250 species of resident and migrant bird species, the results of this study on the invertebrate fauna are also indicative of high conservation value of this wetland. While the present legislation may confer considerable protection to the nature reserve, the integrity of the habitat cannot possibly be maintained without the setting up of a buffer zone where only intermediate levels of use are allowed (MacKinnon *et al.* 1986, p. 93). Again, this appears to be a luxury to wildlife conservation in Hong Kong.

ACKNOWLEDGEMENTS

I would like to thank the following taxonomic experts for their effort to identify the new taxa mentioned in this paper: Prof. J. Sieg (Tanaidacea); Dr J.K. Lowry (Amphipoda); Dr C. Erséus (Oligochaeta); Prof. B. Morton and Mr P.H. Scott (Bivalvia); Dr M. Luxton (Acarida) and Prof. R. Gibson (Nemertea). All other identifications were performed by myself based on published materials, and errors, if any, are of course mine. Part of this work was supported by a John Swire Scholarship in Wetland Ecology, administered by the World Wide Fund for Nature Hong Kong.

REFERENCES

Abernethy, Y. and Turner, R.E. 1987. US forested wetlands: 1940–1980. *BioScience* 37:721–7.
Bawa, K.S., Primack, R. and Woodruff, D. 1990. Conservation of biodiversity: a Southeast Asian perspective. *Trends in Ecology and Evolution* 5:394–96.
Chan, H.T. 1987. Human habitation and traditional uses in the Matang mangrove. In *Mangroves of Asia and the Pacific: Status and Management* (ed. Umali, R.M., Zamora, P.M., Gotera, R.R., Jara, R.S., Camacho, A.S. and Vanucci, M.), 313–7. UNESCO and UNDP.
Choudhury, R.A. 1987. Conversion of mangrove areas to aquaculture. In *Workshop on the Conversion of Mangrove Areas to Aquaculture*, 107-18. UNESCO /UNDP.
de la Cruz, A.A. 1984. A realistic approach to the use and management of mangrove areas in southeast Asia. In *Physiology and Management of Mangroves* (ed. H.J. Teas), 65–8. The Hague: Dr. W. Junk Publishers.
Ehrlich, P.R. 1988. The loss of diversity: causes and consequences. In *Biodiversity* (ed. E.O. Wilson), 21–7. Washington, D.C.: National Academy Press.

Erséus, C. 1990. Marine Oligochaeta of Hong Kong. In *Proceedings of the Second International Marine Biological Workshop: the Marine Flora and Fauna of Hong Kong and Southern China, Hong Kong, 1986* (ed. B. Morton), 259–335. Hong Kong: Hong Kong University Press.

Ewel, K.C. 1990. Multiple demands on wetlands. *BioScience* 40: 660–6.

Field, C.D. and Dartnall, A.J. 1985. *Mangrove Ecosystems of Asia and the Pacific: Status, Exploitation and Management*. Townsville: Australian Institute of Marine Science.

Fortes, M.D. 1988. Mangrove and seagrass beds of east Asia: habitats under stress. *Ambio* 17:207–13.

Freeman, B. 1989. *Environmental Ecology*. San Diego: Academic Press.

Gibson, R. 1990. The macrobenthic nemertean fauna of Hong Kong. In *Proceedings of the Second International Marine Biological Workshop: the Marine Flora and Fauna of Hong Kong and Southern China, Hong Kong, 1986* (ed. B. Morton), 33–212. Hong Kong: Hong Kong University Press.

Gilpin, M.E. and Soule, M. E. 1983. Minimum viable populations: processes of species extinction. In *Conservation Biology. The Science of Scarcity and Diversity* (ed. M.E. Soule), 19–34. Sunderland: Sinaeur Associates.

Irving, R.T.A. and Morton, B. 1988. *A Geography of Mai Po*. Hong Kong: World Wide Fund For Nature Hong Kong.

Kellert, S.R. 1984. Assessing wildlife and environmental values in cost-benefit analysis. *Journal of Environmental Management* 18:355–63.

Lahmann, E.J., Snedaker, S.C. and Brown, M.S. 1987. Structural comparisons of mangrove forests near shrimp ponds in southern Ecuador. *Interciencia* 12:240–3.

Lee, S.Y. 1988. The ecology of a traditional tidal shrimp pond, the production and fate of macrodetritus and implications for management. Ph.D. thesis, University of Hong Kong.

Lee, S.Y. 1989. The importance of inundation frequency and sesariminae crabs (*Chiromanthes* spp.) on the decomposition of mangrove (*Kandelia candel* (L.) Druce) leaf litter in a Hong Kong tidal shrimp pond. *Journal of Experimental Marine Biology and Ecology* 130:23–43.

Lee, S.Y. 1992. The management of traditional tidal ponds for aquaculture and wildlife conservation in southeast Asia: problems and prospects. *Biological Conservation* 63:113-8.

Lugo, A.E. 1988. Estimating reductions in the diversity of tropical forest species. In *Biodiversity* (ed. E.O. Wilson), 58–70. Washington, D.C.: National Academy Press.

MacKinnon, J., MacKinnon, K., Child, G. and Thorsell, J. 1986. *Managing protected areas in the tropics*. Gland: International Union for Conservation of Nature and Natural Resources.

Morton, B. and Scott, P.H. 1989. The Hong Kong Galeommatacea (Mollusca:Bivalvia) and their hosts, with descriptions of new species. *Asian Marine Biology* 6:129–60.

Myers, N. 1988. Tropical forests and their species: going, going ...? In *Biodiversity* (ed. E.O. Wilson), 28–35. Washington, D.C.: National Academy Press.

Naamin, N. 1987. Conversion of mangrove areas to tambak aquaculture in Indonesia. In *Workshop on the Conversion of Mangrove Areas to Aquaculture*, 56-65. UNESCO /UNDP.

Nor, S.M. 1984. Major threats to the mangroves of Asia and Oceania. In *Productivity of the Mangrove Ecosystem: Management Implications* (ed. J.E. Ong and W.K. Gong), 68–78. Penang: Universiti Sains Malaysia.

Poovachiranon, S. 1990. The food of *Chiromanthes bidens* (De Haan, 1835) and *C. maipoensis* (Soh, 1978) (Decapoda:Sesarminae) in Hong Kong. In *Proceedings of the Second International Marine Biological Workshop: the Marine Flora and Fauna of Hong Kong and Southern China, Hong Kong, 1986* (ed. B. Morton), 727–35. Hong Kong: Hong Kong University Press.

Saegner, P. 1987. Mangrove use and conservation. In *Mangrove Ecosystems of Asia and the Pacific: Status, Exploitation and Management* (ed. C.D. Field and A.J. Dartnall), 97–103. Townsville: Australian Institute of Marine Science.

Schuster, W.H. 1952. *Fish Culture in Brackish-water Ponds of Java*. Indo-Pacific Fisheries Council Special Publications, No.1.

Singh, T. 1987. The use of mangrove-managed areas for aquaculture. In *Workshop on the Conversion of Mangrove Areas to Aquaculture*, 47-55. UNESCO/UNDP.

Soh, C.L. 1978. On a collection of sesarmine crabs (Decapoda:Brachyura:Grapsidae) from Hong Kong. *Memoirs of The Hong Kong Natural History Society* 13:9–21.

Tong, K.Y. 1990. The microgastropods of Hong Kong mangroves. In *Proceedings of the Second International Marine Biological Workshop: the Marine Flora and Fauna of Hong Kong and Southern China, Hong Kong, 1986* (ed. B. Morton), 437–48. Hong Kong: Hong Kong University Press.

Umali, R.M., Zamora, P.M., Gotera, R.R., Jara, R.S., Camacho, A.S. and Vanucci, M. 1987. *Mangroves of Asia and the Pacific: Status and Management.* UNESCO/UNDP.

Warren, A. and Goldsmith, F.B. 1983. An introduction to nature conservation. In *Conservation in Perspective* (ed. A. Warren and Goldsmith), 2–15. Chichester: John Wiley & Sons.

Wilson, E.O. 1988. The current state of biological diversity. In *Biodiversity* (ed. E.O. Wilson), 3–18. Washington, D.C.: National Academy Press.

The Marine Biology of the South China Sea
(ed. B. Morton). Proceedings of the First
International Conference on the Marine
Biology of Hong Kong and the South China Sea,
Hong Kong, 28 October – 3 November 1990.
Hong Kong: Hong Kong University Press, 1993.

CONSERVATION OF THE DEEP BAY ENVIRONMENT

Llewellyn Young

Department of Zoology, The University of Hong Kong, Hong Kong

and

David S. Melville

World Wide Fund for Nature Hong Kong, P.O. Box 12721, Hong Kong

ABSTRACT

The Deep Bay area of Hong Kong comprises a mosaic of natural and man-made habitats, which has been recognized both locally and internationally as of great biological importance.

The site supports one of the largest and most diverse mangrove communities along the south China coast. Also, the expanse of intertidal mudflat is an important feeding area for birds that migrate along the East Asian/Australian flyway. A variety of mammals have also been recorded including the otter (*Lutra lutra*), leopard cat (*Felis bengalensis*) and Javan mongoose (*Herpestes javanicus*).

The agricultural habitats found in Deep Bay are good examples of the traditional land-use found in the Hong Kong countryside, but which is now fast disappearing due to encroachment by urban developments.

The biological significance of Deep Bay is now being undermined by pollutants entering into the bay from both Hong Kong and China, as well as from a number of development projects along its coastline and catchment area. If urgent steps are not taken by the Hong Kong government to protect this fragile environment, then it may well be lost in the next few decades.

INTRODUCTION

Deep Bay is situated at $22.41°N$ to $22.53°N$, and $113.88°E$ to $114°E$, separating the north-west coast of the New Territories of Hong Kong from the south-west coast of the Shenzhen Special Economic Zone (SEZ) of the People's Republic of China. It is the largest estuarine area in Hong Kong with a surface area of 112 km^2 and a catchment area of 500 km² (Fig. 1), Despite its name, however, it has an average depth of only 2.9 m and is nowhere deeper than 6 m. At low tide, extensive mudflats covering 1.8 km² are exposed. The tidal flats are fringed with dwarf mangrove, landward of which are shrimp and fish ponds and now, an increasing urban landscape.

From the north-east, Deep Bay receives water from the Shenzhen River and from the south-east, water comes from the Yuen Long and Tin Shui Wai creeks. The water entering Deep Bay then drains into the Pearl River estuary to the south-west (Fig.1). On the flood tide, water from the Pearl River flows back into the bay and is an important source of sediment.

Sixty percent of the human population in the Hong Kong catchment of Deep Bay live in rural villages and 40% are housed in new towns such as Yuen Long and Fanling. With the growth of these new towns and the development of further ones, e.g., Tin Shui Wai, which will eventually house 135,000 people, the urban population in the Deep Bay catchment will increase substantially in the present decade. From a total population of 496,000 living in this area in 1976, the number grew to 800,000 in 1986 and is now

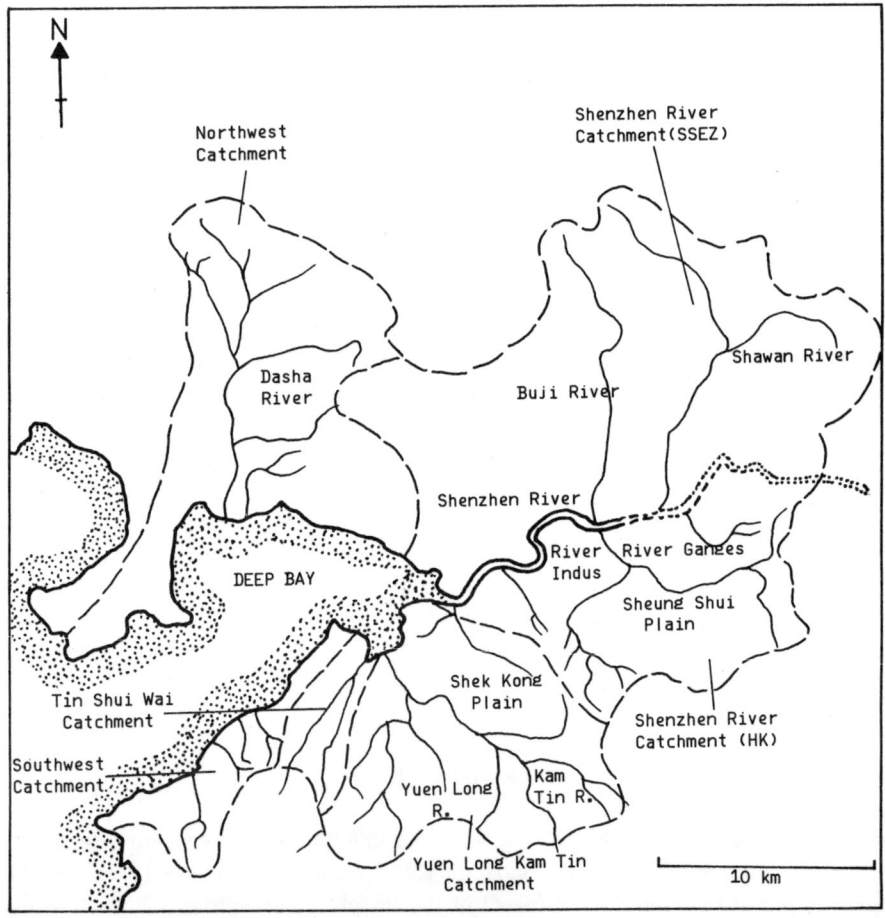

Fig. 1. Map of the Deep Bay catchment area.

expected to rise to 1.5 million by the year 2001 (Melville and Morton 1983; Anon 1988a; Irving and Morton 1988). The population of the Shenzhen SEZ similarly, has increased spectacularly in the past 15 years from a small market town to a major city containing 400,000 people in 1986 (Anon 1986d).

This dramatic increase in the human population together with associated development of industry, housing and infrastructure are placing severe pressures on the bay and its hinterland.

HUMAN HISTORY AROUND DEEP BAY

Before considering the importance of the Deep Bay environment, it is useful to review the human land-use history of the area.

When the first people arrived in Hong Kong around 4000 B.C., they were probably fishermen who settled along the coast. Deep Bay at that time was still fringed by extensive areas of mangrove. Agriculture was introduced to Hong Kong by immigrants from China in the 10th century following which reclamation of the Deep Bay marshes for rice fields began. The first record for land reclamation suggests that this took place some 1000 years ago around Yuen Long. Since then, a further 1700 ha have been reclaimed for mainly agricultural uses. The names of some present day villages gives a clue to their origin, e.g., San Tin, which was founded in the 13th century. Most reclamations were initially on a small scale, the first large scale one being in the early 1920s at Ping Shan when over 325 ha was impounded. In the early days, brackish rice was first grown on the newly reclaimed soils then, as the salt was washed out, freshwater rice could be planted.

In the 1950s, there was an influx of refugees from China into Hong Kong and they brought with them improved methods of market gardening. Soon, this was found to be more economic than rice farming and agricultural land-use began to change in the New Territories as areas of paddi were converted to market vegetable plots. Paddi-fields made up 70.3% (9450 ha) of all agricultural land in 1954, but the area fell to 43.3% (5870 ha) by 1969 and disappeared from Hong Kong by 1986. With a marked increase in demand for freshwater fish in the early 1970s, most of the paddi in the Deep Bay area was converted subsequently to fish-ponds, producing mullet (*Mugil cephalus*) and carp (Cyprinidae) (Irving and Morton 1988; Melville 1989a).

PRESENT LAND-USE AROUND DEEP BAY

The location of each of the main types of agricultural land-use in the Deep Bay area is summarised in Figure 2.

Oyster cultivation

There are extensive areas of oyster beds on the intertidal mudflats of Deep Bay. These oyster beds are the only ones in Hong Kong, having a total area of 4072 ha (Anon. 1988c). However, only relatively small areas of the beds are currently in production.

Two main species of oysters are cultivated, one being the 'white' oyster (*Crassostrea*

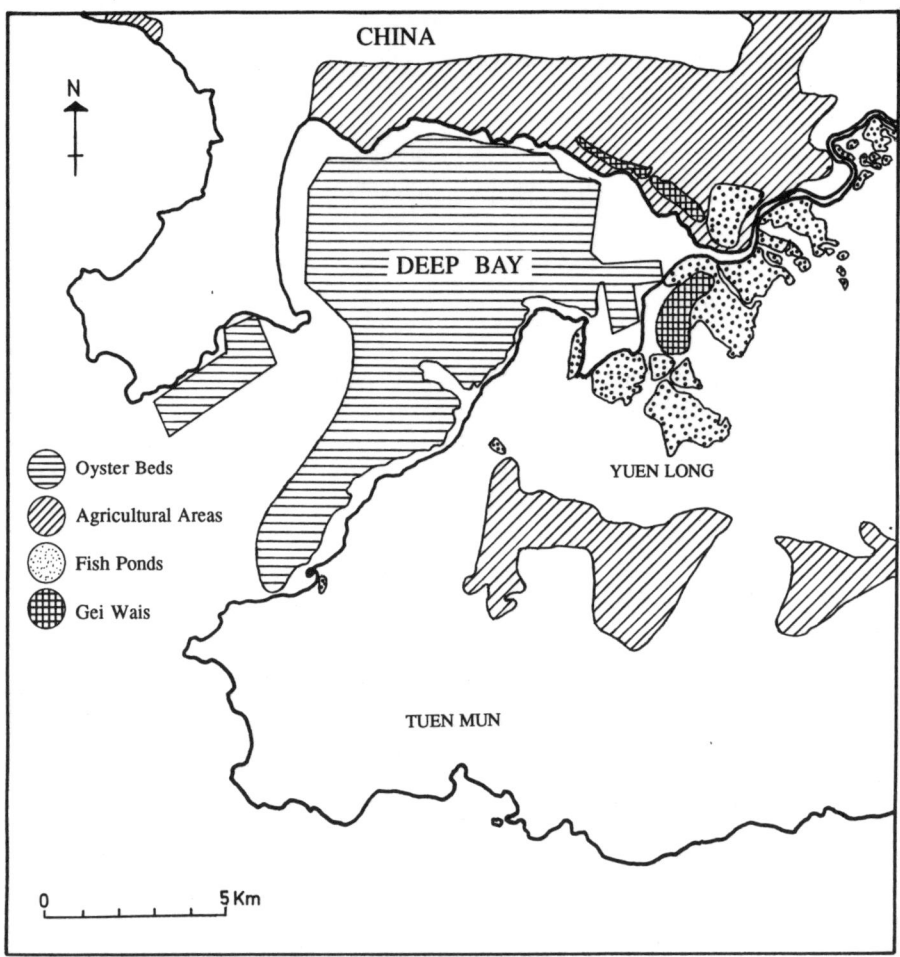

Fig. 2. Agricultural land-use in the Deep Bay area.

gigas), which makes up 70% of the total production, the other is the 'red' oyster (*C. rivularis*). These are grown from spat either collected in Deep Bay or by fattening young oysters imported from elsewhere in the Pearl River estuary. In 1987, local oyster farmers produced 200 tonnes of fresh oyster meat valued at HK$8 million (Lee 1988). Local production usually accounts for only 30–40% of the oysters eaten in the territory, the remaining 60–70% being imported mainly from China. However, since the late 1950s, production in Deep Bay has declined, this being due to a combination of fungal infections, overstocking of the oyster beds, a lack of labour and pollution. The latter is a particular problem, with oysters being contaminated with cadmium and faecal bacteria (Leung *et al*. 1975; Phillips *et al*. 1982). In 1986, 10% of the oyster samples from Deep Bay had wet weight cadmium concentrations in the range 2.1–2.36 ppm compared with the limit for human consumption of 2 ppm (Anon 1988b).

Fishing

While China recognizes Deep Bay as an important fish nursery ground and forbids their fishermen to work the waters there (except for lift nets near Shekou), there is no attempt to control Hong Kong fishermen. However, since only 14% of all fish consumed in Hong Kong is caught locally and that from Deep Bay makes up only 1% of this amount, the contribtion from Deep Bay fisheries is not significant, but disturbance caused by fishermen trapping mudskippers and setting stake nets on the tidal mudflat has an adverse impact on waterfowl. No mariculture is possible due to the shallowness of the bay.

Gei wai farming

Mangroves on the Hong Kong side of Deep Bay were first dug up and converted to *gei wais* in the early 1940s, and there are now 170 ha of *gei wais* found solely at Mai Po.

Gei wais are traditionally operated shrimp ponds which depend on their nutrient input from two sources: (1) litter input via the vegetation growing inside the ponds and (2) organic material brought in from Deep Bay through a single sluice gate by flooding at selected high tides. They thus capitalize on natural productivity. Each of the rectangular *gei wai's* is on average 9 ha in area, and has a single sluice gate on its seaward side which can be opened and shut by placing wooded boards across its opening. Channels have been cut through the mangroves on the outside of the *gei wai* to link the sluice gate with the bay, and along which water can enter the *gei wai*.

In late autumn and winter when the shrimps present in Deep Bay are spawning, their larvae are flushed into the *gei wai* by opening the sluice gate at high tides. On the ebbing tide, the sluice gate is shut again. This way, the shrimp larvae are kept inside the *gei wai* and are allowed to mature there. When the shrimps begin to reach marketable size some three months later, harvesting can be started. This is done at night to coincide with when the shimps are most active, and is also dependent on there being a low tide in the bay. A net is placed across the opened sluice gate at this time and the shrimps are then flushed into the net. The *gei wai* is partially drained by this operation and as a result, the water lost has to be replaced the next morning on the incoming tide by opening the sluice gate again.

Only a small proportion of the total number of shrimps in the *gei wai* is caught each time using this method, so that the operation can be repeated many times over the course of the year. In practise, each *gei wai* can be harvested in this way some eighty times each year to produce a total of up to 600 kg of shrimps.

The shrimp of main economic importance is *Metapenaeus ensis* which is currently worth HK$40–150 between 600 g^{-2}. In 1989, the income generated from the six *gei wais* managed by World Wide Fund for Nature Hong Kong at Mai Po, amounted to HK$283,000 (M.W.N. Lau, personal comment). Apart from shrimps, a variety of fish are also harvested from the gei wais such as the yellow-fined bream (*Sparus latus*) and mullet (*Mugil cephalus*) when the *gei wais* are drained in mid-winter.

The total production of shrimps from these *gei wais* may not be significant when compared to that produced in China and imported into Hong Kong for consumption. However, these gei wai ecosystems are important in terms of the rich fauna they contain, and in maintaining the area of mangrove in Deep Bay. They also serve as an important feeding site for many waterbird species, e.g., herons and waders, which take advantage of the exposed areas of shallow water and mud to find food when the *gei* wais are partially drained for shrimp harvesting. In mid-winter, all the *gei wais* are drained in sequence to harvest the fish found in them. On these occasions, hundreds of waterbirds, especially little egrets (*Egretta garzetta*), can be seen feeding on the small fish and shrimps in the remaining pools of water.

Over recent years, shrimp production has declined due possibly to a combination of a deterioration in the quality of the incoming water from Deep Bay, and silting up of the *gei wais* themselves (Melville et al. 1989).

Freshwater fish ponds

These have existed in Deep Bay since the early 1970s by conversion of the traditional *gei wais* and, later, by additional conversion of the saltwater paddi. From 1954 to 1985, there was a ten fold increase in fish-pond area in Hong Kong to around 1400 ha, 90% of which is located in Deep Bay. These ponds depend on being stocked with fish fry from Deep Bay or elsewhere in spring, and need high inputs of purchased feeds.

There are two main types of fish-ponds. The first and most common, is a polyculture of grey mullet (*Mugil cephalus*) and up to five species of carp: big head (*Aristichthys nobilis*), mud carp (*Cirrhinus molitorella*), grass carp (*Ctenopharyngodon idellus*), common carp (*Cyprinius carpio*) and silver carp (*Hypohthalmichthys molitrix*). This is often integrated with the rearing of other types of farm animals such as ducks and chickens the droppings of which are used as fertilizer. The other type of ponds are monocultures of carnivorous fish, e.g., snakehead (*Ophiocephalus*) sp. or catfish (*Clarias fuscus*). While the average production from monoculture ponds is 12 tonnes·ha^{-1}yr^{-1}, that from polyculture ponds is 5.2 tonnes·ha^{-1}yr^{-1}. In 1987, of the 6500 tonnes of fish produced from these ponds, 5800 tonnes came from Deep Bay. However, since 86% of the fish consumed in Hong Kong is imported, the commercial contribution from these ponds is not generally considered significant (Anon. 1988a). Ecologically, however, these ponds are important in providing year round feeding sites for many species of herons (Ardeidae), especially in winter when the ponds are completly drained for fish harvesting. At that time, they can serve also as high tide roost sites for ducks and waders. However, large areas of these ponds are now being filled in for new developments such as the Tin Shui Wai new town, which will lead to the loss of 500 ha of fish-ponds. Smaller areas have also been lost recently by conversion to open storage areas for car dumps and container parks.

Mudskipper collection

Traditionally, the mudflats on the Hong Kong side of Deep Bay have supported local fishermen harvesting mudskippers, mainly *Boleophthalmus boddarti* which can fetch HK$40·600 g^{-1}. Recently, with the movement of people into the towns to find work, traditional local mudskipper collection has declined but their place has been taken up by fishermen from China who also catch other mangrove-associated fauna, e.g., the mangrove crab (*Scylla serrata*), and the large goboid fish (*Bostrichthys sinensis*).

No detailed work has been done on the amount of mudskippers collected by these fishermen, but it is estimated to be between 2.5–3 kg·fisherman·$^{-1}$day^{-1}, with a maximum of 70 to 80 collectors on the mudflat during spring when mudskipper densities are highest (K.W. Ho pers. comm.).

A crude estimate of the effect of this harvesting on the prey base for birds can be made if certain assumptions are made: i.e., the average weight of a mudskipper = 8 g; each collector catches 2.5 kg of mudskippers$\cdot^{-1}$day; there are on average, 50 collectors on the mudflat mudskipper catching mainly takes place over 60 days from April to June; density of mudskippers = 5$\cdot$m^{-2} area of mudflat = 3.5 km^2

Therefore, 15,625 mudskippers are caught each day, which is equivalent to 937,500 over the main collecting season. Total number of mudskippers on the mudflat is, therefore, 17,500,000. This indicates that approximately 5.4% of the total mudskipper population is being removed from the mudflat during their breeding season, and the individuals taken are the largest, i.e., the breeding adults. Although this is only a crude estimate, it does indicate that the effect of collecting mudskippers at present levels could have a significant effect on the population.

The effect of disturbance caused by the collectors to birds feeding on the mudflat is also potentially severe. Although no counts have been made of the numbers of collectors on the mudflat each year, there is no doubt that over the past seven years, at least, they have been increasing in number each spring when both the mudskipper and bird density is highest. If this is the case, then the number of these collectors must be controlled to avoid serious disturbance to the birds and the mudflat fauna.

THE CASE FOR NATURE CONSERVATION IN DEEP BAY

Flora

The Deep Bay estuary with its high productivity and variety of habitats types, is able to support a great diversity of flora and fauna. The area is unique in having 500 ha of dwarf mangrove swamp (Anon. 1988e), forming the largest area of mangrove in Hong Kong and one of the most extensive along the south China coast. The Deep Bay mangrove community comprises six species: *Acanthus ilicifolius, Aegiceras corniculatum, Avicennia marina, Bruguiera gymnorrhiza, Excoecaria agallocha* and *Kandelia candel.* Although mangroves occur as far north as Japan (*Kandelia candel* at 32°N), the Deep Bay mangal is one of the most northerly locations to support a wide assemblage of typical mangal species of both flora and fauna.

Associated with the intertidal mangroves on the Hong Kong side (and also at Fu Tien, Shenzhen SEZ), are small areas of *Halophila beccarii,* the only place in the territory where this species is found (Hodgkiss and Morton 1978). *Ruppia maritima* has recently been found in the gei wais at Mai Po — the first record for Hong Kong since 1905. Landwards, behind the mangroves, are extensive areas of reed-beds (*Phragmites communis/australis*) located inside the *gei wais.*

Invertebrates

Thirteen invertebrate species have been recorded from Mai Po and Tsim Bei Tsui and which are either new species or new records for the Territory (Lee 1993). With more research in the area, it is likely that other species will be discovered.

Mammals

Until recently, little work had been done on the mammals of Hong Kong, even on such basics as their distribution and abundance. Thus, it is not surprising that sometimes new species for the Territory are recorded, such as the Javan mongoose at Mai Po in November 1989.

Other mammals recorded from the Hong Kong side of Deep Bay include the pangolin (*Manis pentadactyla*), Chinese leopard cat (*Felis bengalensis*), crab-eating mongoose (*Herpestes urva*), seven-banded civet (*Viverricula indica*) and various Muridae, e.g.; bandicoot rat (*Bandicota indica*), Soricidae, e.g., house shrew (*Crocidura murinus*), and bats such as *Pipistrellus abramus*. Otters (*Lutra lutra chinensis*), were quite common in the bay until the 1950s but now are seen only occasionally. The last record was in January 1991, when footprints were found in a drained *gei wai* at Mai Po. The Pearl River Delta of which Deep Bay is part, is also the type locality for the Chinese white dolphin (*Sotalia (Sousa) chinensis*), and this is seen occasionally as far upstream in the Shenzhen River as Lok Ma Chau.

Birds

Over 270 birds have been recorded from the Deep Bay/Mai Po area. Most of these are regarded as being common, but twelve are listed by Collar and Andrews (1988) as either being rare or threatened (Table 1). Of these, Deep Bay supports 1% or more of the world population of four of these species. It supports the second largest known group of Saunders' gulls (*Larus saundersi*) (Melville, in prep.) and one sixth of the world population of the black-faced spoonbill (*Platalea minor*) (Kennerley 1990). Of the total number of species recorded, only some 44 (approximately 16%) are 'residents', most others being migrants or winter visitors.

Table 1
Threatened bird species recorded from the Deep Bay area.
(Wv= winter visitor, Ss= spring/summer visitor, Owv= occasional winter visitor, Sam= Spring/autumn migrant).

Species	Scientific name	Status	Recent highest count	Estimated % of the world population using Mai Po
Dalmatian pelican	*Pelecanus crispus*	Wv	37 (declining)	0.5%
Chinese egret	*Egretta eulophotes*	Ss	< 5	0.9%
Oriental white stork	*Ciconia boyciana*	Owv	120	5.0%
Black-faced spoonbill	*Platalea minor*	Wv	65	17.0%
Baikal teal	*Anas formosa*	Owv	–	–
Baer's pochard	*Aythya baeri*	Wv	–	–
Imperial eagle	*Aquila heliaca*	Wv	–	–
Spoon-billed sandpiper	*Eurynorhyncus pygmaeus*	Sam	< 10	0.2%
Asiastic dowitcher	*Limnodromus semipalmatus*	Sam (exceptional)	> 340	6.80%
Spotted greenshank	*Tringa guttifer*	Sam	< 60	6.0%
Saunder's gull	*Larus saundersi*	Wv (2nd largest wintering population)	> 160	16.0%
Relict (Mongolian) gull	*Larus relictus*	Owv	–	–

Results from ringing studies at Mai Po since 1979 have shown, increasingly, the importance of the Deep Bay/ Mai Po area as a staging ground for migrant birds, especially shorebirds, to build up fat stores to provide fuel for the next stage of their migration (Melville 1981a and unpublished data). For example, the Curlew sandpiper (*Calidris ferruginea*) breeds in arctic Siberia and spends the non-breeding season along the coasts of southeast Asia and Australia. Movements of ringed birds (Table 2) have revealed that birds passing through Hong Kong in spring come from as far south as Tasmania.

Table 2
Movements of ringed birds to/from Mai Po, Hong Kong.
(After Melville 1981, 1987, 1988, 1989 and unpublished data).

Species	Ringed	Controlled/Recovered	Distance (km)
Red-necked stint	Mai Po	Tasmania	8,010
Calidris ruficollis	Mai Po	SE Australia	7,467
	Tasmania	Mai Po	8,021
Curlew sandpiper	Mai Po	NW Australia	4,790
Calidris ferruginea	Tasmania	Mai Po	8,021
	SE Australia	Mai Po	7,479
	SE Australia	Mai Po (San Tin)	7,200
	SE Australia	Mai Po	7,446
	NW Australia	Mai Po	4,750
Black-tailed godwit			
Limosa limosa	Mai Po	N Vietnam	840
Bar-tailed godwit	Mai Po	NW Australia	4,569
Limosa lapponica			
Redshank	Mai Po	S China	136
Tringa totanus			
Terek sandpiper	Mai Po	W Malaysia	2,531
Xenus cinereus	Mai Po	NW Australia	4,582
	Mai Po	NE China	
Grey-rumped sandpiper	NW Australia	Mai Po	4,684
Heteroscelus brevipes			
Bluethroat	Mai Po	NE China	2,053
Erithacus svecia			
Great reed warbler	Mai Po	Japan	2,384
Acrocephalus arundinaceus	Mai Po	Japan	2,808
	Mai Po	Japan	2,362
	Japan	Mai Po	2,384

Various formulae have been developed to estimate the flight range of birds and these have been discussed by Davidson (1984). However, they do provide an indication of likely range such as with the estimated flight ranges of Curlew sandpipers from Mai Po based on estimated fat loads (Table 3). In spring, the birds would be able to fly to the Bo Hai, northeast China (a distance of about 2600 km), which is known to be another important staging post for shorebirds. The autumn weight suggest that birds might be able to fly direct to northwest Australia (a distance of about 4750 km) but, at present, it is not known whether they do this, or use an intermediate staging post.

Table 3

A, Estimates of the flight range of the Curlew sandpiper *Calidris ferruginea* from Mai Po, Hong Kong and B, parameters used for estimates.

A. Formula used	Estimated spring weights	Flight range (Autumn range)	(Kms) from max. weight
McNeil and Cadieux (1972)	3469	3340	4726
Summers and Waltner (1979)	4074	3863	5904
Davidson (1984)	3396	3252	4944
Greenwalt (1975)	3414	3177	4830

B. Parameters used for estimates

	Spring weight	Autumn weight*	max. weight range
Arrival weight	48.6 g	61.4 g	48.4 g
Departure weight	76.5 g	92.3 g	92.3 g
Flight speed	75 kph	75 kph	75 kph

* Minimum autumn weights (n = 4) are considerably higher than those in spring. Fat-free body mass is unlikely to vary to such an extent seasonally and thus the estimates for 'max. weight range' are likely to be more realistic for autumn birds.

The ability of birds, such as Curlew sandpipers, to put on fat quickly put on fat at rich feeding areas is essential to their survival. If feeding areas such as Deep Bay are lost, the implications are far wider than just within Hong Kong.

In recent years, following the establishment and management of the World Wide Fund Hong Kong Mai Po Marshes Nature Reserve and consequent habitat improvement, the habitat has become a moulting ground used by both shorebirds and yellow-nib ducks (*Anas poecilorhyncha*).

Deep Bay is also an important wintering ground for over 80 species of waterbirds, as shown by counts made in mid-winter by the Hong Kong Bird Watching Society since 1979 (Fig. 3). Possible factors affecting the results of these annual counts have been reviewed by Melville (1989c). The counts show an upward trend for most bird groups counted. Factors which are likely to have contributed to this increase include a total ban on hunting in Hong Kong since 1981, the destruction of wetlands in adjacent areas of China, and possibly changes in food supply in Deep Bay due to increasing organic pollution.

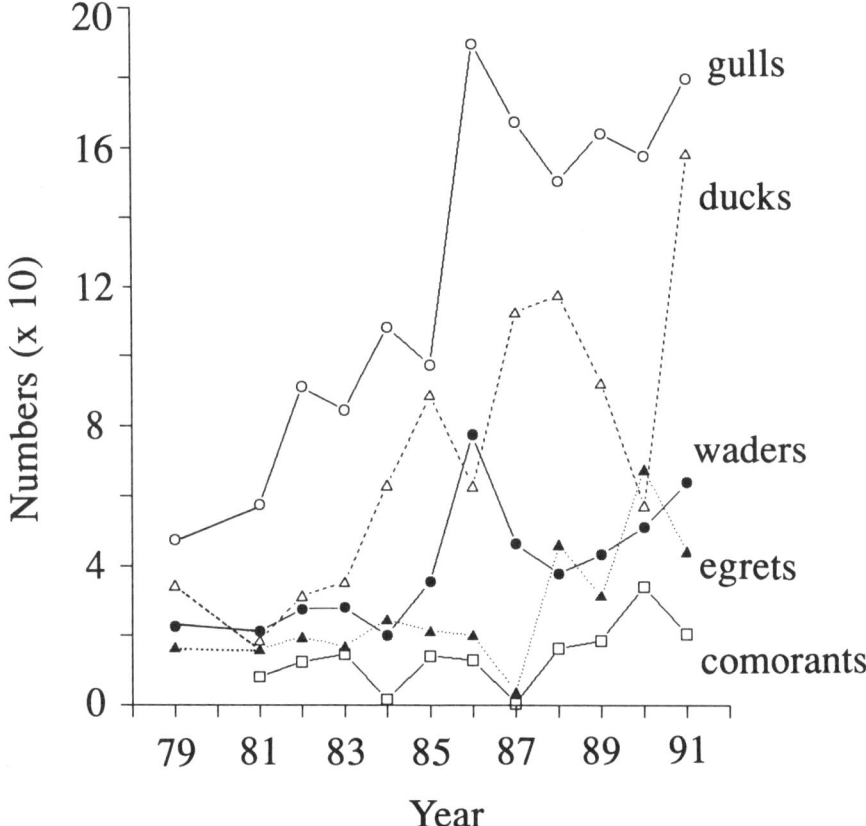

Fig. 3. Results of mid-January waterfowl counts in Deep Bay. (Data courtesy of the Hong Kong Bird Watching Society).

There is no doubt that the Deep Bay/Mai Po area qualifies for inclusion in the 'List of Wetlands of International Importance' under the Ramsar Convention on Wetlands of International Importance Especially as Waterfowl Habitat, with respect to at least three categories (Appendix 1). The area also is deserving of protection under the Bonn Convention on the Conservation of Migratory Species of Wild Animals, especially since two species regularly occuring in the area are listed in Appendix 1 of that Convention (Appendix 2). Hong Kong is a party to both Conventions, but so far the government has taken no formal steps to gain international recognition for the site.

PROTECTED AREAS IN DEEP BAY

Currently, there are four Sites of Special Scientific Interest (SSSIs) located on the Hong Kong side of Deep Bay, and one National Nature Reserve, Fu Tien, on the Shenzhen SEZ side (Fig. 4).

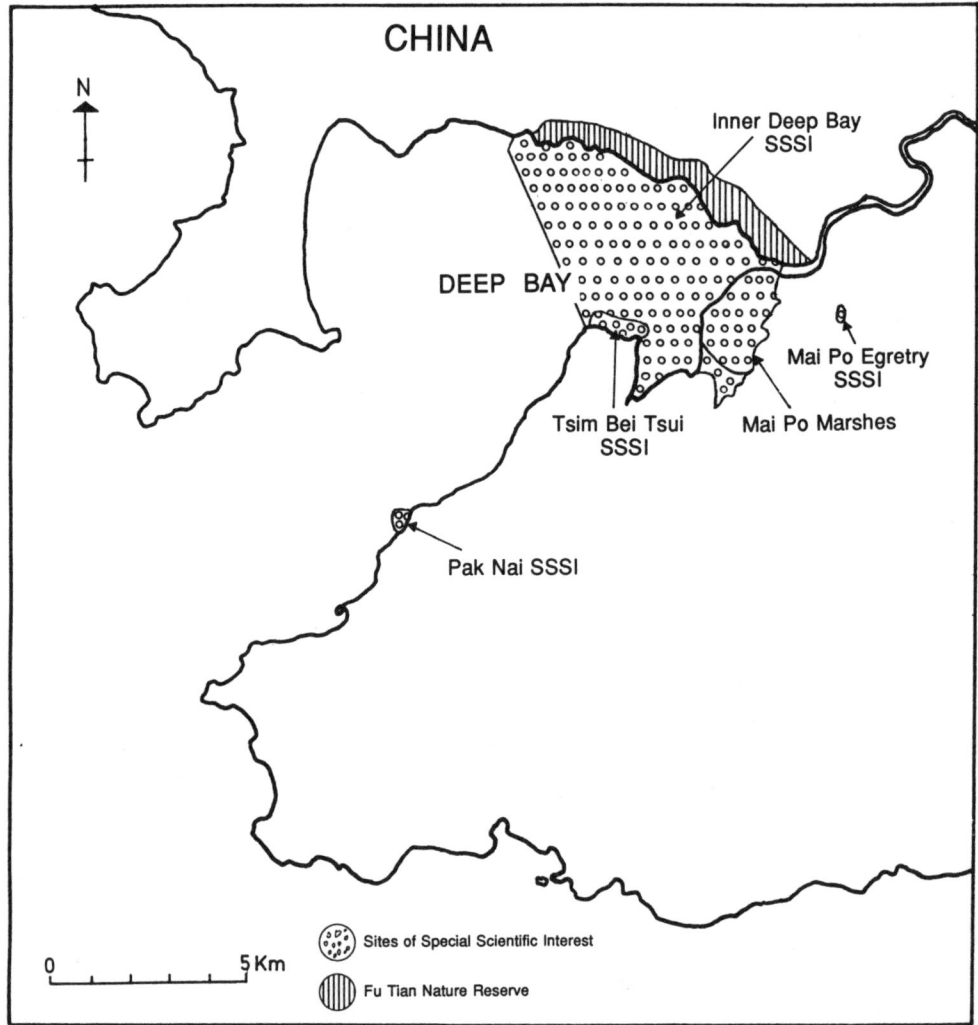

Fig. 4. Areas of conservation importance in Deep Bay.

Fu Tien Nature Reserve

Of 300 ha, Fu Tien is similar in size to Mai Po but is much longer and narrower. There are six species of mangrove found here, with *Avicennia marina* being the most common. The mangroves are relatively short, reaching a maximum height of only 4.5 m. Disturbance to the inland section of the mangrove has halted succession, so that only the pioneer community is present. Recently, reserve management has included attempts to diversify the mangal by introducing species from Hainan, but these have largely been unsuccessful.

Fish and shrimp-ponds make up half of the reserve area and inland is a 200 m buffer strip of agricultural land. Due to the growth of Shenzhen, there are strong development pressures on the reserve. Already, large areas have been lost for an industrial park and more could be lost from other proposed developments, e.g., widening of the Shenzhen River (Anon. 1988a).

The SSSIs located on the Hong Kong side of Deep Bay are:

Mai Po Marshes

This site covers an area of 381 ha and consists of 172 ha of dwarf mangrove and 209 ha of traditional and modified *gei wais* and fish ponds. The area is important in providing a rich feeding site for migrating and resident birds, as well as nesting habitat for a number of species. The area is currently being managed by the World Wide Fund for Nature Hong Kong, whose education centre is visited by over 30,000 people each year, thus providing an important recreational and educational service for the people in Hong Kong, as well as visitors from abroad (Melville 1989a).

Pak Nai

The 15.5 ha sandpit site was formerly an important high tide roost site for wintering gulls and tern in the Deep Bay area but, due to disturbance, is now seldom used.

Mai Po village egretry

This *'feng shui'* wood covering about 53 ha, has been the site of a mixed breeding colony of five heron species since the early 1970s. Several hundred nests have been counted in recent years at the site.

Tsim Bei Tsui

This consists of a 4.8 ha little egret woodland breeding colony, and a 2.1 ha mangrove community. The latter holds the mangrove *Bruguiera gymnorrhiza* which is now becoming rare in Hong Kong, and is the only known habitat in the territory for the large mangrove pulmonate snail *Ellobium polita*.

Inner Deep Bay

This 2300 ha site contains a variety of habitats from shallow water to intertidal and estuarine mudflat. It is important for the large area of dwarf mangrove, and the highly productive mudflat which provides a feeding ground for large numbers of visiting and resident birds. The site also supports a variety of organisms of economic importance, e.g., oysters, fish, crabs and shrimps, and scientific value, e.g., the pulmonate snail (*Ellobium polita*) and the crab (*Chiromanthes maipoensis*).

Although all of these sites have been designated SSSIs, this was only an administrative status and did not confer any legal protection on them. Following the revision of the Town Planning Ordinance, these SSSIs have now become a designated land-use and only a limited number of activities are allowed inside them. Nonetheless, in view of the increasing pressure from development, their physical integrity cannot be assured. Another problem that these sites face, is that (with the exception of Mai Po) there is unrestricted access and, they are therefore prone to disturbances. The need to prevent further deterioration of water quality in Deep Bay is also of paramount importance for all of the SSSIs. Those species which inhabit tidal areas are directly dependent upon the bay while herons and egrets at the Mai Po and Tsim Bei Tsui SSSIs, are dependent on the bay to a large extent for feeding.

THREATS TO DEEP BAY

The preceding sections have illustrated the biological, economic and educational importance of Deep Bay. However, 28 major development projects have been identified in the bay's catchment (Fig. 5) which will increase the threat to the area from water pollution, habitat loss and disturbance (Anon. 1988c). Unless steps are taken to reduce these threats and/or implement mitigatory measures, the enviroment will be severely damaged and its international conservation importance lost.

Water quality in Deep Bay is presently poor and it suffers regular and severe oxygen depletion. In 1986–87, two-thirds of the water quality samples taken from Inner Deep Bay recorded less than 50% oxygen saturation and, of these, half showed less than 10% saturation. The major sources of pollution entering Deep Bay waters are from agricultural wastes, domestic sewage and industrial effluents (Table 4). Domestic sources of pollution are largely due to untreated sewage entering Deep Bay, while agricultural sources are mainly due to pig and chicken rearing. Industrial pollutants come from a variety of sources, such as bleaching and dyeing, paper manufacturing, laundries, etc. Seventy-five percent of the total pollution load is from the Shenzhen River and the Yuen Long-Kam Tin catchments enters directly into Inner Deep Bay — the most environmentally significant part of the bay (Anon. 1988a).

Table 4
Sources of pollution loading into Deep Bay in terms of biological oxygen demand (EPA 1985).

	Sources of pollution loading (kg·day^{-1})			
	Domestic	Agricultural	Industrial	Total
Hong Kong	13,162 (21%)	47,006 (75%)	2,581 (4%)	62,470 (100%)
Shenzhen SEZ	6,239 (79%)	1,075 (14%)	576 (7%)	7,890 (100%)

The concentration of faecal bacteria in Deep Bay water is extremely high, averaging 1281·100 mL^{-2} in 1987–88 (Lam 1989) and is due to the input of untreated agricultural and domestic wastes. Such high levels may constitute a health risk because the oysters at Lau Fau Shan are frequently found to be contaminated (Leung *et al.* 1975).

There is, presently, little reliable data on the amounts of toxic metals in the bay's water, but that available suggests that there is insignificant contamination at the moment. However, with the increasing urban and industrial development of the catchment, and projects such as the Tsang Tsui Pulverised Fuel Ash (PFA) lagoons and the Western New Territories (WENT) landfill, there could be more risk of direct discharge and leachate entering Deep Bay.

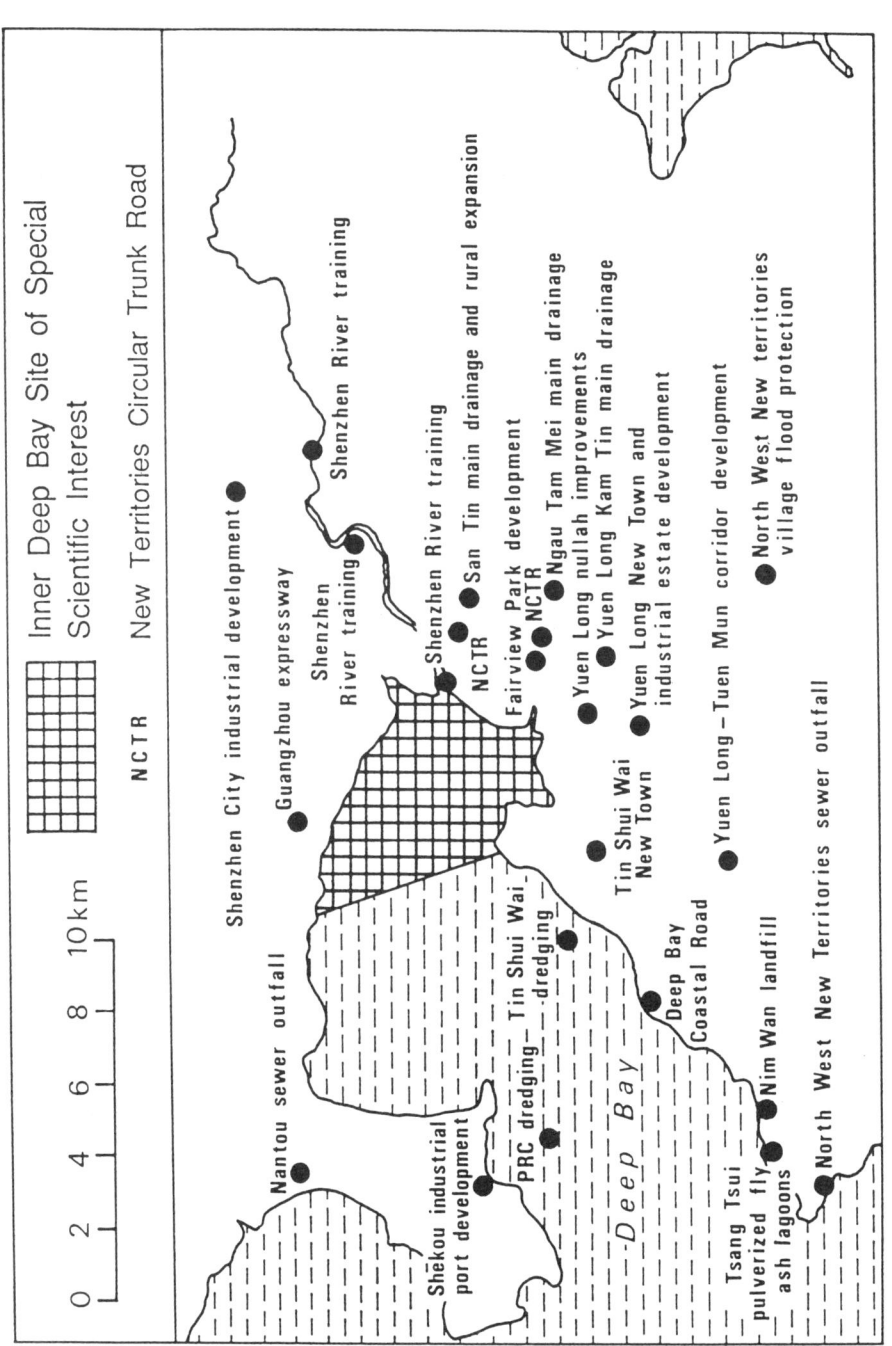

Fig. 5. Present and proposed developments in the Deep Bay area (After Irving and Morton 1988).

Certain organic macropollutants are presently found in significant concentrations in the waters and sediments of Deep Bay such as alpha-BHC, gamma-BHC (Lindane) and DDE which is a metabolite of DDT degradation, but DDT itself has not been found (Anon. 1988d).

If attempts are not made to reduce the levels of pollution entering Deep Bay, the marine flora and fauna will be severely impoverished, oyster contamination will become even more serious and algal blooms will occur more often, placing further demands on the dissolved oxygen levels in the water.

Deep Bay receives a large sediment input from the Pearl River, in the order of 2700 tonnes per day (Anon. 1988a). Due to this input, there is unlikely to be any overall change in the sediment regime of the bay due to development in the immediate catchment. However, two development projects in Inner Deep bay could increase sediment levels locally (the Shenzhen River Flood Control Project and the Yuen Long-Kam Tin main drainage works), and reduce primary production by 10–20% in the short term. This could then have knock on effects through the food chain but the overall effects are not certain. Perhaps more important are the possible effects on water movements in the bay due to those projects which will result in increased flushing rates. This also may result in increased pollution of Inner Deep Bay.

Much of the traditional landscape and areas of ecological and economic importance in Deep Bay are under threat from the increasing land-use changes in the catchment due to urban development and associated infrastructure.

Among the development projects which have been identified as potentially damaging the traditional Deep Bay landscape are:

— creation of the drainage channels for Yuen Long-Kam Tin, Ngau Tam Mei and Tin Shui Wai which will destroy 5% of the remaining 500 ha of mangrove. Four further projects may also reduce the area of coastal mangrove, e.g., Shenzhen River Works;

— at least eleven separate projects will involve the loss of fish-pond area from the 1400 ha remaining;

— stage II of the Shenzhen River Works could destroy some of the Mai Po Marshes SSSI;

— development of the Guangzhou expressway and the New Territories circular road will disturb and encroach upon the Fu Tien Nature Reserve and Mai Po Egretry SSSI;

— the overall disturbance in Inner Deep Bay from the various projects, especially river and drainage projects, could adversely affect feeding and breeding areas used by resident and migrant birds.

— The possible impacts of these projects on the Deep Bay environment are shown in Figure 6.

It has been suggested that although the Deep Bay catchment does contribute significantly to food production in Hong Kong, it may not be appropriate to retain agricultural activities such as fish-ponds and arable lands, as an economic priority (Anon. 1988b). From an economic point of view, these statements may be true; ecologically, they would be damaging to the wildlife in the catchment. Many of the tens of thousands of waterbirds which winter in Deep Bay are either wholly or partially dependent on the draining of *gei wais* and fish-ponds for their food supply. Also, many of the heron species breeding at the Mai Po and Tsim Bei Tsui SSSIs, collect more than 50% of their food for the young chicks from around the fish-ponds. Further loss of fish-pond area would then increase the winter mortality of birds around Deep Bay, and decrease chick survival during the breeding season (Young, in prep.).

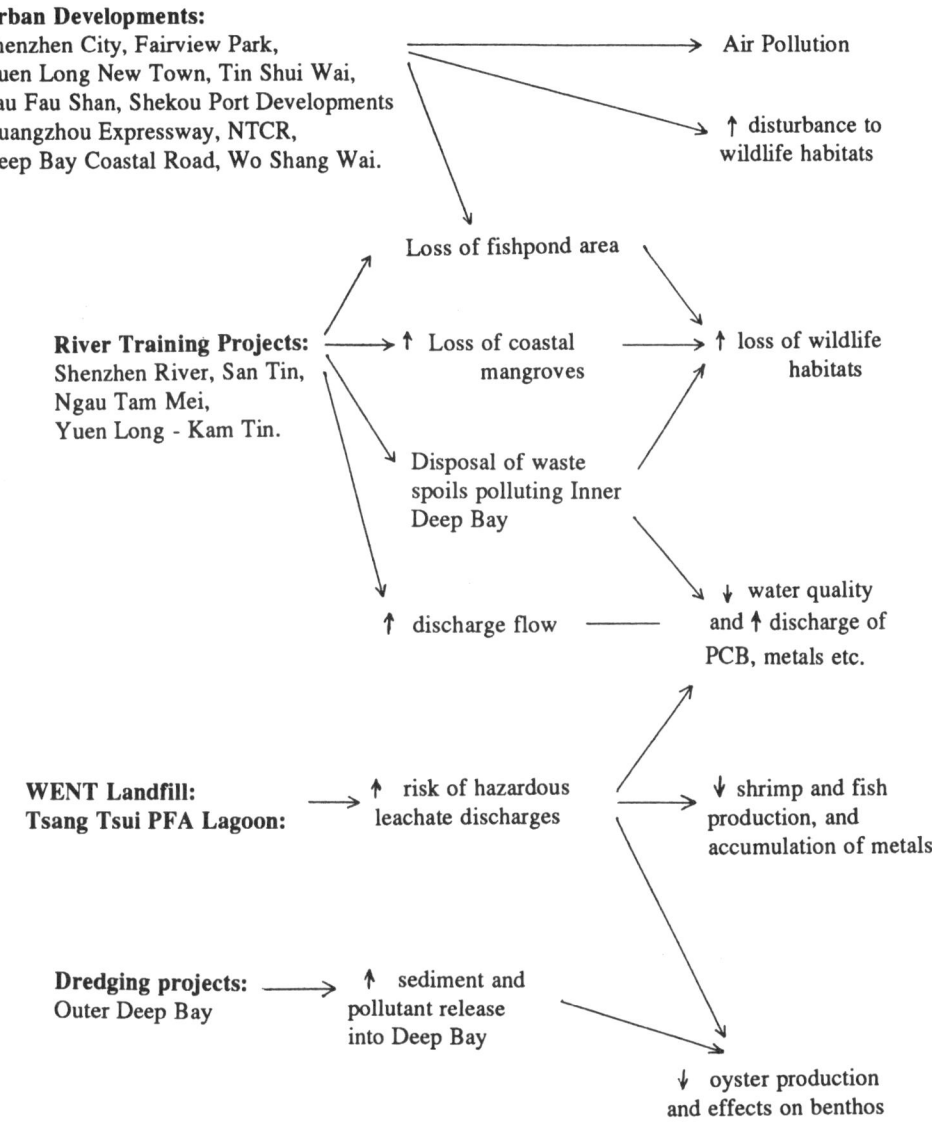

Fig. 6. The possible impact of various projects on the Deep Bay environment.

PROTECTION MEASURES FOR DEEP BAY

The Deep Bay environment is important primarily as an international site for its birdlife and its mangrove community. Traditional land-use in the area also represents a landscape that is fast disappearing from the territory. If pollution into the bay and habitat loss is not controlled, then the value of the site for both scientific research and conservation will be lost, as well as its educational and recreational significance.

A recent published report commissioned by the Hong Kong government on enviromental management of Deep Bay (Anon. 1988c), proposed recommendations to protect the importance of the site at the institutional, policy and project levels. It also put forward specific objectives for the quality of the water and air in and over the bay.

On the institutional level, the report proposed the setting up of a joint Hong Kong, Guangdong and Shenzhen committee to direct environmental protection in Deep Bay, and a Deep Bay Enviromental Management Committee in Hong Kong to oversee the Hong Kong side of the work. It was recommended that these groups be advised on particular scientific and conservation issues by experts from within and outside government. Some steps have now been taken to implement this and the first meeting of the Joint Group was held in September 1990, but to date, there has been no involvement by NGOs.

At the policy level, the report recommends the Hong Kong government to establish objectives already stated as part of the report, on water and air quality, conservation and other enviromental issues. The recommended water quality objectives are given in Appendix 3. The Enviromental Protection Department is currently finalising the Deep Bay report.

The report also asks the government to urgently consider the following:

— designating a protected 'buffer' zone around Inner Deep Bay, with the most sensitive sites having a restricted area status;

— developing a conservation management plan for the five SSSIs and 'buffer' zone areas, with the possibility of managing all these areas as an integrated unit;

— designating Inner Deep Bay as a Ramsar site;

— producing codes of practice for developers on dredging and construction impacts in Deep Bay.

On the project level action, the report suggests that for all proposed and future projects in Deep Bay, there should be either a full Enviroment Impact Assessment (EIA) for major projects, or other project studies and recommendations on specific mitigation measures. It goes on to list specific projects where a full EIA should be produced such as the Shenzhen River flood control works and the Yuen Long-Kam Tin main drainage scheme, as well as other projects where partial EIAs are needed.

In January 1991, the Town Planning Ordinance was amended in order to extend its provisions to control land use throughout the territory. Interim development permission areas have been gazetted and all the land areas immediately adjacent to the inner Deep Bay SSSI are now subject to planning control. This should halt the previous widespread filling of fish ponds for conversion to open storage areas and should provide a strong weapon for controlling land use. In particular, it should play an important role in conserving the Deep Bay area.

The Hong Kong government is also undertaking various projects which should lead to an improvement of water quality in Deep Bay. These include the implementation of the livestock waste control regulations, which prohibit the discharge of untreated livestock wastes into water courses. Controls should be effective throughout the Hong Kong catchment by the end of 1993, but the programme has slipped considerably in the past year.

Another project of importance, is the construction of the northwest New Territories trunk sewer which will take both domestic and industrial effluent from much of the Yuen Long/Tin Shui Wai area and discharge it into Urmston Road off Tuen Mun. However, the Yuen Long treatment plant will continue to discharge into Deep Bay.

Model studies indicate that there should not be any significant movement of effluent from the outfall into Deep Bay. This sewer will also collect leachate from the Nim Wan landfill site. A study is about to start to investigate ways of controlling and/or treating sewage discharge from the smaller villages within the catchment area.

The present activities by the Hong Kong government to control land use and improve water quality in the bay are to be applauded. However, there is still a tendency for engineers to ride roughshod over enviromentalists when designing drainage projects such as with the Kam Tin/Yuen Long main drainage project, and this is likely to lead to increasing conflicts. It is essential that the Draft Deep Bay Guidelines developed by the Enviromental Protection Department be finalised and implemented without delay.

The Deep Bay/Mai Po area is a wetland of international importance. The Hong Kong and Shenzhen authorities face a major challenge to ensure that this site retains its ecological character for future generations — both of humans and wildlife.

ACKNOWLEDGEMENTS

Many thanks to M.L. Chalmers, Phoebe Chan, Ho Kin-Wing, Peter Kennerley and Michael Lau Wai-Neng for providing valuable information concerning Deep Bay during the writing of this paper.

REFERENCES

Anonymous 1988a. *Environment Review: Deep Bay Management. Working paper 1: Status of Deep Bay*. Hong Kong: Environmental Resources Ltd.
Anonymous 1988b. *Deep Bay Integrated Environmental Management. Key Issues*. Hong Kong: Environmental Resources Ltd.
Anonymous 1988c. *Environment Review: Deep Bay Management. Executive Summary*. Hong Kong: Environmental Resources Ltd.
Collar, N.J. and Andrew, P. 1988. *Birds to Watch: The ICBP World Checklist of Threatened Birds*. Cambridge: International Council for Bird Preservation.
Davidson, N.C. 1984. How valid are flight range estimates for waders? *Ringing and Migration* 5:49–64.
Greenwalt, C.H. 1975. The flight of birds. *Transactions of the American Philosophical Society* 65:1–67.
Enviromental Protection Agency. 1985. *The Deep Bay Water Monitoring Study*. Report no. EPA/tm38/85. Hong Kong: Government Press.
Hodgkiss, I.J. and Morton, B. 1978. *Halophila beccarii* Ascherson (Potamogetanaceae) — a new record from Hong Kong, with notes on other *Halophila* species. *Memoirs of the Hong Kong Natural History Society* 13:28–32.
Irving, R. and Morton, B. 1988. *A Geography of the Mai Po Marshes*. Hong Kong: World Wildlife Fund Kong Kong.
Kennerley, P.R. 1990. A review of the status and distribution of the Black-faced Spoonbill. *Hong Kong Bird Report 1989*, 116–25.
Lam, C.W.Y., Lui, P.H. and Kong, M.F. 1989. *Marine water quality in Hong Kong*. Enviromental Protection Department Report no. EP/TR/2/89. Hong Kong: Government Press.
Lee, L.H.Y. 1988. Agr*iculture and Fisheries. Annual Departmental Report 1987–88*. Hong Kong: Government Press.
Leung, C., Shortridge, K.F., Morton, B. and Wong, P.S. 1975. The incidence of faecal bacteria in the tissues of the commercial oyster *Crassostrea gigas* Thunberg 1793 correlated with

the hydrology of Deep Bay, Hong Kong. *Proceedings of the Pacific Science Association Special Symposium on Marine Sciences,Hong Kong 1973*, (ed. B. Morton) 114–27.Hong Kong: the Government Printer.

McNeil, R. and Cadieux, F. 1972. Numerical formulae to estimate flight range of some North American shorebirds from fresh weight and wing length. *Bird Banding* 43:107–13.

Melville, D.S. 1981a. Spring measurements, weights and plumage status of *Calidris ruficollis* and *C. ferruginea* in Hong Kong. *Wader Study Group Bulletin* 33:18–21.

Melville, D.S. 1988b. Report on Bird Ringing in Hong Kong in 1987. *Hong Kong Bird Report 1987*, 56–63.

Melville, D.S. 1989a. Hong Kong. In *A Directory of Asian Wetlands* (ed. D.A. Scott), 283-94. Gland: IUCN.

Melville, D.S. 1989b. Report on Bird Ringing in Hong Kong in 1988. *Hong Kong Bird Report 1988*, 63–72.

Melville, D.S. 1989c. Wintering waterfowl in Deep Bay, Hong Kong. In *Wetlands and Waterfowl Conservation in Asia* (ed. D. Parish and R.C. Prentice), 180–7. Kuala Lumpur: Asian Wetland Bureau/International Waterfowl Research Bureau.

Melville, D.S. and Morton, B. 1983. *Mai Po Marshes*. Hong Kong: World Wildlife Fund Hong Kong.

Melville, D.S., Lee, S.Y.and Cheng, W.W. 1989. Some aspects of the management of the Mai Po Marshes, Deep Bay, Hong Kong. In *Wetlands and Waterfowl Conservation in Asia* (ed. D. Parish and R.C. Prentice), 94–104. Kuala Lumpur: AWB/IWRB.

Phillips, D.J.H., Ho, C.T. and Ng, L.H. 1982. Trace elements in the Pacific Oyster in Hong Kong. *Archives of Environmental Contamination and Toxicology* 11:533–7.

Summers, R.W. and Waltner, M. 1979. Seasonal variations in the mass of waters in southern Africa, with special reference to migration. *Ostrich* 50:21–37.

APPENDIX 1

Three criteria used to designate 'wetlands of international importance' under the terms of the Ramsar convention apply to Inner Deep Bay.

Criterion 1: The site should be 'a particularly good example of a specific type of wetland characteristic of its region.' The dwarf mangrove community at Mai Po and Fu Tien is such an example, being an ecosystem that is being destroyed or drastically changed in much of southern China. It is the largest remaining mangal in mainland China.

Criterion 2: The designated site should support an appreciable number of individuals of rare, vulnerable or endangered species or sub-species. Table 1 shows that Deep Bay supports such rare species and that some occur in significant numbers, that is, greater than 1% of their world population.

Criterion 3: The site should 'regularly support more than 20,000 waterfowl.' Deep Bay regularly supports larger numbers of waterfowl particularly in winter. In January 1991, nearly 49,000 waterfowl were counted using the bay.

Therefore, Inner Deep Bay is eligible as a Ramsar site on at least three counts. Other current Ramsar sites have been designated on only one criterion.

APPENDIX 2

How Inner Deep Bay is eligible for protection under the Bonn Convention.

Of the Bonn Convention's two Appendices, Appendix 1 lists endangered migratory species while Appendix 2 lists species of unfavourable conservation status. For the former Appendix, Article 3.4(a) of the Convention states that Range States of Appendix 1 migratory species should endeavour:

— 'to conserve and, where feasible and appropriate, restore those habitats of the species which are of importance in removing the species from extinction.'

Inner Deep Bay supports two Appendix 1 species, Saunders' gull (*Larus saundersi*) and the Dalmatian pelican (*Pelecanus crispus*).

Three other Appendix 1 species also occur regularly in inner Deep Bay, the Chinese egret (*Egretta eulophotes*), the Oriental white stork (*Ciconia boyciana*) and the Relict (Mongolian) gull (*Larus relictus*).

POLLUTION
PLENARY PAPER

The Marine Biology of the South China Sea
(ed. B. Morton). Proceedings of the First
International Conference on the Marine
Biology of Hong Kong and the South China Sea,
Hong Kong, 28 October – 3 November 1990.
Hong Kong: Hong Kong University Press, 1993.

BIOMONITORING OF MARINE HEAVY METAL POLLUTION AND ITS APPLICATION IN HONG KONG WATERS

P.S. Rainbow

School of Biological Sciences, Queen Mary and Westfield College, University of London, Mile End Road, London E1 4NS, UK

ABSTRACT

Biomonitors provide a time-averaged measure of the abundance of bioavailable metals in local aquatic habitats, without the disadvantages associated with the quantification of such metals in water or underlying sediments. The employment of biomonitors to assess the extent and significance of heavy metal pollution in coastal waters is well established in temperate European and North American waters, using now classic sentinel organisms such as the mussel *Mytilus edulis*. Research in Hong Kong has pioneered the extension of these techniques into tropical and subtropical waters. Initial work concentrated on the bivalves *Saccostrea cucullata* and *Crassostrea gigas* (Ostreidae), and the green mussel *Perna viridis* (Mytilidae). Subsequently, comparative biomonitoring work has included barnacles, particularly *Balanus amphitrite* (Cirripedia), and the littoral strandline beach-hopper *Platorchestia platensis* (Amphipoda). Hong Kong has proved to be an ideal site for the development of biomonitoring procedures with local geographical and temporal variation along gradients of heavy metal bioavailability. In turn, biomonitoring has provided information to Hong Kong authorities on previously unrecognized sources of metal contamination, particularly at Chai Wan Kok.

THE BIOMONITORING OF HEAVY METAL POLLUTION

Metals included under the loose and usually undefined heading of 'heavy metals' are all potentially toxic to living organisms, often at a very low threshold availability. Many of these metals are essential for life in small doses, whereas no such essential metabolic role has been described (perhaps as yet) for the others (non-essential metals). The term 'trace metal' may be used synonymously with 'heavy metal', but alternatively may be restricted to essential heavy metals only. The biochemistry and ultimately toxic action of heavy metals are dependent on their chemical properties, and therefore definitions of heavy metals on weight criteria alone fall down because of the ineligibility of the larger Group IA and IIA metals. Although high in atomic weight, these latter metals are chemically similar to the biologically 'major' metals sodium, potassium, calcium and magnesium in the same groups of the Periodic Table. The major metals are very stable as the hydrated ion in aqueous media and do not have the tendency of heavy metals to form bonds with sulphur and nitrogen, for example in protein molecules. The major metals are, therefore, biochemically distinct from heavy metals. Strictly it is necessary to resort to chemical criteria to categorize metals, for example in terms of Lewis acids and bases (see Nieboer and Richardson 1980). Nevertheless the term heavy metal is used here for convenience, but heavy metals are pedantically defined as metals with ions falling into categories B and Borderline of Nieboer and Richardson (1980). In practice the term refers here to the essential metals chromium, cobalt, copper iron, manganese, molybdenum, nickel, tin, vanadium and zinc; and the non-essential metals cadmium, gold, lead, mercury and silver.

Heavy metals, whether essential or not, are toxic and therefore of potential danger to life in aquatic habitats receiving metal-rich effluents. It is thus necessary for marine biologists and government scientists to make an assessment of toxic metal pollution in local coastal waters, for example to measure variation in time and/or space. It is much more difficult to assess the toxicological effects on local marine communities which are directly attributable to enhanced metal levels (see Langston 1990), but comparative measures of local metal pollution do provide an important basis for explanation of differences between the biological communities of coastal habitats. Moreover, such toxic metals may be accumulated by local marine organisms and therefore represent the ultimate source of metals in seafood with potential impacts on human health.

Three measures of toxic metal levels in coastal habitats are available— namely concentrations in waters, sediments and biota. The measurement of dissolved metal levels presents analytical problems. Such concentrations are typically low, often at the limits of detectability of analytical techniques, and liable to inadvertent contamination during collection and analytical handling. Dissolved concentrations vary greatly in time, for example with tidal cycle, season, freshwater run off, etc., and therefore repeated measurements are required over extended periods to provide a representative picture of metal pollution. Such sampling programmes are expensive in terms of laboratory chemicals and time. More importantly, however, measurements of dissolved metal provide an assessment of total metal present, not of that portion of the total metal which is bioavailable— that is available for uptake and accumulation by local biota. It is the bioavailable fraction that is potentially toxic and therefore of ecotoxicological relevance.

The use of sediments overcomes some of these disadvantages. Heavy metals tend to accumulate in sediments, particularly in those which are organically rich. Sediment metal concentrations are therefore high, easily measured and not liable to be affected by contamination. Moreover, sediments offer an element of time integration, overcoming the worst effects of temporal variability of metal availability. However, metal accumulation by sediments is affected by characteristics of the sediment which might well vary between the sites being compared, the most important characteristics being particle size and organic carbon content (Luoma 1990). Crucially again, however, the metal concentration measured is that of total (not bioavailable) metal, and there is no simple method of relating the two (Luoma 1983, 1989; Tessier and Campbell 1987).

Heavy metals are significantly accumulated by many marine organisms to very high tissue and hence body concentrations. Such concentrations are easily measured, not liable to contamination and provide a time-integrated measure of metal supply, over weeks, months or even years according to the organism under examination. Most importantly, the metal accumulated by organisms is a time-integrated measure of the supply of bioavailable metal, as opposed to total metal, i.e., the fraction of direct ecotoxocological relevance is measured directly. Organisms used to quantify heavy metal bioavailability are now employed widely, particularly in temperate waters, and are variously termed bio-indicators, sentinel organisms and biomonitors (Phillips 1990). The term bio-indicator is, however, also used for an organism indicating particular hydrological conditions by its mere presence or absence. The term biomonitor is used here.

Individual biomonitors respond differentially to different sources of bioavailable metal— for example in solution, sediment-bound or incorporated in food. Thus, to make an assessment of total metal bioavailability in a marine habitat it is necessary to make use of a suite of biomonitors covering all sources. Such a requirement can be used to advantage, for the comparative use of different biomonitors might allow identification of the particular source of a contaminant metal (Phillips and Rainbow 1988; Phillips 1990).

Species used as biomonitors need to fulfil several criteria (Phillips 1977a, 1980, 1990; Bryan et al. 1980), these being as follows:

— sessile or sedentary, therefore representative of the study area
— abundant, long lived, easy to identify and sample at all times of the year, and large enough to provide sufficient tissue for analysis
— hardy, tolerating high levels of metals and large ranges of salinity, and permitting laboratory studies of metal kinetics
— a net accumulator of metal with a simple correlation between metal concentration in tissues (body) and average ambient bioavailable metal concentration over a recent time period; this correlation should be the same at all study sites.

Clearly, not all marine organisms fulfil these criteria. Most critically, a biomonitor should be a strong net accumulator of the metal in question. Marine organisms in fact fall along a gradient of metal accumulation strategies from regulators (maintaining a constant body concentration of metal across a wide range of ambient metal bioavailabilities), through partial regulators, weak net accumulators and strong net accumulators, (Phillips and Rainbow 1989; Rainbow and White 1989; Rainbow 1990; Rainbow et al. 1990; Depledge and Rainbow 1990). It is important to know the metal accumulation strategy of a chosen biomonitor, incorporating a knowledge of metal kinetics including rates of uptake and loss, thereby defining the period over which the biomonitor reflects the ambient metal bioavailability (Phillips 1990). Such data are collected more easily in laboratory experiments (Rainbow and White 1989; Rainbow et al. 1990) but should be complemented by field data (Phillips 1990), such as those from transplant experiments (Okazaki and Panietz 1981).

Phillips (1990) has reviewed the development and present status of heavy metal biomonitoring in estuaries and coastal waters using macroalgae and invertebrates. Early uses of biomonitors quantified radionuclides (^{54}Mn, ^{60}Co and ^{65}Zn) released from the Hanford reactors via the Columbia River into Californian coastal waters in the early 1960s. Thereafter, various biomonitoring programmes for heavy metals have been undertaken, particularly in northern temperate waters such as those of the United States (Goldberg et al. 1983; Phelps et al. 1985), Canada (Bourget and Cossa 1976; Popham and D'Auria 1982), the UK (Preston et al. 1972; Bryan et al. 1980, 1985; Langston 1986) and Scandinavia (Phillips 1977b, 1978; Lyngby and Brix 1987). Biomonitoring work is now carried out worldwide (see Phillips 1991) including Australia (Ayling 1974; Klumpp and Burdon-Jones 1982; Talbot 1985a, 1985b), New Zealand (Nielsen and Nathan 1975), South Africa (Watling and Watling 1976), and (albeit to a lesser extent) in the tropics such as in Thailand (Phillips and Muttarasin 1985) and Brazil (Lima et al. 1986).

Biomonitoring organisms most commonly used in temperate waters are mussels, oysters, tellinid bivalves and fucoid macroalgae (Phillips 1990).

Mussels of the genus *Mytilus* are particularly important in biomonitoring programmes over wide areas (Goldberg 1975), involving for example *Mytilus edulis* in the United States (Goldberg et al. 1983), Canada (Bourget and Cossa 1976; Popham and D'Auria 1982), Scandinavia (Phillips 1977b, 1978; Lyngby and Brix 1987), the UK (Bryan et al. 1985; Langston 1986) and elsewhere in western Europe (De Wolf 1975; Theede et al. 1979); *Mytilus galloprovincialis* in the Mediterranean (Capelli et al. 1978) and the Adriatic (Crisetig et al. 1984); *Mytilus edulis planulatus* in Australia (Ritz et al. 1982, Coleman et al. 1986); and *Mytilus californianus* in the western United States (Gordon et al. 1980 Smith et al. 1986).

Oysters of the genera *Ostrea*, *Crassostrea* and *Saccostrea* have been used as biomonitors: for example in the UK *O. edulis* (Bland et al. 1982; Bryan et al. 1985) and *C. gigas* (Boyden and Phillips 1981); in the United States *C. virginica* (Zaroogian et al. 1979; Okazaki and Panietz 1981; Phelps et al. 1985) and *C. gigas* (Okazaki and Panietz 1981); in Australia *C. gigas* (Ayling 1974; Thomson 1982), *S. commercialis* (Ward 1982), *S. cucullata* (Talbot 1985b), and *S. echinata* (Denton and Burdon-Jones 1981); in New Zealand *S. glomerata* (Nielsen and Nathan 1975); in South Africa *O. edulis*, *C. gigas* and *C. margaritacea* (Watling and Watling 1976); in Brazil *C. brasiliana* (Lima et al. 1986) and in Thailand *S. cucullata* (Brown and Halley 1982). It is necessary to beware of confusion in oyster nomenclature and it is likely that some of the species named in the genera *Crassostrea* and *Saccostrea* are in fact synonymous (Stenzel 1971; Ahmed 1975).

Tellinid bivalves include *Scrobicularia plana* and *Macoma balthica* used in extensive biomonitoring studies in Britain (Bryan and Uysal 1978, Bryan et al. 1980, 1985; Langston 1986). *Macoma balthica* has also been introduced into San Francisco Bay where it is therefore available for biomonitoring work (Cain and Luoma 1985).

In addition, fucoid seaweeds have been used widely for biomonitoring, for example in Britain (Preston et al. 1972; Bryan and Hummerstone 1973; Morris and Bayle 1975, Bryan et al. 1985; Langston 1986) and in the United States (Seeliger and Edwards 1977).

In the design of a biomonitoring programme, it is important to use more than one biomonitor to ensure coverage of the various possible sources of bioavailable metal. Of the above biomonitors, mussels and oysters, as suspension feeding lamellibranch bivalves, would be expected to accumulate metals from solution and from small suspended particles including phytoplankton and detritus. Tellinids are deposit feeders sucking up superficial sediments via the inhalant siphon, thereby obtaining much of their accumulated metal from the sediment. Fucoid seaweeds, unless in contact with sediments, would obtain all accumulated metals from solution. Of other biomonitors, barnacles obtain metals from water and suspended food particles (Phillips and Rainbow 1988, Chan *et al.* 1990), nereid polychaetes from food and the interstitial solution of the sediments through which they move, and infaunal deposit-ingesting worms from interstitial solution and from ingested sediment particles. Shorehoppers (talitrid amphipods) (see Rainbow *et al.* 1989) appear to obtain most accumulated metal from their food source— cast-up strandline algae (Rainbow 1992).

MARINE HEAVY METAL POLLUTION IN HONG KONG

Although relatively little marine biomonitoring work has been carried out in the tropics as opposed to temperate waters (Phillips 1991), much of the pioneering tropical work has been carried out in Hong Kong.

Wong and colleagues in the 1970s investigated the effect of iron ore tailings on the local coastal environment at the base of Ma On Shan in the southwest corner of Tolo Harbour (Wong and Li 1977; Wong *et al.* 1978; Wong *et al.* 1979). Iron ore from the Ma On Shan iron mine was crushed and separated, and the solid waste dumped along the coast of Tolo Harbour north of Tai Shui Hang village (Wong *et al.* 1978) near the present position of the Hang On estate, an area clearly much altered in recent years by reclamation and development.

Wong and Li (1977) measured the local metal contamination of the littoral bivalve *Paphia* sp. (possibly a misidentification of *Tapes* sp.?). Concentrations of iron and manganese were elevated in the tissues of *Paphia* sp. from the area of the iron-ore tailings dump, with no evidence for raised bioavailability of cadmium, copper, lead or zinc. Metal levels in the littoral ocypodid crab *Scopimera intermedia* from the same area similarly indicated increased bioavailability of iron and manganese, and possibly very locally of copper, lead and zinc (Wong *et al.* 1978). *Scopimera intermedia* fits fewer of the criteria listed above for a heavy metal biomonitor and has less potential than *Paphia* spp. for future work. Wong *et al.* (1979) turned to two local littoral marine algae— *Chaetomorpha brychagona* and *Enteromorpha crinita*, comparing Tolo Harbour samples against samples from Stanley Bay (*C. brychagona*) and Shek O (*E. crinita*), both on the south coast of Hong Kong island. Again, iron and manganese bioavailabilities were clearly raised near Ma On Shan, with some evidence for elevated lead and possibly zinc bioavailability locally (Wong *et al.* 1979). *C. brychagona* had higher accumulated concentrations of iron, manganese, lead and zinc than *E. crinita*.

Wong *et al.* (1982) used another green alga, the sea lettuce *Ulva lactuca*, in a biomonitoring investigation of copper, iron, lead and zinc further afield in Tolo Harbour in comparison to levels at Shek O and Stanley Bay. *U. lactuca* was collected at four littoral sites between Sha Tin and Tai Po in July 1978, in a farsighted attempt to establish a basis for future comparison, after the then proposed establishment of heavy industry locally. The metal contents of the Tolo Harbour algae were even then generally higher than those of the two south Hong Kong Island sites. A new study of the metal contents of Tolo Harbour *U. lactuca* (if present) would certainly be of interest, and would fulfil the original aims of Wong *et al.* (1982) to establish an historical basis for comparison.

Phillips (1979) carried out the first large scale biomonitoring survey in Hong Kong waters, investigating the heavy metals cadmium, copper, iron and zinc. Phillips (1979) used the oyster *Saccostrea glomerata* from 54 sites (sampled in March/April 1978) extending from Deep Bay in the northwest, the Soko Islands and Po Toi in the south, to Long Ke Wan and Chek Chau in the east. *S. glomerata* (or *Crassostrea glomerata*), if correctly identified, may well be synonymous with *Crassostrea commercialis, S. commercialis* and/or *S. cucullata* (see Phillips 1979). The Hong Kong oyster will be referred to as *Saccostrea cucullata* hereafter (Morton, personal communication). The soft tissues of the oyster exhibited a remarkable ability to accumulate heavy metals, and the oyster appeared to be a reliable and significant biomonitor.

The study conducted in spring 1978 revealed elevated metal bioavailabilities in several areas, and exemplified the use of statistical analysis to confirm relationships between known areas of contamination and high metal concentrations in the oysters (Phillips 1979). Statistical analysis of profiles of heavy metal contamination split the samples into two groups— one of oysters collected from the area of Victoria Harbour, and a second group consisting of all the remainder. Oysters from Victoria Harbour had significantly raised concentrations of copper, iron and zinc but not cadmium. It was possible to subdivide the second group further but with less clear definition. Of the two subgroups thereby produced, those oysters with higher metal concentrations tended to have been collected form inlets whilst the rest included samples from more offshore sites with high flushing rates (Phillips 1979). Thus, it was concluded that Victoria Harbour was contaminated by anthropogenic sources of copper and zinc (industrial and domestic discharges), particularly in the eastern part of the harbour. There was little evidence of a west-east gradient of heavy metal bioavailability as might be expected if the Pearl River constituted a major heavy metal source or caused changes in metal bioavailability indirectly via salinity variations (Phillips 1979). The Pearl River has a major effect on the hydrology of Hong Kong waters, creating a west-east gradient of hydrological parameters such as salinity and turbidity (Morton and Wu 1975). This study of Phillips (1979) first indicated the particular suitability of Hong Kong waters as a test site for marine biomonitoring techniques, given the range of environments from metal-polluted to clean. This suitability allowed Phillips and Yim (1981) for example to make a comparative evaluation of oysters, mussels and sediments as monitors of trace metals.

Another oyster in Hong Kong water, the Pacific oyster *Crassostrea gigas*, has also been analysed for heavy metals, particularly because it is cultured for human consumption and represents a dietary source of toxic metals (Wong *et al.* 1981; Phillips *et al.* 1982). *C. gigas* is cultured in Deep Bay in north-west Hong Kong, some of the oysters being transferred there temporarily from waters of the People's Republic of China (Phillips *et al.* 1982). Such transfers tend to confuse biomonitoring studies on local oysters, but metal analyses of the oyster soft tissues are required in order to monitor potential dangers to human health, for example via the local market at Lau Fau Shan. Lead and zinc levels in Deep Bay *C. gigas* soft tissues were considered low in comparison to published data from elsewhere in the world, and copper concentrations were not unusual (Phillips *et al.* 1982). Cadmium and mercury concentrations were, however, clearly enriched in the oysters (Phillips *et al.* 1982), but given the import of exogenous oysters into the Deep Bay oyster beds, this cannot be taken *per se* as concrete biomonitoring evidence for raised cadmium and mercury bioavailabilities in Deep Bay.

Saccostrea cucullata (as *S. glomerata*) collected from Deep Bay in the extensive study of Phillips (1979) fell into the higher metal concentration subgroup of the larger grouping of oysters. Deep Bay *S. cucullata* did not exhibit the high copper, iron and zinc concentrations of those from Victoria Harbour but did show some evidence of raised cadmium concentrations (Phillips 1979). Thus oysters from Deep Bay have provided some evidence of moderately raised cadmium bioavailability there. This increased bioavailability may be a feature of the low salinity in Deep Bay, cadmium bioavailability being increased with decreased salinity (Phillips 1980), rather than being indicative of a local cadmium point source.

The comparative study of Phillips and Yim (1981) involved the first use of a mussel— *Septifer virgatus* (misidentified as *S. bilocularis* in the original publication) in a biomonitoring survey in Hong Kong. Phillips and Yim (1981) reported data on copper, iron and zinc concentrations in *Saccostrea cucullata* (as *S. glomerata*) (20 sites, August 1978), *S. virgatus* (23 sites, March/April and August 1978) and surficial sediments (210 sites September 1975 to February 1977). The oyster data showed good agreement with the sediment data, both confirming the high copper and zinc biovailabilities in Victoria Harbour already indicated by the high concentrations of copper and zinc in the Victoria Harbour oysters collected in April 1978 (Phillips 1979). *S. virgatus* also exhibited high concentrations of copper in Victoria Harbour, but only a minor enrichment of zinc, suggesting a degree of regulation of zinc by the mussel (Phillips and Yim 1981). There was no parallelism between iron concentrations in sediments, oysters and mussels. The oysters contained higher accumulated heavy metal concentrations than the mussels, and Phillips and Yim (1981) concluded that *S. virgatus* is much less suitable as a biomonitor. Phillips (1989) reported previously unpublished results of this study indicating that the greatest concentrations of nickel were also found in Victoria Harbour samples.

More recently, attention (Phillips 1985; Chan 1988a; Phillips and Rainbow 1988; Chan *et al.* 1990) has turned to another mussel, the green-lipped mussel *Perna viridis*— also known as *Mytilus viridis* and *M. smaragdinus* amongst other names (see Siddall 1980). Phillips (1985) evaluated the capacity of *P. viridis* to act as a biomonitor for cadmium, copper, lead, mercury and zinc in Hong Kong coastal waters. He concluded that *P. viridis* is an excellent biomonitor for copper and lead. The mussels from Victoria Harbour exhibited high copper and lead concentrations in agreement with general trends already detected (Phillips 1979; Phillips and Yim 1981) of metal contamination in the harbour from sewage and industrial discharges. The mussels from Rennies Mill in Junk Bay contained extremely high concentrations of lead.

Phillips (1985) concluded, however, that more studies were needed to assess the use of *Perna viridis* for mercury and cadmium biomonitoring. Soft tissue concentrations of mercury were below a detection limit of 0.11 µg g^{-1} dry weight in all mussel samples except those from Kwun Tong and North Point (eastern Victoria Harbour), suggesting some mercury biomonitoring ability on the part of the mussel. In the absence of major sources of cadmium in Hong Kong waters (Phillips 1979), it was not possible to provide a rigorous test of the suitability of *P. viridis* as a biomonitor of cadmium, although the mussel cadmium data (Phillips 1985) did agree generally with earlier biomonitoring data (Phillips 1979; Phillips and Yim 1981).

Soft tissue concentrations of zinc in the mussels varied only over a 2-fold range, compared to ranges of 43-fold for lead, 33-fold for copper and 21-fold for cadmium (Phillips 1985). Since earlier biomonitoring work (Phillips 1979; Phillips and Yim 1981) had shown high zinc bioavailability in Victoria Harbour, this narrow range of zinc concentrations in the mussel indicated an ability on the part of *Perna viridis* to partially regulate body zinc concentrations (Phillips 1985), as indicated previously for *Septifer virgatus* (Phillips and Yim 1981). The partial regulation of body zinc by *P. viridis* was also apparent in later field monitoring studies (Chan 1988a; Phillips and Rainbow 1988; Chan *et al.* 1990), and was confined experimentally by Chan (1988b). Such partial regulation reduces the suitability of the green-lipped mussel for use as a biomonitor for zinc.

The biomonitoring surveys of Chan (1988a), Phillips and Rainbow (1988) and Chan *et al.* (1990) involved collections of *Perna viridis* from 14 to 16 sites in April 1986, with follow-up collections by Chan (1988a) in January 1987. The April 1986 mussel data confined high bioavailabilities of copper, lead and zinc (despite the low mussel zinc concentration range) in Victoria Harbour, and produced new evidence for high chromium, nickel and silver bioavailabilities therein, probably again from domestic and industrial point discharges (Phillips and Rainbow 1988; Chan *et al.* 1990).

Lead and zinc bioavailabilities were high in Junk Bay (Rennies Mill and Hang Hau), and Chai Wan Kok (north of Tsing Yi) emerged to have staggeringly high bioavailabilities of chromium and copper, and high bioavailabilities of lead, nickel and silver (Phillips and Rainbow 1988; Chan *et al.* 1990). There was some evidence of raised cadmium bioavailability to the mussel at Rennies Mill and at Reef Island (The Brothers) north of Lantau, the latter possibly as a low salinity effect. *Perna viridis* collected form Tolo Harbour in April 1986 were almost invariably to the bottom to rank order lists of sites in decreasing order of heavy metal concentration (Phillips and Rainbow 1988; Chan *et al.* 1990).

Chan (1988a) additionally reported on manganese and iron concentrations in *Perna viridis*. Manganese bioavailabilities were somewhat raised north of Lantau and in Tolo Harbour (Chan 1988a), possibly in reflection of the relatively high sediment load of the water. Iron concentrations in the mussels in April 1986 were also highest in sites north of Lantau (Chan 1988a). Iron in fact was the only metal to show differences in concentrations in the mussels between the two sampling periods (April 1986, January 1987), those in April 1986 being the higher (Chan 1988a). Chan (1988a) suggested that iron concentrations may be affected by the discharge of the Pearl River with associated sediment load, the mussels in western waters showing the greatest seasonal differences in iron concentrations.

An important aspect of the April 1986 biomonitoring survey (Phillips and Rainbow 1988; Chan *et al.* 1990) was that it was a comparative study of the biomonitoring capabilities of mussels and barnacles, again making use of the ideal nature of Hong Kong waters for such studies, given the well-defined asymmetry of contaminating discharges (Phillips 1989). Three littoral barnacle species were used in order to cover sites of a range of wave action and tidal current conditions, i.e., *Balanus amphitrite* (sheltered), *Tetraclita squamosa* (moderate wave action and current) and *Capitulum mitella* (strong wave action and current) (Wu 1973). It is not possible to compare absolute body metal concentrations between barnacle species, but it is possible to make intraspecific comparisons of accumulated metal concentrations down a rank order of sites containing the same barnacle species and to make comparisons interspecifically between ranks, for example by Spearman's rank correlation (Phillips and Rainbow 1988; Chan *et al.* 1990).

In such studies it is also important to allow for the effect of body size on accumulated metal concentration. In the case of the mussels, tissues were pooled from mussels of similar sizes from each site and mean metal concentrations compared by analysis of variance (ANOVA) after logarithmic transformation (Phillips and Rainbow 1988). In the case of the smaller barnacles, the largest available barnacles were collected at each site and 10 dissected bodies analysed individually. For the small *B. amphitrite*, 15 bodies were pooled in each of 10 samples. Body dry weights (or mean body dry weights when pooled) were regressed linearly against metal concentration after double logarithmic transformation, and log regression lines compared by analysis of covariance (ANCOVA). ANCOVA tests for significant differences in y (metal concentration) between regression lines having allowed for differences in x (dry weight), with the precondition that the slopes of the lines do not differ. Such data may for convenience be expressed in terms of estimated metal concentrations of bodies of a particular barnacle species from several sites at a standardized body dry weight (Phillips and Rainbow 1988; Chan et al. 1990). Examination of the significance of the regression lines produced confirmed that this procedure was necessary for each metal, to eliminate an observed effect of barnacle body size on accumulated metal concentration at at least one site.

Results for the three barnacle species and the green-lipped mussel showed remarkable agreement in the rank ordering of sites, despite absolute differences in accumulated metal concentrations. The barnacle data similarly showed high chromium, copper, lead, nickel, silver and zinc bioavailabilities in Victoria Harbour, high lead and zinc bioavailabilities in Junk Bay and high chromium, copper, lead, silver and nickel bioavailabilities at Chai Wan Kok (Phillips and Rainbow 1998; Chan et al. 1990). Metal bioavailabilities to barnacles were low in Tolo Harbour in 1986. As in the case of the mussels, there was no strong contamination gradient for the bioavailability of cadmium to barnacles in Hong Kong waters, and as a probable consequence the correlation of site rankings between barnacles and mussel broke down.

The general agreement between heavy metal contamination profiles for the barnacles and mussels in Hong Kong waters implies that the relative bioavailabilities of the metals are similar to the three barnacle species and the mussel (Phillips and Rainbow 1988). All are microphagous filter feeders moving feeding and respiratory currents across permeable surfaces, with the likelihood therefore that dissolved metal and metal associated with small suspended particles (food) are the dominant sources of bioavailable metal. It is likely that the range of particle sizes filtered by *Perna viridis* would approach most closely that taken by *Balanus amphitrite*, for *Tetraclita squamosa* and *Capitulum mitella* would be expected to take large zooplanktonic particles (Anderson 1981). Since the different barnacle species probably feed on different sized particles yet show close agreement in identifying areas of high metal bioavailability, it seems that dissolved metals are the major source of bioavailable metals to the barnacles, and by extension to the mussels (Chan et al. 1990).

Rainbow and Smith (1992) made collections of barnacles from some of the same sites in April 1989, allowing an investigation of changes in metal bioavailabilities in the period 1986 to 1989. Collections were make at the same time of year, thus eliminating possible seasonal effects, and all barnacle samples were treated identically to those of Chan et al. (1990). In a direct comparison with 1986 data, *Balanus amphitrite* were collected from three sites in Tolo Harbour and from the 1986 metal hotspots at Chai Wan Kok and Hang Hau (Junk Bay). An additional collection of *B. amphitrite* was made at Tsim Bei Tsui (Deep Bay). In 1986 the Victoria Harbour sites at Kowloon Pier and Queen's Pier were typified by barnacles preferring wave action (*Tetraclita squamosa* and *Capitulum mitella*), but by 1989 there appeared to have been a change to more sheltered conditions with *B. amphitrite* replacing *C. mitella* (Rainbow and Smith 1992). This change might be a reflection of changed tidal flow with harbourside development, or may be associated with a reduction of wash from shipping.

The major temporal changes in metal bioavailabilities detected by Rainbow and Smith (1992) concern the three sites in Tolo Harbour, these being Ma Liu Shui (named Sha Tin by Chan *et al.* 1990), Wu Kai Sha and Tai Po Kau. The bioavailabilities to *Balanus amphitrite* of cadmium, chromium, copper and zinc had increased significantly at all three sites between 1986 and 1989; that of lead was raised at two of the three sites; and that of silver at one of the three sites (Rainbow and Smith, 1992, Table 1). Metal bioavailabilities to *B. amphitrite* at Chai Wan Kok were still high but were unchanged between the surveys for copper, nickel and silver; increased in 1989 for cadmium and even further increased in 1989 for chromium and lead, with no change for zinc (Rainbow and Smith 1992).

At Hang Hau, metal bioavailabilities to *B. amphitrite* were raised in 1989 for lead (from an already high 1986 base), cadmium chromium, cobalt, nickel and silver but decreased for copper and zinc (Rainbow and Smith 1992). 1989 metal bioavailabilities at Tsim Bei Tsui were very high for zinc but not atypical for other metals. In Victoria Harbour, *Tetraclita squamosa* indicated raised bioavailability of nickel and possibly of lead between 1986 and 1989, a rise and fall in zinc bioavailability on either side of the harbour, and alternately a fall and no change in copper bioavailability on either side (Rainbow and Smith, 1992).

This biomonitoring study using *Balanus amphritrite* has the potential to be ongoing and provide valuable comparative data in time, particularly in Tolo Harbour, whether its fate brings further making habitat degradation or an improvement in water quality.

Recently, beach-hoppers specially, the temperature talitrid amphipod crustacean *Orchestra gammarellus* have been proposed (Rainbow *et al.* 1989) as pragmatic biomonitors of copper and zinc in temperate coastal habitats. Rainbow (1992) has extended this study to Hong Kong in an evaluation of the potential of the widespread cosmopolitan beach-hopper *Platorchestia platensis* as a tropical biomonitor for coastal copper and zinc. *P. platensis* showed no variation in copper or zinc concentration over the moult cycle and exhibited proportional net accumulation of each metal when feeding on metal-enriched food (cast-up seaweed). Body copper and zinc concentrations in amphipods from 4 sites (Wu Kai Sha, Hoi Ha Wan, Cape d'Aguilar and a Mai Po gei wai) in April 1989 showed significant differences by ANCOVA, and Rainbow (1992) concluded that *P. platensis* is a suitable biomonitor for copper and zinc in Hong Kong.

In the case of copper, the amphipods from Wu Kai Sha (Tolo Harbour) had significantly raised copper concentrations, with no significant differences between the other sites (Table 2). The Wu Kai Sha amphipods also exhibited significantly raised zinc concentrations, whilst the Mai Po amphipods had significantly reduced zinc concentrations (Table 2), possibly as a result of feeding on mangrove leaf litter as opposed to cast-up seaweed (Rainbow 1992). The 1989 amphipod data therefore complement the 1989 barnacle data for Tolo Harbour (Rainbow and Smith 1992), indicating raised copper and zinc bioavailabilities.

Thus, there has been a considerable amount of marine biomonitoring work in Hong Kong, which has proved an ideal site for the development of biomonitoring procedures with local geographical and temporal variation along gradients of heavy metal bioavail-

Table 1

Heavy metal concentrations ($\mu g\ g^{-1}$) in Tolo Harbour *Balanus amphitrite* (0.004 g standardized mean body weight) with 95% confidence limits (CL) as estimated from best fit double log regressions. Samples showing any common letter in the 1989 ANCOVA column for each meal are not significantly different. In the 1986 ANCOVA column P is the probability that there is no significant difference between 1989 and 1986 metal concentrations (NS P > 0.05) (adapted from Rainbow and Smith 1992).

	1989			1986		
	Metal Conc.	ANCOVA CL		Metal Conc.	ANCOVA CL	
Cadmium						
Ma Liu Shui	22.1	27.5, 17.8	A	2.1	2.5, 1.7	P < 0.001
Wu Kai Sha	16.2	21.2, 12.4	B	4.4	5.0, 3.9	P < 0.001
Tai Po Kau	11.9	39.0, 3.6	C	4.1	7.4, 2.2	P < 0.001
Chromium						
Tai Po Kau	15.7	36.8, 0.7	A	0.22	6X10^8, 0	P < 0.05
Ma Liu Shui	11.6	16.6, 8.1	A	3.4	4.1, 2.8	P < 0.001
Wu Kai Sha	7.2	8.8, 5.9	B	1.8	2.3, 1.4	P < 0.001
Copper						
Ma Liu Shui	1808	1988, 1643	A	116	136, 98.5	P < 0.001
Wu Kai Sha	658	760, 570	B	213	244, 187	P < 0.001
Tai Po Kau	239	596, 95.7	C	142	235, 86.2	P < 0.001
Zinc						
Ma Liu Shui	14818	17410, 12612	A	3214	3578, 2887	P < 0.05
Wu Kai Sha	9865	11261, 8642	B	4671	5201, 4195	P < 0.001
Tai Po Kau	5677	30137, 1069	C	4381	5620, 3415	P < 0.01
Lead						
Ma Liu Shui	15.5	19.5, 12.3	A	1.7	2.4, 1.3	P < 0.001
Wu Kai Sha	11.1	23.0, 5.3	A	9.2	12.1, 7.0	NS
Tai Po Kau	10.6	411, 0.27	A	3.8	8.3, 1.7	P < 0.05
Silver						
Ma Liu Shui	3.3	4.0, 2.6	A	1.1	1.6, 0.8	P < 0.001
Wu Kai Sha	2.1	2.8, 1.6	B	1.8	2.2, 1.4	NS
Tai Po Kau	1.4	20.0, 0.1	B	1.7	4.3, 0.7	NS
Nickel						
Ma Liu Shui	11.6	14.2, 9.5	A	12.2	13.8, 10.9	*
Wu Kai Sha	9.3	13.8, 6.3	A	8.4	10.7, 6.7	NS
Cobalt						
Wu Kai Sha	3.6	4.6, 2.9		2.9	3.7, 2.2	NS

* Slopes significantly different

Table 2

Copper and zinc concentrations (µg g^{-1} dry weight) with 95% confidence limits (CL) in *Platorchestia platensis* (standardized 5 mg dry weight) as estimated from best fit double log regressions of metal concentration against dry weight. Samples showing any letter in the ANCOVA column are not significantly different (adapted from Rainbow 1992).

	Metal conc.	95% CL	ANCOVA
Copper			
Wu Kai Sha	130	227, 74.6	A
Hoi Ha Wan	71.4	81.2, 62.7	B
Cape d'Aguilar	71.1	92.3, 54.7	B
Mai Po	61.4	75.2, 50.1	B
Zinc			
Wu Kai Sha	354	583, 354	A
Hoi Ha Wan	199	242, 163	B
Cape d'Aguilar	193	284, 131	B
Mai Po	109	141, 83.7	C

ability. Work in Hong Kong has confirmed the suitability of the oyster *Saccostrea cucullata*, the mussel *Perna viridis*, the barnacle *Balanus amphitrite* and the beach-hopper *Platorchestia platensis* as heavy metal biomonitors in the tropics. In turn, in addition to confirming the metal contamination of Victoria Harbour, biomonitoring has allowed the recognition of previously unrecognized sources of metal contamination, for example at Chai Wan Kok and at Hang Hau (Junk Bay). Biomonitoring is now also sounding warnings of increasing bioavailable metal pollution in Tolo Harbour with the potential for ecotoxicological consequences.

Future heavy metal biomonitoring programmes in Hong Kong should use a suite of biomonitors in order to identify different bioavailable sources of toxic metals. Such biomonitoring programmes should probably include the bivalves *Saccostrea cucullata* and *Perna viridis* (with a qualification against zinc biomonitoring in this latter case), and the barnacle *Balanus amphitrite*. In sites of more wave action *Tetraclita squamosa* should replace *B. amphitrite*. *Platorchestia platensis* needs particular experience for correct identification but does have potential as a biomonitor of the more common metals copper and zinc. As inhabitants of soft shores, paphiid Venus-shells of their genera *Paphia* and *Tapes*, especially *T. philippinarum*, have biomonitoring potential and deserve thorough investigation, as do tropical deposit-feeding tellinid bivalves.

A comprehensive study of possible seaweed biomonitors is also needed. Littoral macroalgae in Hong Kong have the disadvantage of seasonal variations in abundance, but green algae of the genera *Chaetomorpha*, *Enteromorpha* and *Ulva* and brown seaweeds like *Sargassum heimiphyllum* may be of some biomonitoring value.

Marine biologists in Hong Kong have the opportunity to continue the pioneering assessment of the suitability of tropical coastal heavy metal biomonitors, and moreover have a role to play in protecting local marine resources.

ACKNOWLEDGEMENTS

I am grateful to Professor Brian Morton for the opportunity to present this paper and to the British Council for funding. My thanks go to collaborative researchers with whom I have worked on Hong Kong material, particularly David Phillips, Geoff Moore, Laurie Chan, Jason Weeks and Brian Smith.

REFERENCES

Ahmed, M. 1975. Speciation in living oysters. *Advances in Marine Biology* 13:357–97.

Anderson, D.T. 1981. Cirral activity and feeding in the barnacle *Balanus perforatus* Bruguiere (Balanidae) with comments on the evolution of feeding mechanisms in thoracican cirripedes. *Philophical Transactions of the Royal Society of London* B. 291:411–49.

Ayling, G.M. 1974. Uptake of cadmium, zinc, copper, lead and chromium in the Pacific oyster, *Crassostrea gigas*, grown in the Tamar River, Tasmania. *Water Research* 8:729–38.

Bland, S., Ackroyd, D.R., Marsh, J.G. and Millward, G.E. 1982. Heavy metal content of oysters from the Lynher estuary, U.K. *The Science of the Total Environment* 22:235–41.

Bourget, E. and Cossa, D. 1976. Mercury content of mussels from the St. Lawrence estuary and the northwestern Gulf of St. Lawrence, Canada. *Marine Pollution Bulletin* 7:237–9.

Boyden, C.R. and Phillips, D.J.H. 1981. Seasonal variation and inherent variability of trace elements in oysters and their implications for indicator studies. *Marine Ecology–Progress Series* 5:29–40.

Brown, B.E. and Holley, M.C. 1982. Metal levels associated with tin dredging and smelting and their effect upon intertidal reef flats at Ko Phuket, Thailand. *Coral Reefs* 1:131–7.

Bryan, G.W. and Hummerstone, L.G. 1973. Brown seaweed as an indicator of heavy metals in estuaries in south-west England. *Journal of the Marine Biological Association of the United Kingdom* 53:705–20.

Bryan, G.W., Langston, W.J. and Hummerstone, L.G. 1980. The use of biological indicators of heavy metal contamination in estuaries. *Occasional Publications of the Marine Biological Association of the United Kingdom* 1:1–73.

Bryan, G.W., Langston, W.J. Humerstone, L.G. and Burt, G.R. 1985. A guide to the assessment of heavy metal contamination in estuaries using biological indicators. *Occasional Publications of the Marine Biological Association of the United Kingdom* 4:1–92.

Bryan, G.W. and Uysal, H. 1978. Heavy metals in the burrowing bivalve *Scrobicularia plana* from the Tamar estuary in relation to environmental levels. *Journal of the Marine Biological Association of the United Kingdom* 58:89–108.

Cain, D.J. and Luoma, S.N. 1985. Copper and silver accumulation in transplanted and resident clams (*Macoma balthica*) in South San Francisco Bay. *Marine Enviromental Research* 15:115–35.

Capelli, R., Contardi, V., Fassone, B. and Zanicchi, G. 1978. Heavy metals in mussels (*Mytilus galloprovincialis*) from the Gulf of La Spezia and from the promontory of Portofino, Italy. *Marine Chemistry* 6:179–85.

Chan, H.M. 1988a. A survey of trace metals in *Perna viridis* (L.)(Bivalvia: Mytilacea) from the coastal waters of Hong Kong. *Asian Marine Biology* 5:89–102.

Chan, H.M. 1988b. Accumulation and tolerance of cadmium, copper, lead and zinc by the green mussel *Perna viridis*. *Marine Ecology– Progress Series* 48:295–303.

Chan, H.M., Rainbow, P.S. and Phillips, D.J.H. 1990. Barnacles and mussels as monitors of trace metal bio-availability in Hong Kong waters. In *Proceedings of the Second International Marine Biological Workshop. The Marine Flora and Fauna of Hong Kong and Southern China, Hong Kong, 1986* (ed. B. Morton), 1239–68. Hong Kong: Hong Kong University Press.

Coleman, N., Mann, T.F., Mobley, M. and Hickman, N. 1986. *Mytilus edulis planulatus*: an 'integrator' of cadmium pollution? *Marine Biology* 92:1–5.

Crisetig, G., Cattani, O. and Vivani, R. 1984. Mettali tossici nei mitili dell' alto e medio Adriatico. *Archivio Veterinario Italiano* 35:10–6.

Denton, G.R.W. and Burdon-Jones, C. 1981. Influence of temperature and salinity on the uptake, distribution and depuration of mercury, cadmium and lead by the black oyster *Saccostrea echinata*. *Marine Biology* 64:317–26.

Depledge, M.H. and Rainbow, P.S. 1990. Models of regulation and accumulation of trace metals in marine invertebrates. *Comparative Biochemistry and Physiology* 97C:1–7.

De Wolf, P. 1975. Mercury content of mussels from West European coasts. *Marine Pollution Bulletin* 6:61–3.

Goldberg, E.D. 1975. The mussel watch— the first step in global marine monitoring. *Marine Pollution Bulletin* 6:111.

Goldberg E.D., Koide, M., Hodge, V., Flegal, A.R. and Martin, J. 1983. U.S. mussel watch: 1977–1978 results on trace metals and radionuclides. *Estuarine, Coastal and Shelf Science* 16:69–93.

Gordon, M., Knauer, G.A. and Martin, J.H. 1980. *Mytilus californianus* as a bioindicator of trace metal pollution: variability and statistical considerations. *Marine Pollution Bulletin* 11:195–8.

Klumpp D.W. and Burdon-Jones, C. 1982. Investigations of the potential of bivalve molluscs as indicators of heavy metal levels in tropical marine waters. *Australian Journal of Marine and Freshwater Reseach* 33:285–300.

Langston, W.J. 1986. Metals in sediments and benthic organisms in the Mersey Estuary. *Estuarine, Coastal and Marine Science* 23:239–61.

Langston, W.J. 1990. Toxic effects of metals and the incidence of metal pollution in marine ecosystems. In *Heavy Metals in the Marine Environment* (ed. R.W. Furness and P.S. Rainbow), 101–22. Boca Raton, Florida: CRC Press, Inc.

Lima, N.R.W., de Lacerda, L.D., Pfeiffer, W.C. and Fiszman, M. 1986. Temporal and spatial variability in Zn, Cr, Cd and Fe concentrations in oyster tissues (*Crassostrea brasiliana* Lamarck, 1819) from Sepetiba Bay, Brazil. *Environmental Technology Letters* 7:453–60.

Luoma, S.N. 1983. Bioavailability of trace metals to aquatic organisms— a review. *Science of the Total Environment* 28:1–22.

Luoma, S.N. 1989. Can we determine the biological availability of sediment bound trace elements? *Hydrobiologia* 176/177:379–96.

Luoma, S.N. 1990. Processes affecting metal concentrations in estuarine and coastal marine sediments. In *Heavy Metals in the Marine Environment* (ed. R.W. Furness and P.S. Rainbow), 51–66. Boca Raton, Florida: CRC Press, Inc.

Lyngby, J.E. and Brix, H. 1987. Monitoring of heavy metal contamination in the Limfjord, Denmark, using biological indicators and sediment. *The Science of the Total Environment* 64:239–52.

Morris, A.W. and Bale, A.J. 1975. The accumulation of cadmium, copper, managanese and zinc by *Fucus vesiculosus* in the Bristol Channel. *Estuarine, Coastal and Marine Science* 3:153–63.

Morton, B. and Wu, R.S.S. 1975. The hydrology of the coastal waters of Hong Kong. *Environmental Research* 10:319–47.

Nieboer, E. and Richardson, D.H.S. 1980. The replacement of the nondescript term 'heavy metals' by a biologically and chemically significant classification of metal ions. *Environmental Pollution* B1:3–26.

Nielsen, S.A. and Nathan, A. 1975. Heavy metal levels in New Zealand molluscs. *New Zealand Journal of Marine and Freshwater Research* 9:467–81.

Okazaki, R.K. and Panietz, M.H. 1981. Depuration of twelve trace metals in tissues of the oysters *Crassostrea gigas* and *C. virginica*. *Marine Biology* 63:113–20.

Phelps, H.L., Wright, D.A. and Mihursky, J.A. 1985. Factors affecting trace metal accumulation by estuarine oysters *Crassostrea virginica*. *Marine Ecology– Progress Series* 22:187–97.

Phillips, D.J.H. 1977a. The use of biological indicator organisms to monitor trace metal pollution in marine and estuarine environments— a review. *Environmental Pollution* 13:281–317.

Phillips, D.J.H. 1977b. The common mussel *Mytilus edulis* as an indicator of trace metals in Scandinavian waters. I. Zinc and cadmium. *Marine Biology* 43:283–91.

Phillips, D.J.H. 1978. The common mussel *Mytilus edulis* as an indicator of trace metals in

Scandinavian waters. II. Lead, iron and manganese. *Marine Biology* 46:147–56.
Phillips, D.J.H. 1979. The rock oyster *Saccostrea glomerata* as an indicator of trace metals in Hong Kong. *Marine Biology* 53:353–60.
Phillips, D.J.H. 1980. *Quantitative aquatic biological indicators: Their use to monitor trace metal and organochlorine pollution.* London: Applied Science Publishers.
Phillips, D.J.H. 1985. Organochlorines and trace metals in green-lipped mussels *Perna viridis* from Hong Kong waters: a test of indicator ability. *Marine Ecology– Progress Series* 21:251–8.
Phillips, D.J.H. 1989. Trace metals and organochlorines in the coastal waters of Hong Kong. *Marine Pollution Bullletin* 20:319–27.
Phillips, D.J.H. 1990. Use of macroalgae and invertebrates as monitors of metal levels in estuaries and coastal waters. In *Heavy Metals in the Marine Environment* (ed. R.W. Furness and P.S. Rainbow), 81–99. Boca Raton, Florida: CRC Press, Inc.
Phillips, D.J.H. 1991. Selected trace elements and the use of biomonitors in subtropical and tropical marine ecosystems. *Reviews of Environmental Contamination and toxicology* 120:105–29.
Phillips, D.J.H., Ho, C.T. and Ng, L.H. 1982. Trace elements in the Pacific oyster in Hong Kong. *Archives of Environmental contamination and toxicology* 11:533–7.
Phillips, D.J.H. and Muttarasin, K. 1985. Trace metals in bivalve molluscs from Thailand. *Marine Environmental Research* 15:215–34
Phillips, D.J.H. and Rainbow, P.S. 1988. Barnacles and mussels as biomonitors of trace elements: a comparative study. *Marine Ecology– Progress Series* 49:83–93.
Phillips, D.J.H. and Rainbow, P.S. 1989. Strategies of trace metal sequestration in aquatic organisms. *Marine Environmental Research* 28:207–10
Phillips, D.J.H. and Yim, W.W.S. 1981. A comparative evaluation of oysters, mussels and sediments as indicators of trace metals in Hong Kong waters. *Marine Ecology- Progress Series* 6:285–93.
Popham, J.D. and D'Auria, J.M. 1982. Effects of season and seawater concentrations on trace metal concentrations in organs of *Mytilus edulis*. *Archives of Environmental Contamination and Toxicology* 11:273–82.
Preston, A., Jefferies, D.J., Dutton, D.W.R., Harvey, B.R. and Steele, A.K. 1972. British Isles coastal waters: the concentrations of selected heavy metals in sea water, suspended matter and biological indicators— a pilot survey. *Environmental Pollution* 3:69–82.
Rainbow, P.S. 1990. Heavy metal levels in marine invertebrates. In *Heavy Metals in the Marine Environment* (ed. R.W. Furness and P.S. Rainbow), 67–79. Boca Raton, Florida: CRC Press, Inc.
Rainbow, P.S. 1992. The talitrid amphipod *Platorchestia platensis* as a potential biomonitor of copper and zinc in Hong Kong: Laboratory and field studies. In *Proceedings of the Fourth International Marine Biological Workshop: The Marine Flora and Fauna of Hong Kong and Southern China, Hong Kong 1989* (ed. B. Morton), 599–610. Hong Kong: Hong Kong University Press.
Rainbow, P.S., Moore, P.G. and Watson, D. 1989. Talitrid amphipods (Crustacea) as biomonitors for copper and zinc. *Estuarine, Coastal and Shelf Science* 28:567–82.
Rainbow, P.S., Phillips, D.J.H. and Depledge, M.H. 1990. Viewpoint. the significance of trace metal concentrations in marine invertebrates: A need for laboratory investigation of accumulation strategies. *Marine Pollution Bulletin* 21:321–24.
Rainbow, P.S. and Smith, B.D. 1992. Biomonitoring of Hong Kong coastal trace metals by barnacles, 1986–1989. In *Proceedings of the Fourth International Marine Biological Workshop: The Marine flora and fauna of Hong Kong and Southern China, Hong Kong, 1989* (ed. B. Morton), 585–97. Hong Kong: Hong Kong University Press.
Rainbow, P.S. and White, S.L. 1989. Comparative strategies of heavy metal accumulation by crustaceans: zinc, copper and cadmium in a decapod, an amphipod and a barnacle. *Hydrobiologia* 174:245–62.
Ritz, D.A., Swain, R. and Elliot, N.G. 1982. Use of the mussel *Mytilus edulis planulatus* (Lamarck) in monitoring heavy metals in seawater. *Australian Journal of Marine and Freshwater Research* 33:491–506.
Seeliger, U. and Edwards, P. 1977. Correlation coefficients and concentration factors of copper and lead in seawater and benthic algae. *Marine Pollution Bulletin* 8:16–9.

Siddall, S.E. 1980. A clarification of the genus *Perna* (Mytilidae). *Bulletin of Marine Science* 30:858–70.

Smith, D.R., Stephenson, M.D. and Flegal, A.R. 1986. Trace metals in mussels transplanted to San Francisco Bay. *Environmental Toxicology and Chemistry* 5:129–38.

Stenzel, H.B. 1971. Oysters. In *Treatise on Invertebrate Paleontology* (ed. K.C. Moore), N953-N 1224 pp. Part IV, vol. 3, Mollusca 6. Boulder: Geological Society of America Inc. and the University of Kansas.

Talbot, V. 1985a. Relationship between cadmium concentrations in seawater and those in the mussel *Mytilus edulis*. *Marine Biology* 85:51–4.

Talbot, V. 1985b. Heavy metal concentrations in the oysters *Saccostrea cuccullata* and *Saccostrea* sp. from the Dampier archipelago, Western Australia. *Australian Journal of Marine and Freshwater Research* 36:169–75.

Tessier, A. and Campbell, P.G.C. 1987. Partitioning of trace metals in sediments: Relationships with bioavailability. *Hydrobiologia* 149:43–52.

Theede, H., Andersson, I. and Lehnberg, W. 1979. Cadmium in *Mytilus edulis* from German coastal waters. *Meeresforschung* 27:147–55.

Thomson, J.D. 1982. Metal concentration changes in growing Pacific oysters, *Crassostrea gigas*, cultivated in Tasmania, Australia. *Marine Biology* 67:135–42.

Ward, T.J. 1982. Laboratory study of the accumulation and distribution of cadmium in the Sydney rock oyster *Saccostrea commercialis* (I & R). *Australian Journal of Marine and Freshwater Research* 33:33–44.

Watling, H.E. and Watling, R.J. 1976. Trace metals in oysters from Knysna Estuary. *Marine Pollution Bulletin* 7:45–8.

Wong, M.H., Chan, K.C. and Choy, C.K. 1978. The effect of iron ore tailings on the coastal environment of Tolo Harbour, Hong Kong. *Environmental Research* 15:342–56.

Wong, M.H., Chan, K.Y., Kwan, S. H. and Mo, C.F. 1979. Metal contents of the two marine algae found on iron ore tailings. *Marine Pollution Bulletin* 10:56–9.

Wong, M.H., Choy, C.K., Lau, W.M. and Cheung, Y.H. 1981. Heavy metal contamination of the Pacific oysters (*Crassostrea gigas*) cultured in Deep Bay, Hong Kong. *Environmental Research* 25:302–9.

Wong, M.H., Kwok, T.T. and Ho, K.C. 1982. Heavy metals in *Ulva lactuca* collected within Tolo Harbour, an almost landlocked sea. *Hydrobiological Bulletin* 16:223–30.

Wong, M.H. and Li, M.W. 1977. An ecological survey of the heavy metal contamination of the edible clam *Paphia* sp. on the iron ore tailings of Tolo Harbour, Hong Kong. *Hydrobiologia* 56:265–72.

Wu, R.S.S. 1973. The distribution of littoral barnacles in Hong Kong. In *Proceedings of Pacific Science Association Special Symposium on Marine Science*, 164–82. Hong Kong: Hong Kong Government Printer.

Zaroogian, G.E., Morrison, G. and Heltshe, J.F. 1979. *Crassostrea virginica* as an indicator of lead pollution. *Marine Biology* 52:189–96.

POLLUTION
SESSION PAPERS

The Marine Biology of the South China Sea
(ed. B. Morton). Proceedings of the First
International Conference on the Marine
Biology of Hong Kong and the South China Sea,
Hong Kong, 28 October – 3 November 1990.
Hong Kong: Hong Kong University press, 1993.

THE EFFECTS OF POLLUTANTS ON THE FILTRATION RATE OF *PERNA VIRIDIS* (BIVALVIA:MYTILIDAE)

Wang Chusheng, Zhou Xiulan and Cheng Rongzhong

Third Institute of Oceanography, State Oceanic Administration, Xiamen, China

ABSTRACT

The effects of pollutants on the filtration rate of *Perna viridis* were studied in the laboratory. The filtration rate in seawater containing unicellular algae was measured over a feeding period. Filtration rate varied among individuals although a relationship between filtration rate (FR) and shell length (L) was established, i.e., FR = 2.95 $L^{-3.02}$ (mL·hr^{-1}·cm^{-1}). On exposure to cadmium, copper, mercury and the soluble fraction of diesel oil, 96 hour EC_{50} values inhibiting filtration were 1.25, 0.10, 0.002 and 0.40 mg·L^{-1}, respectively. After 20 days of exposure to low concentrations, i.e., 30 and 60 µg·L^{-1} of copper, filtration rate was inhibited by 59 and 81%, respectively. Polluted seawater also inhibited filtration rate.

INTRODUCTION

Marine bivalves take suspended food particles and oxygen from seawater by means of filtering a water current drawn into their body by the gills. Previous research (Abel 1976; Widdows 1978, 1985; Martin 1984) demonstrated that the filtration behaviour of bivalves was influenced by environmental stress or toxic pollutants. The mechanism by which pollution affects filtration rate is not well known but likely involves actions of chemical substances on the organism's chemoreceptors (Hara 1984). As a result, the filtration rate of bivalves has been suggested as a physiological index for detecting water quality changes (Abel 1976; Widdows 1985). In the experiments reported upon here, the factors influencing filtration rate as well as the effects of some pollutants and polluted seawater on the green mussel *Perna viridis* were studied in order to obtain a simple and quick method of toxicity testing for marine pollution monitoring.

MATERIALS AND METHODS

Experimental mussels

Individuals of *Perna viridis* were collected from a test raft in Xiamen Harbour, and transferred into the laboratory. After removing encrusting organisms and cleaning shell surfaces, individuals were maintained in seawater in the laboratory. During the acclimation period, seawater was renewed and the mussels were fed with cultured algae. Samples were used in the experiments after acclimation for 7 days or more.

Filtration rate measurements

The test mussels were transferred from the seawater to 1L test vessels with the filtered seawater containing monocultures of unicellular algae, i.e., either *Dicrateria zhanjiangensis* or *Chaetoceros calcitrans*. The concentration of algae was $2-4 \times 10^4$ cell·mL^{-1}. The salinity and temperature of test water were matched with the acclimation seawater. For algal concentration measurements, an initial 50 mL sample was taken from each vessel at the start of the experiment and a second 50 mL sample after 1-2 hours. Concentrations of unicellular algae in the samples were determined by an electronic counter, Model MZ Coulter Counter. Filtration rate is give by the formula of Coughlan (1969):

$$FR = \frac{V \ln (C_o - C_t)}{Nt}$$

where FR = filtration rate in litres·hour^{-1},
V = volume of test seawater in litres,
N = number of animals in the test vessel,
Co = algal concentration in initial sample,
Ct = algal concentration in final sample,
t = test time between the two samples in hours,

Filtration rate is expressed as the volume of seawater filtered·animal^{-1}·hour^{-1}.

Exposure experiments

For the exposure tests, the pollutant were used in the following forms: cadmium and copper as sulphate ($CdSO_4$ and $CuSO_4$); mercury as mercuric chloride ($HgCl_2$); the soluble fraction of diesel oil as a solution isolated from a mixture of oil and seawater by stirring and filtration. For each exposure test, filtered seawater was used as a control, and test solutions containing different concentrations were placed in a series of vessels. Test individuals of similar body size were randomly selected, 10 for each vessel. During the exposure period, test solutions were renewed daily. After the exposure, the filtration rate of mussels in each vessel was measured. Polluted seawater was collected from Yangdan Bay near Xiamen Bay which receives a large amount of urban and industrial waste and has an exchange with the sea. Samples were filtered to remove suspended matter and adjusted to approximately the same salinity and pH as the test seawater. Different concentrations of the polluted seawater (0, 12.5, 25, 50, 100%) were used for the exposure test. Filtration rates for each exposure test were treated to give filtration inhibition rates by comparison with the control. Probit analysis of the concentration-filtration inhibition rate data using the maximum likelihood method (Hobert 1984) were performed to give the values of EC_{50}, the effective concentration of a pollutant required to inhibit filtration rate by 50%.

RESULTS AND DISCUSSION

Factors influencing mussel filtration rate

Filtration rate as a physiological response to pollution is known to be disturbed by environmental parameters such as salinity, temperature, dissolved oxygen and concentrations of suspended matter. In order to either reduce or minimize test variances, appropriate controls were established.

Because the filtration rate was determined by an indirect method measuring the decrease in algal cell concentration of the test medium in relation to time, the computation equation applied to this measurement was based on several assumptions. It was assumed that algal cells or suspended particles were homogeneously dispersed in the test medium and that algal extraction by the test animals was 100% efficient. In accordance with the requirement for homogeneous dispersion, two species of cultured algae, *Dicrateria zhanjiangensis* and *Chaetoceros calcitrans*, were found to be satisfactory. Some species, such as *Platymonas subcordiformis* which is phototaxic, gather together or sink to the bottom, and caused errors.

Figure 1 shows that filtration rate fell markedly with increasing algal concentrations ranging from $4-12 \times 10^4$ cell·mL^{-1}. The production of pseudofaeces observed in tests with high algal concentrations was likely to have a negative effect, as un-ingested algae might return to the water to elevate the apparent amount of algae. The maximum values of filtration rate in Figure 1 occurred at a concentration of 2×10^4 cell·mL^{-1}. The test concentration selected ($2-4 \times 10^4$ cell·mL^{-1}) ensured that the final algal concentration in the filtration tests could be measured accurately.

Increasing the volume of test seawater caused a decrease in filtration rate (Fig. 2). Because, in these experiments, stirring was not used in order to avoid disturbing the test mussels, the assumption of homogenous dispersion was difficult to satisfy. In this case, filtration rate could be underestimated as the water filtered by the test mussel caused the algal concentration around its body to locally fall. Such decreases, however, were not evident in tests with a smaller water volume (0.5–2.0 L) (Fig. 2). This seems to imply that a small volume is better for experimental purposes. To ensure sufficient dissolved oxygen in the test medium, the volume of test seawater was selected as 1 L·test^{-1} mussel^{-1}.

Salinity and temperature generally influence filtration rate. The experiments showed that abrupt changes in salinity and temperature stressed the test mussels to inhibit filtration rate. In some cases, the valves closed. In order to avoid such abrupt changes, salinity and temperature were kept constant. Based on information regarding the filtration rate of *Perna viridis* from May 1986 to March 1987, Table 1 lists means and standard deviations for filtration rates in different months and corresponding ranges of temperature and salinity of test seawater. Mussels of shell length 5.4–6.8 were meas-

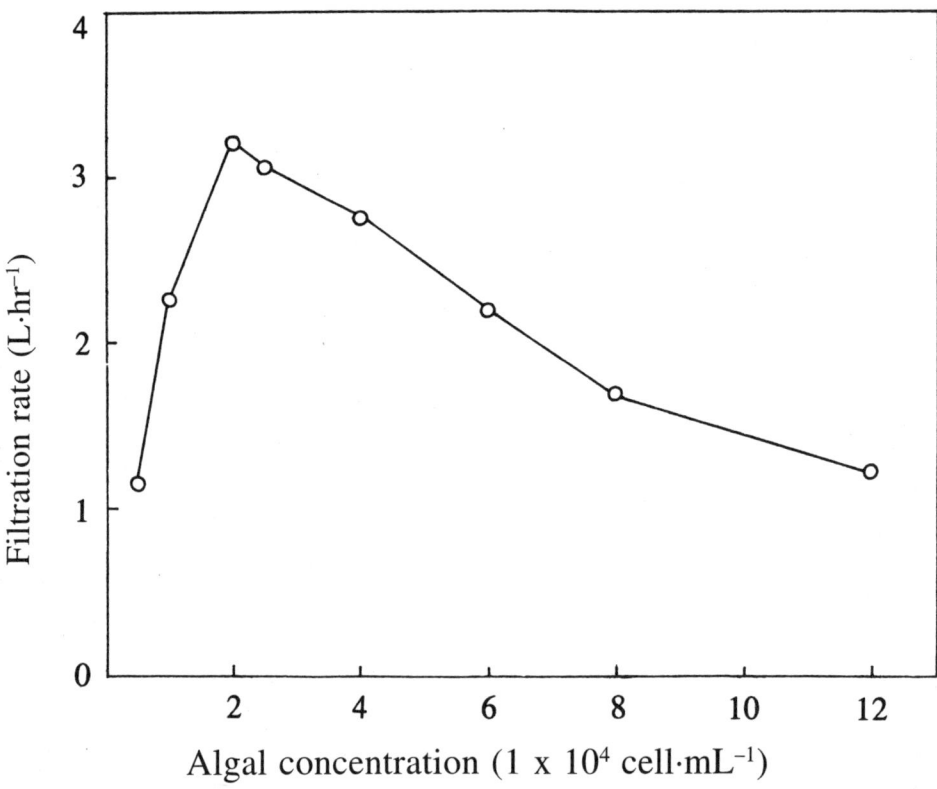

Fig. 1. *Perna viridis.* Filtration rate in relation to algal concentration, at 24°C and 30‰ S. Shell length = 6.4–7.1 cm.

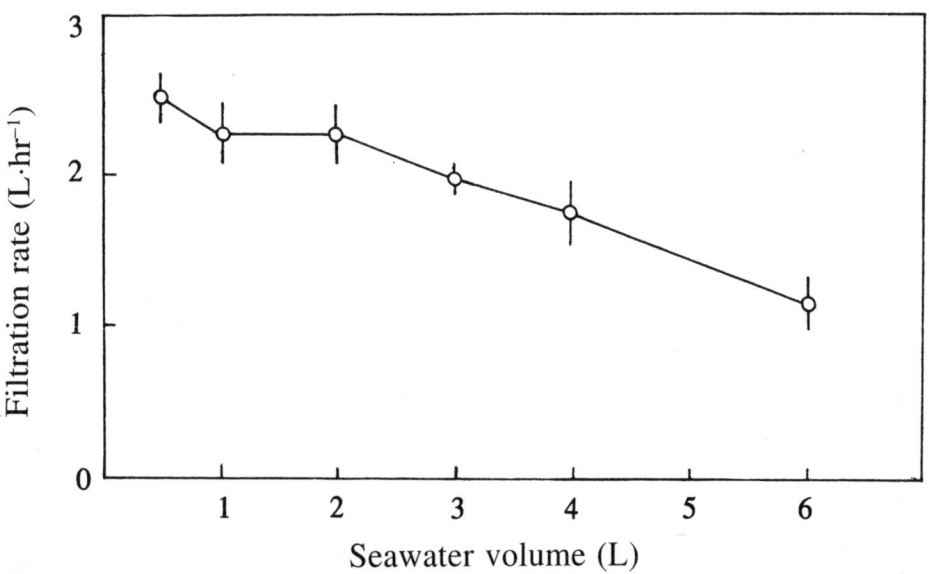

Fig. 2. *Perna viridis.* Filtration rate in relation to the volume of test seawater, at 28°C and 29‰ S. Shell length = 5.3–5.7 cm.

ured at 17–30°C and salinities of between 24–30‰. The total average was 2.26 L·hr^{-1}, the lowest value of 1.92 L·hr^{-1} occurred at 17–19°C and the highest at 20–22°C. However, the differences among these mean values were not statistical significant using a paired sample t-test, ($P > 0.05$) except the lowest value ($P < 0.05$). It is suggested that the filtration rate of *Perna viridis* is not subject to seasonal variation and is temperature dependent, provided there is no abrupt change of environmental conditions.

Table 1
Filtration rates of *Perna viridis* in different months.

Month	Temperature (°C)	Salinity (‰)	Filtration rate(L·hr^{-1}) Mean ± SD
May, 1986	26–28	24–28	2.39 ± 0.54
July, Aug., 1986	28–30	27–30	2.21 ± 0.48
Sep., Oct., 1986	23–25	29–30	2.32 ± 0.39
Nov., 1986	20–22	30	2.47 ± 0.43
Feb., Mar., 1987	17–19	28–30	1.92 ± o.31

Individual variability

It is known that variation in physiological responses exist between populations and individuals. The physiological behaviour of individuals from the same population also varies according to size, age and stage of development. The allometric model was used to express the relationship between physiological rate and body weight rate = a·weight^b, where a and b are fitted parameters (Widdows 1978; Bayne 1981). Since the shell length of bivalves is related to body weight and represents body size, a similar relationship exists between physiological rate and shell length. Figure 3 shows the relationship between filtration rate and shell length of *Perna viridis*. The regression equation is:

$$FR = 2.95 \ L^{3.02} \ (mL·hr^{-1}·cm^{-1}),$$

where FR = filtration rate,
and L = shell length in cm.

From Figure 3 and this equation, it is clear that filtration rate is dependent on body size. On the other hand, variation also exists among individuals of the same body length. In experiments on two groups of mussels with shell lengths of between 5.4 ± 0.24 and 5.3 ± 0.16 cm, the filtration rates were 1.78 ± 0.90 and 1.77 ± 0.40 L·hr^{-1}, respectively. The coefficients of variation were only 4.4 and 3.0% for shell length but up to 51% and 36% for filtration rate. An increase in sample size will reduce experimental variation. Making eight individuals a test group, reduced the coefficient of variation to 16%. To reduce individual variance and to improve the precision of the pollution test, individuals of similar body size were selected and ten individuals were used as the test group.

Pollution effects

Four pollutants, cadmium, copper, mercury and the soluble fraction of diesel oil were

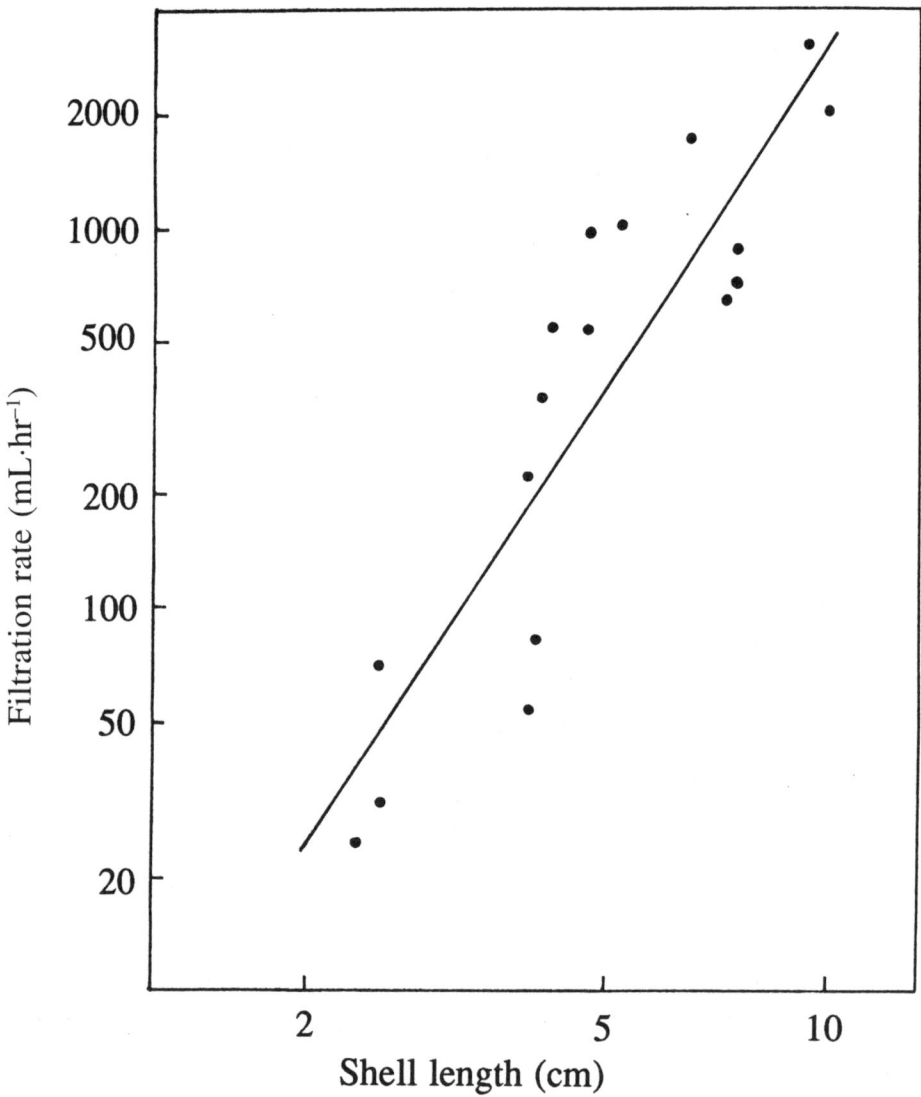

Fig. 3. *Perna viridis*. Relationship between filtration rate and shell length. The regression equation was logy = 3.02 logx + 0.47 (n = 17, r = 0.90).

Table 2
96 hour EC_{50} values for four pollutants upon *Perna viridis*.

Pollutant	Cadmium	Copper	Mercury	The soluble fraction of diesel oil
EC_{50} (mg·L^{-1})	1.25	0.10	0.002	0.40

used in the test experiments. After 96 hours exposure, the EC_{50} values inhibiting filtration are listed in Table 2. By comparing the EC_{50} values in Table 2, the toxic sequence of these pollutants was: mercury > copper > the soluble fraction of diesel oil > cadmium. Some test individuals were killed by the high concentration of pollutants. The concentrations causing mortality were 0.1 mg·L^{-1} for mercury, 0.5 mg·L^{-1} for copper, 8 mg·L^{-1} for the soluble fraction of diesel oil, and 10 mg·L^{-1} for cadmium. This lethal toxic sequence is the same as the sublethal response sequence giving a reliable reflection of the relative toxic effects of the pollutants.

In the test with low copper concentrations, the test mussels were exposed to 30 and 60 µg·L^{-1} copper in the medium for 20 days without mortality. The results of the filtration rate measurements ($P < 0.01$) were: 2.36 ± 0.53 L·hr^{-1} for the control, 0.96 ± 0.37 L·hr^{-1} for the test with 30 µg·L^{-1} of copper and 0.45 ± 0.16 L·hr^{-1} for 60 µg·L^{-1} of copper. In comparison with the control, filtration rate was inhibited by 59 and 81%, respectively. This response also reflects the toxicity of the pollutant at low concentrations when exposed for a longer test time. This method was used to assay the effect of polluted seawater collected from Yangdan Bay. Test individuals were exposed to different concentrations of polluted seawater and filtration rates were measured at 1, 48 and 96 hrs. From Figure 4, filtration rate was inhibited as the concentration of polluted seawater increased to more than 50%; the inhibition rate ranged from 30–40% for 48 and 96 hours exposure, respectively. No inhibition occurred with 12.5% polluted seawater during 96 hours exposure. From Figure 4, the inhibition impact decreased with

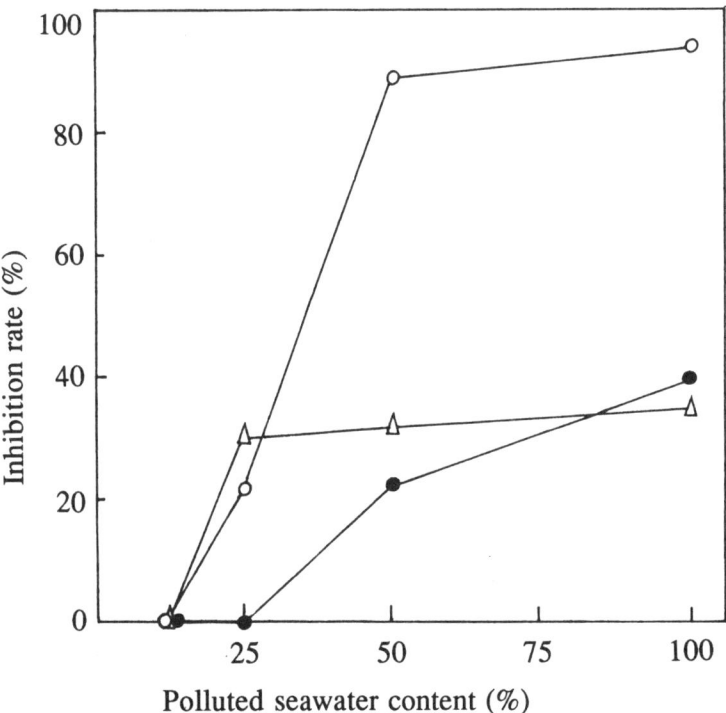

Fig. 4. *Perna viridis*. Filtration inhibition rate in different concentrations of polluted seawater at 27°C and 26‰ S for 1 (○), 48 (Δ) and 96 (●) hrs exposure.

extension of the exposure time, reflecting the adaptability of test individuals to the test solution. This adaptability was particularly evident at low concentrations, complete recovery in filtration rate occurring within 96 hours in 25% polluted seawater.

Filtration rate, as a test for pollution monitoring can be simple and quick. A small scale test does not require expensive equipment, giving short-time responses without elaborate procedures. Some other advantages are evident. Mussels are widely distributed geographically and are easy to collect and maintain in the laboratory. A physiological response is far more sensitive than lethal tests, and are ecologically significant as an animal's capacity to feed influences growth and development of the individual and the population.

REFERENCES

Abel, P.D. 1976. Effects of some pollutants on the filtration rate of *Mytilus. Marine Pollution Bulletin* 7:228-31

Bayne, B.L., Clarke, K.R. and Moore, M.N. 1981. Some practical considerations in the measurement of pollution effects on bivalve molluscs, and some possible ecological consequences. *Aquatic Toxicology* 1:159–74.

Coughlan, J. 1969. The estimation of filtering rate from the clearance of suspensions. *Marine Biology* 2:356–8.

Hara, T.J., Brow, S.B. and Evans, R.E. 1984. Pollutants and chemoreception in aquatic organisms. In *Aquatic Toxicology* (ed. J.O. Nriagu), 247–306. New York: John Wiley and Sons Inc.

Hubert, J.J. 1984. Bioassay (2nd ed.). Kendal Hunt Publishing Company.

Martin, M., Ichikawa, G., Goetzl, J., de los Reyes and Stephenson, M.D. 1984. Relationships between physiological stress and trace toxic substance in the bay mussel, *Mytilus edulis* from San Francisco Bay, California. *Marine Environmental Research* 11:91–110.

Widdows, J. 1978. Combined effects of body size, food concentration and season on the physiology of *Mytilus edulis. Journal of the Marine Biological Association of the United Kingdom* 58:109–24.

Widdows, J. 1985. Physiological responses to pollution. *Marine Pollution Bulletin* 16:129–34.

ANALYSIS AND ASSESSMENT OF HEAVY METAL POLLUTION IN HONG KONG'S MARINE ENVIRONMENT

Y.S. Fung

Department of Chemistry, The University of Hong Kong, Hong Kong

ABSTRACT

Analytical methods available for the monitoring of trace amounts of heavy metal in the marine environment is reviewed and new developments in analytical methodology identified. New analytical procedures for analysing trace metals in seawater, sediment and marine animals have been developed using a gold film mercury vapour analyser and two electroanalytical techniques, the differential pulse anodic stripping voltammetry (DPASV) and the differential pulse cathodic stripping voltammetry (DPCSV). The advantages and limitations of the analytical methods developed are given and the problems facing the analysis of ultra-trace levels of heavy metals are discussed, in particular with reference to the monitoring of background pollutant levels in parts per trillion concentrations. Procedures for automation of the analytical technique using Flow Injection Analysis are also given and shown to be capable analysing ppt levels of mercury in seawater. An assessment of the impact of heavy metal pollution on Hong Kong's marine environment will be given with regard to the lead poisoning of fisherman's children and by tracing the pollution profile of heavy metals in sediments over the past twenty years.

INTRODUCTION

The rapid urbanisation of Hong Kong in recent years has led to increasing amounts of various kinds of pollutants discharged into different water bodies such as rivers, ponds, coastal shores and man-made reservoirs. The pressure for space due to the rapid increase in population density from natural growth and from external sources, the demand for more living space per person, and the increase in numbers of small families in Hong Kong creates a huge market for development of residential, commercial and industrial lands. The above human activities, create an anthropogenic flux of many substances, both natural and synthetic, into neighbouring waters and in many cases this flux is several orders of magnitude higher than that resulting from natural processes such as weathering.

Amongst the numerous pollutants discharged to various aquatic systems, heavy metals have received the most concern as a result of their persistency and subsequent bioaccumulation. Many of the heavy metals are known to cause toxification of aquatic organisms and their predators including man himself via the food chain. Metals such as Be, Co, Ni, Cu, Zn, As, Te, Ag, Cd, Au, Hg, Pb are classified as very toxic and relatively accessible metals (Wool 1974) and their hazardous effects to plants and animals had been reviewed in general by various authors such as Burns and Higgins (1975) and Whittmann (1979). The effects of specific metals had also been discussed by other authors such as Ngiagu (1981) for cadmium, Ngiagu (1979) for copper, Boggess and Wixson (1979) for lead, Ngiagu (1980) for nickel and zinc.

The analysis of heavy metals in the marine environment faces the normal problems of environmental pollutant monitoring— sensitivity and speed of analysis. This is particularly so for toxic heavy metals which are present in trace amount in the environment. The most demanding analysis is to monitor background toxic metal levels which involves analysis at the parts per trillion level. Thus, this paper will present the results and discuss the experiences we have had in the development of analytical methodology for trace metal analysis in the marine environment. A brief description will also be given for our work for assessing the impact of heavy metal pollution in the marine environment in Hong Kong.

MATERIALS AND METHODS

Apparatus and materials

For analysis using the DPASV and the DPCSV method, the Metrohm Polarographic Analyser was used. For AAS studies, the Varian atomic absorption spectrophotometer and graphite furnace were employed. For mercury analysis, the Varian cold vapour generation kit and the Jerome Gold film mercury vapour analyser (model 511) were set up. The FIAstar 5020 Analyser was used for flow injection analysis.

The NBS 1645 river sediment was used to check the results on sediment analysis and standard trace metal solutions in seawater were made by appropriate dilution of standards in given amounts of artificial seawater.

Procedures

For digestion of seawater samples for mercury analysis, 60 mL of HNO_3 + H_2SO_4 + HCl (4:2:1) were mixed with 60 mL of a mixture of HCl + (0.1 N $KBRO_3$ + 1% KBr) in the ratio of 5:3. 500 mL of the seawater sample was added and the solution was sonificated for 4 minutes at 20°C.

The sampling of sediment involves obtaining sediment cores at selected harbour locations with no history of dredging by a 3 inch Phleger core sampler with a tube length of 2.5 ft. The sampler was placed in water about 1 foot from the surface and then set free to fall towards the bottom sediment. The core sediment was stored in an acrylic tube and cut into 1–2 cm sections immediately after transfer to the laboratory.

The sediment was digested by reflux with AR grade 65% nitric acid for 24 hours. The digested sediment was then cooled and filtered with a sintered glass filter prior to dilution to 25 mL in a volumetric flask. Standard addition method was employed for analysing the metal content in the sediment using the AAS method or the gold film mercury vapour analyser.

RESULTS

Development of an analytical methodology

For heavy metal determinations at trace levels, the most common method of analysis is using the Atomic Absorption Spectrophotometer (AAS). In general, the technique is satisfactory for measuring heavy metals at ppm levels using flame Atomic Absorption Spectrophotometry. At lower levels such as at ppb concentration, one has to use the graphite furnace AAS. This technique is less satisfactory due to the high running cost, long analysis time and poor repeatability in particular for samples with high salt content. The use of a background correction employing a deuterium lamp or Zeeman effect AAS can offset some of the problems, but the high cost of the equipment and its limited scope of applicability makes it less attractive as a general technique for measuring ppb levels of heavy metals in the marine environment.

In order to increase the sensitivity of the method, various ways of generation of the vapour prior to atomisation have been used so as to improve the transfer of analyte to the analytical zone for AAS determination. Two methods have been successfully used such as the hydride generation method and the cold vapour technique. The former method is applicable to As, Bi, Ge, Pb, Se, Sb and Te under a suitable reducing atmosphere. Very high sensitivity was obtained and the concentration can be determined down to the ppb level. The cold vapour technique can only be applicable to mercury analysis which reduces the mercury ions to the metallic state in vapour phase at very low concentrations. The mercury atoms show strong absorption of UV light and thus can be detected at ppb levels. Both the cold vapour and hydride generation techniques use a chemical method to convert the analyte in the seawater to a form suitable for atomisation, which departs from the sample solution in the vapour state prior to actual analysis. Thus, the high salt content in the samples does not affect the use of the above two techniques.

The advance in the Inductively Coupled Plasma-Atomic emission spectroscopy (ICP-AES) enables simultaneous determination of several metallic elements and hence a reduction in the analysis time per element per analysis. The linear range is very wide, over several orders of magnitude from ppb to ppm concentrations.

The electroanalytical method provides a particularly suitable technique for analysis in seawater as the presence of salt provides the supporting electrolyte needed in the method (Florence and Battey 1977). Currently, there are two electroanalytical methods commonly used for trace metal analysis in seawater— differential pulse anodic stripping voltammetry (DPASV) and differential pulse cathodic stripping voltammetry (DPCSV). The DPASV method uses the electrolytic method to deposit metals onto the mercury electrode surface to form an amalgam prior to stripping anodically using the differential pulse voltammetric technique. This method is applicable to metal ions having less anodic deposition potential as compared to a hydrogen reduction potential at the mercury electrode surface (Gillain and Duyckaerls 1979).

The DPCSV method makes use of the surface adsorption of organometallic complexes onto the mercury electrode as a preconcentration step prior to analysis using the differential pulse voltammetric technique. The difference in the DPASV method is that it may not involve electron transfer in the first stage and the metal ions to be determined can exist in a high valency state in the form of a complex during adsorption (Berg 1984; Berg and Huang 1984). The reduction step may involve the changes in valency state of the complexed metal or the reduction of the ligand of the complex. Thus, its scope of application is wider than the DPASV method which restricts its application for analysing metals deposited on mercury (Nurnberg et al. 1976). Both techniques are capable of measuring trace metal concentration down to the ppb level and the drawback of the electroanalytical methods is the rather long analysis time.

Another lately developed analytical technique for trace metal analysis is the gold film mercury vapour analyser. The method was first developed to measure mercury vapour in air for occupational health reasons. It makes use of the selective adsorption of mercury at a gold film electrode, which subsequently leads to changes in the electrical resistance. Thus, by measuring the change in resistance, one can measure the mercury vapour concentration indirectly. This method is very sensitive and capable of measuring ng amounts of mercury vapour.

For measuring mercury in seawater, the cold vapour method was used to generate the mercury vapour which is detected by the gold film mercury vapour analyser in place of the AAS method. This method was shown to be more sensitive than the cold vapour AAS method due to the inherent sensitivity of the gold film technique. We have applied the gold film technique for analysing mercury in 10 given seawater samples and the results are shown in Table 1. It is clear that the gold film technique offers a better analytical technique for measuring mercury in seawater.

The current research work undertaken to improve the analytical methodology concentrates on the following areas: First, it focuses on improvement of the detection limit of the analytical methods. The development of the gold film mercury analyser for seawater and sediment analysis is one direction and the development of DPCSV for trace

Table 1
The application of the gold film mercury vapour analyser for analysing mercury in seawater.

Sample	Gold-film	Technique Cold vapour ASS
1	0.5	<1
2	0.8	<1
3	0.6	<1
4	3.7	3.9
5	1.2	1.0
6	2.1	2.4
7	4.8	5.0
8	0.7	<1
9	0.9	<1
10	1.8	1.5

Note: Concentrations given are expressed in ppb w/w.

metal analysis is another. The results of using the electroanalytical technique for monitoring heavy metals in seawater is shown in Table 2. In order to analyse a large number of seawater and sediment samples daily, automation of the analytical procedures is needed. Thus, an automatic analytical procedure utilising flow injection analysis with the use of the gold film mercury analyser was developed. A schematic diagram showing the procedure is given in Figure 1. Detection limit down to ppt of mercury has been achieved using the gold film method. The analytical procedure and the precision of the method is given in Table 3.

Table 2
Concentration of heavy metals in seawater at Deep Water Bay as determined by the developed electroanalytical technique.

Heavy Metal	Concentrations, ppb		
	August	September	October
Zn	2.3	1.3	5.1
Cd	0.090	0.12	0.24
Pb	0.39	1.1	0.55
Cu	0.64	0.66	1.00
Ni	0.46	0.61	0.83
Co	N.D.	0.021	0.021
Fe	76	50	85

Note: The data given are the average of two samplings taken during that month.

Table 3
Determination of seawater samples at ppt levels using the gold film mercury vapour analyser.

1. Digestion conditions
   $HNO_3 + H_2SO_4 + HCl$ 4:2:1 (60 mL)
   and
   $HCl = (0.1N\ KBrO_3 + 1\%\ KBr)$ 5:3 (60 mL)
   Sonificate 4 minutes at 20°C

2. Working range:
   0–1700 ng Hg
   0–100 ppt for 500 mL sample

3. Precision:

Conc. (ppt)	RSD, (%)
5	23
10	17
20	8.2
30	6.2
100	2.5
500	1.1

The second area of research is developing methods for speciation of metallic elements. The use of the DPCSV is one method and the other is making use of the differential volatility of metallic complexes at different valency states. This method was found to be useful for differentiating Cr (III) and Cr (VI) using ß-diketo chelate as the complex prior to analysis using the graphite AAS with suitable temperature setting at the atomisation stage. The third area of work is developing automatic analytical procedures. The development of flow injection analysis method coupled with gold film mercury vapour sensor or cold vapour ASS is a promising approach for increasing the analysis speed of the method (Fig. 1). The various analytical methods developed had been applied for analysis of trace metals in seawater and sediment. Some of the results will be shown in the next section.

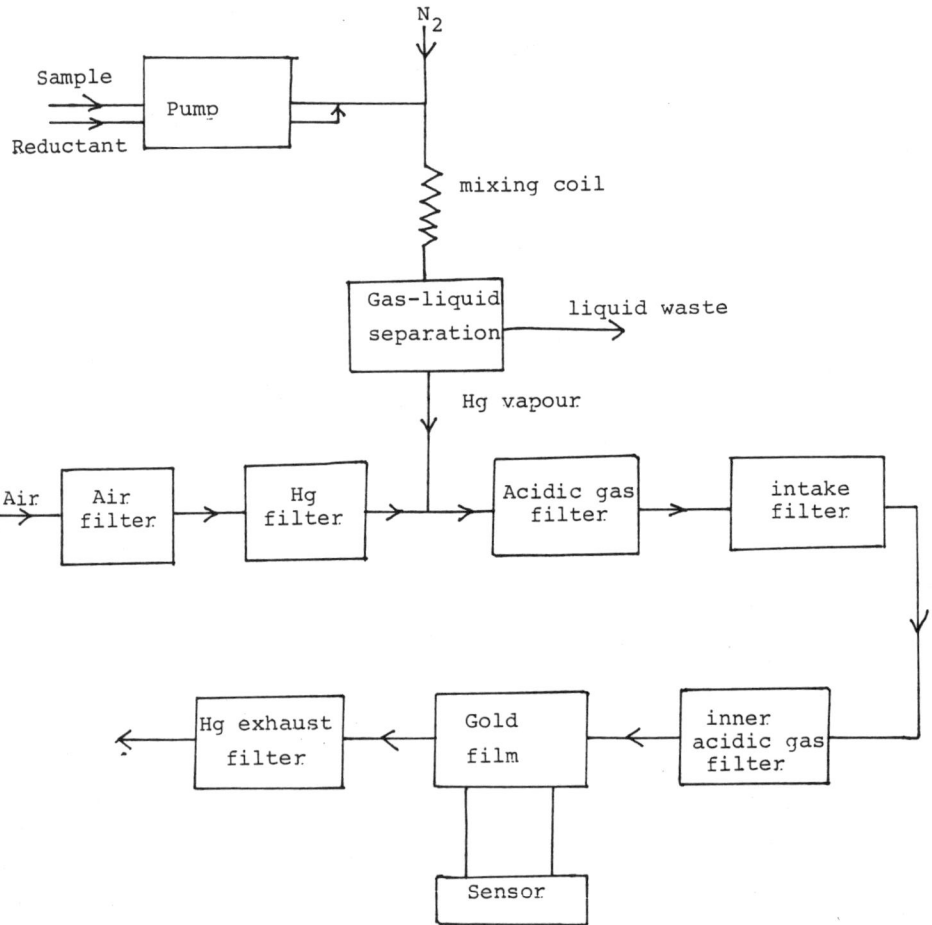

Fig. 1. Schematic diagram showing the automation of the gold film mercury vapoour analyser using flow injection analysis.

Impact assessment of heavy metal pollution

Two projects are currently being undertaken to assess heavy metal pollution in the marine environment of Hong Kong. The first project collaborates with the Centre of Environmental Studies, Civil Engineering Department, Hong Kong Polytechnic. It involves measuring heavy metal pollution profiles in sediment. As heavy metals are quickly absorbed onto fine grained settling particles in the water body leading to entrapment in the sediment, the level of contamination over different time spans are recorded in different vertical sections of the sediment, provided that the pollutants are persistent and the sediment stratum has not been seriously disturbed by human activities such as dredging. Thus, the pollution history of a particular persistent pollutant can be revealed by constructing a temporal pollution profile, which is basically a plot of pollution level versus time. The construction of the profile requires knowledge of the concentration of pollutants in layers of sediment and its real time of deposition. We have used the analytical methods developed to obtain such a chemical composition. Time information can be obtained either by measuring the sedimentation rate or using the radionuclide dating method. The first method suffers the disadvantage of the inevitable variation in sedimentation rate due to the increase in human activity near the coast. Thus, the latter method would provide a much better way of estimating time. Of the various dating methods, the Pb-210 dating technique is more recent and very useful for dating sediments up to 100 years old as the Pb-210 natural radionuclide has a half life of 22.3 years and a short atmospheric residence time after its generation from the decay of gaseous Ru-222.

The preliminary results of a core taken near the coast at Cheung Kwan Oh indicate that the concentrations of heavy metal has increased rapidly near the surface of the sediment (Figs. 2 and 3) and is more or less constant throughout the rest of the core. This trend was observed markedly for Cd, Cu, Cr and Pb (Table 4). Ni also shows a similar but less marked trend. The results clearly indicate that the event of heavy metal pollution is relatively recent and is accelerating rapidly as indicated by the jump in concentration near the surface sediment. This is shown clearly in the case of cadmium which was virtually zero in concentration for a long period of time prior to an escalating increase in concentration near the surface sediment. Our work using Pb-210 dating is currently in progress and we should be able to obtain the time scale after the given set of experiments has finished.

Our second project was done in collaboration with the Paediatrics Department, Faculty of Medicine, The University of Hong Kong. It involves measuring the blood lead level in fisherman's children. During a preliminary survey undertaken in 1984, the blood lead and zinc protoporphyrin (a metabolite resulting from chronic lead absorption or iron deficiency anaemia) content in the fisherman's children at Aberdeen was found to be abnormally high as compared to other school children in the same area, in particular those living on boats. The average number children with high blood lead levels were 2.2 per boat (Ho 1984). Thus a comprehensive survey was performed to obtain the statistical data for comparison of the blood lead content of fisherman's children with other groups of children in the same school. Environmental factors were also recorded with an aim to determine factors leading to the increase in the blood lead content in fisherman's children. The project is currently in progress and results are expected in the summer of next year.

DISCUSSION

A comparison of the various analytical techniques for trace metal analysis in seawater are given in Table 2 in terms of scope, working range, detection limit, analysis time,

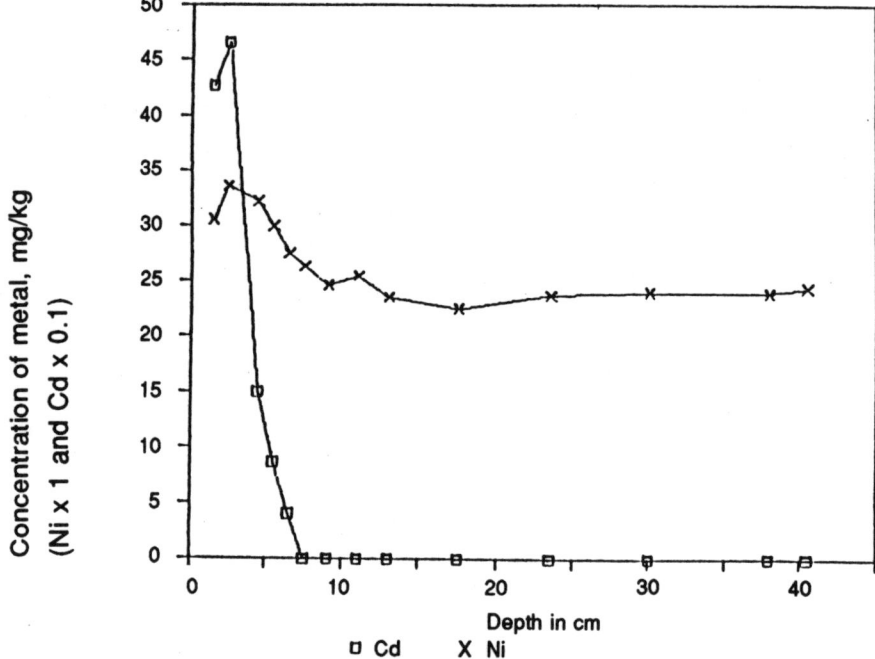

Fig. 2. The vertical profile of Cd and Ni in a sediment core taken at Cheung Kwan Oh.

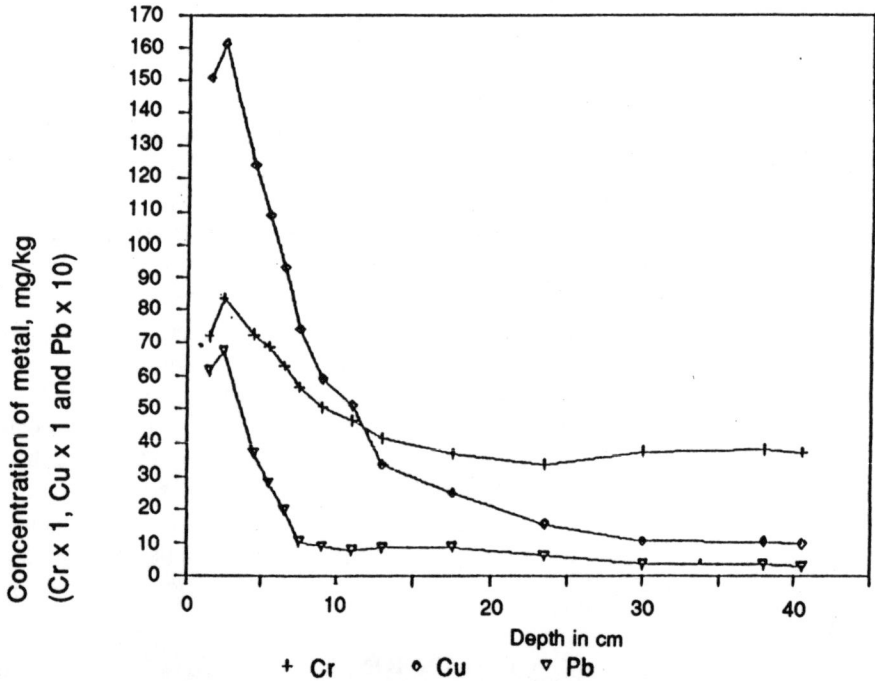

Fig. 3. The vertical profile of Cr, Cu and Pb in a sediment core taken at Cheung Kwan Oh.

Table 4
The trace metal concentrations [mg·kg dry wt.$^{-1}$] in Core JB sediments from Cheung Kwan Oh.

	Depth (cm)	Cd Mean	Cd Std	Cr Mean	Cr Std	Cu Mean	Cu Std	Ni Mean	Ni Std	Pb Mean	Pb Std	Colour
JB-1	1.5	42.7	0.00	71.9	0.0	151	–	30.5	–	61.6	–	light brown
JB-2	2.5	46.5	0.96	83.5	0.7	161	1.2	33.6	0.0	67.4	1.3	light brown
JB-3	4.5	14.9	0.43	72.4	0.9	124	0.7	32.3	0.3	36.9	0.3	light brown
JB-4	5.5	8.63	1.20	68.6	1.3	109	1.4	29.9	0.5	28.1	0.9	light brown
JB-5	6.5	3.92	0.37	63.1	1.9	93.0	1.3	27.5	0.8	19.8	0.4	light brown
JB-6	7.5	0.00	0.00	56.8	0.3	74.0	1.5	26.3	0.8	10.4	0.0	light brown
JB-7	9.0	0.00	0.00	50.7	0.6	59.3	1.8	24.6	0.8	8.9	0.4	brown
JB-8	11.0	0.00	0.00	46.7	0.4	51.5	8.0	25.4	0.5	7.7	0.7	brown
JB-9	13.0	0.00	0.00	41.5	0.7	33.7	0.4	23.5	0.3	8.5	0.1	light brown
JB-10	17.5	0.00	0.00	37.0	1.1	25.1	0.4	22.4	0.2	8.7	0.4	light brown
JB-11	23.5	0.00	0.00	33.8	0.6	15.7	0.2	23.6	0.6	6.2	0.1	light brown
JB-12	30.0	0.00	0.00	37.5	1.3	10.6	0.6	23.9	0.5	3.5	0.1	brown
JB-13	38.0	0.00	0.00	37.9	0.9	10.4	0.9	23.8	0.7	3.6	0.3	grey
JB-14	40.5	0.00	0.00	37.0	1.3	9.9	0.2	24.3	0.8	3.0	0.1	brown

Note: Cd concentration multiplied by 10.
pb concentration multiplied by 0.1.

Table 5
Comparison of various analytical techniques for analysing trace metals in seawater.

Techniques	Scope	Working Range	Detection Limit	Analysis Time	Capital Cost	Running Cost	Others
FAAS	wide	good	ppm	10 sec	fair	fair	Versatile technique
GFAAS	wide	fair	ppb	10–15 min	fairly high	high	1) suffers interference from NaCl 2) Problems of repeatability of results
ZGFAAS	fair	fair	ppb	10–15 min	high	high	1) Concentration roll-back for some elements 2) Solves some problem due to NaCl absorption
HGAAS	limited	low	ppb	20-30 min	fair	fair	Only aplicable to As, Bi, Ge, Pb, Se, Sb and Te
CVAAS	limited	low	ppb	20–30 min	fair	fair	Only applicable to mercury
ICP-AES	wide	very good	ppb-ppm	10 sec	high	high	Capable of multi-element analysis
DPASV	wide	good	ppb	20 min	fair	low	Applicable to metal ions less anodic than H+
DPCSV	wide	good	ppb	20 min	fair	low	Applicable to metals with variable valency and can be used for very electro-positive metals
GFMVA	limited	low	ppt	20 min	fair	fair	Applicable to mercury only

Note: FAAS - Flame atomic absorption spectrophotometry.
GFAAS - Graphite furnance atomic absorption spectrophotometry.
ZFGFAAS - Zeeman effect graphite furnance atomic absorption spectrophotometry.
HGAAS - Hydride generation atomic absorption spectrophotometry.
CVAAS - Cold vapour atomic absorption spectrophotometry.
ICP-AES - Inductively coupled plasma-atomic emissin spectrophotometry.
DPASV - Differential pulse anodic stripping voltammetry.
DPCSV - Differential pulse cathodic stripping voltametry.

capital cost, running cost and other considerations. It clearly indicates that the flame AAS offers the most versatile technique, though the detection limit is not low enough for many toxic elements. For analysing trace metals at ppb levels, the use of the electroanalytical technique is recommended for laboratories which do not have a large analytical load. For a laboratory requiring high sample throughout, the ICP-AES method is recommended. The graphite furnace AAS, though offers good sensitivity, is not the method of choice due to the interference of NaCl and the high cost and limited scope of application of various form of background correction methods. For analysis of mercury in seawater, the gold film mercury vapour analyser is shown to be a promising technique for analysing samples with a low mercury content.

The results of the analysis of a trace metal profile in sediment cores indicate an escalating increase in heavy metal pollution in recent years as shown by the alarming increase in the Cd, Cr, Pb and Cu content in the sediment core sampled. The rapid rate of increase in heavy metal pollution in the marine environment leads to concern about their health implications as heavy metals can accumulate via the marine food chain and eventually affect human health. Although the origin of the elevation in the blood lead level in Aberdeen fisherman's children has not yet been identified, it exemplifies the potential impact on human health due to heavy metal pollution. The work done on the two projects for assessing heavy metal pollution is in progress at present and results will be published as soon as they are ready.

ACKNOWLEDGEMENTS

The continued support of the Hong Kong University Research Grant Committee on the analytical and environmental activities in our research group is gratefully acknowledged. The work described in the above article are currently carried out by the following persons: Mr C.K. Lo, Mr W.C. Sham, Mr Andrew C.K. Tsang, and Mr C.C. Lau.

REFERENCES

Berg, C.M.G. Van den. 1984. Determination of copper in sea water by cathodic stripping voltammetry of complexes with catechol. *Analytica Chimica Acta* 164:195–207.

Berg, C.M.G.Van den and Huang, Z.Q. 1984. Determination of iron in sea water using cathodic stripping voltammetry preceded by adsorptive collection with the hanging mercury drop electrode. *Journal of Electroanalytical Chemistry* 177:269–80.

Boggess, W.R. and Wixson, B.G. 1979. *Lead in the environment* [Parts I and II]. Castle House Publications.

Burns, R.G. and Higgins, I.J. 1975. *The chemistry and microbiology of pollution.* New York: Academic Press.

Florence, T.M. and Battey, G.E. 1977. Determination of copper in sea water by anodic stripping voltammetry. *Journal of Electroanalytical Chemistry* 75:791–8.

Gillain, G. and Duyckaerts, G. 1979. Direct and simultaneous determinations of Zn, Cd, Pb, Cu, Sb and Bi dissolved in sea water by differential pulse anodic stripping voltammetry with a hanging mercury drop electrode. *Analytica Chimica Acta* 106:23–37.

Ngiagu, J.O. 1981. *Cadmium in the environment.* New York: Wiley Interscience.

Ngiagu, J.O. 1979. *Copper in the environment* [Part I and II]. New York: Wiley Interscience.

Ngiagu, J. O. 1980. *Nickel in the environment* [Part I and II]. New York: Wiley Interscience.

Ngiagu, J.O. 1980. *Zinc in the environment* [Part I and II]. New York: Wiley Interscience.

Nurnberg, H.W., Valenta, P., Raspor, M.B. and Sipos, L. 1976. Applications of polarography and voltammetry to marine and aquatic chemistry II. The polarographic approach to the determination and speciation of toxic trace metals in the marine environment. *Zeitschrift für Analytische Chemie* 282:357–67.

Whittmann, G.T. 1979. Toxic Metals. In *Metal Pollution in the Aquatic Environment* (ed. U. Forstner and G.T. Whittmann), 3–68. New York: Springer-Verlag.

Wool, J.W. 1974. Biological cycles for toxic elements in the environment. *Science* 183:1049–52.

A GRAY MODEL FOR PREDICTING RED TIDES

Wang Zhaoding, Peng Yunhui and Lin Yongshui

South China Sea Institute of Oceanology, Academia Sinica,
164 West Xin Gang Road, Guangzhou, China

ABSTRACT

The application of a gray model (based on the gray control theory) for predicting red tide occurrences is discussed. Assuming that the red tide organisms show no clear relationship with environmental variables, the model is established by selecting various factors, e.g., salinity, dissolved oxygen, pH, and PO_4–P, and used to determine red tide occurrences and to predict occurrence time and frequencies. The examples given in this paper (including the prediction of red tide frequencies in Tolo Harbour, Hong Kong), reveal that, although only a few variables were used to establish the model, it has high prediction precision.

INTRODUCTION

With marine pollution becoming more and more serious, the frequency of red tide occurrences in the marine environment are increasing. In recent years there have been many research reports concerned with predicting red tides (Ikeda 1987). Most authors lay stress on using multiple linear regression and discriminant analysis as well as map-analysis, in studies of the relationship between red tides and marine conditions (Ouchi and Takayama 1981, 1984; Ouchi 1982, 1984), the relationship between red tides and eutrophication (Zou et al. 1983), and the discrimination between red tides/non-red tides (Kato et al. 1985). In other words, one has to be seek prediction approaches from a statistical analysis of recorded data, since the mechanism by which red tides occur is not clear. Previous studies have, however, led to a better understanding of how red tides occur.

We report upon a gray model that is considered of practical use in the prediction of red tide occurrences. According to Deng (1986), the gray system gives a differential equation-described picture of red tide dynamics, and the equation can be used to discriminate between and to predict their development. This paper consists of three sections. The first section summarizes the basic theory on the gray control system and the methods used to establish the model. The second section discusses the formulation of the gray model for red tide prediction. In the third section, we discuss some problems of model application.

THEORY AND METHODS FOR MODELLING

The gray model

According to gray control system theory, the inverse process of the abstract system is named as a gray inverse process, i.e., behaviour is followed by the model. The model obtained from this inverse process is called the gray model (GM(n,h)). Its mathematical basis is briefly summarized as follows.

The GM(n,h) model, which means that the model consists of nth order and h of the variables, has a differential equation as follows

$$\frac{d^n X_1^{(1)}}{dt^n} + \frac{d^{n-1} X_1^{(1)}}{dt^{n-1}} + \ldots + a_n X_1^{(1)} = b_1 X_3^{(1)} + b_2 X_3^{(1)} \ldots + b_{h-1} X_h^{(1)} \tag{1}$$

This equation is built from Yn, an array of known data, and A, B, known data matrices

$$Y_n = A \begin{Bmatrix} a_1 \\ \vdots \\ a_{n-1} \end{Bmatrix} + B \begin{Bmatrix} a_n \\ \vdots \\ b_{h-1} \end{Bmatrix} = [A\!:\!B] \begin{Bmatrix} a_1 \\ \vdots \\ a_{n-1} \\ \cdots \\ a_n \\ \vdots \\ b_{h-1} \end{Bmatrix} = (A\!:\!B)\hat{a} \tag{2}$$

In which, $X_1^{(1)}$ is the accumulated value of $X_1^{(0)}$ (i.e., $X_1^{(1)}(i) = \sum_{k=1}^{i} X_1^{(0)}(k)$); (A:B) is the partitional matrices built by B following A (i.e., $(A\!:\!B) \triangleq \text{block}(A\!:\!B)$; $Y_n = [a^{(n)}(X_1^{(n)}, 2),$
$a^{(n)}(X_1^{(n)}, 3), \ldots, a^{(n)}(X_1^{(n)}, N)]^T$. The structures of matrices A and B are listed as follows:

$$A = \begin{Bmatrix} -a^{(n-1)}(X_1^{(1)}, 2), -a^{(n-2)}(X_1^{(1)}, 2), \ldots, -a^{(1)}(X_1^{(1)}, 2) \\ -a^{(n-1)}(X_1^{(1)}, 3), -a^{(n-2)}(X_1^{(1)}, 3), \ldots, -a^{(1)}(X_1^{(1)}, 3) \\ \cdots\cdots\cdots \\ -a^{(n-1)}(X_1^{(1)}, N), -a^{(n-2)}(X_1^{(1)}, N), \ldots, -a^{(1)}(X_1^{(1)}, N) \end{Bmatrix}$$

$$B = \begin{Bmatrix} -\frac{1}{2}(X_1^{(1)}(2), + X_1^{(1)}(1)), \ X_2^{(1)}(2), \ldots, X_n^{(1)}(2) \\ -\frac{1}{2}(X_1^{(1)}(2), + X_1^{(1)}(2)), \ X_2^{(1)}(3), \ldots, X_n^{(1)}(3) \\ \cdots\cdots\cdots \\ -\frac{1}{2}(X_1^{(1)}(N), + X_1^{(1)}(N-1)), \ X_2^{(1)}(N), \ldots, X_n^{(1)}(N) \end{Bmatrix}$$

Based on least square approximation, we get a discriminating formula:

$\hat{a} = [(A\!:\!B)^T (A\!:\!B)]^{-1} (A\!:\!B)^T Y_N.$

The undetermined discriminating coefficient vector of the differential equation â (=[a_1, a_2, ..., a_n : b_1, ..., b_{h-1}]^T), can be gained from the discrimination formula. Obtaining the differential equation of the substantial model and solving the equation, we can correspondingly get a response time function ($\hat{X}_1^{(1)}(t)$) and a discrete function ($\hat{X}_1^{(1)}(k)$).

$$\hat{X}_1^{(1)}(t) = X_1^{(0)}(0) + (\frac{b}{a}) X_2^{(1)}(t)) e^{-at} + (\frac{b}{a}) X_2^{(1)}(t) +$$
$$+ (\frac{c}{a}) X_3^{(1)}(t) + (\frac{d}{a}) X_4^{(1)}(t) + (\frac{e}{a}) X_5^{(1)}(t)$$

$$\hat{X}_1^{(1)}(k) = (X_1^{(0)}(0) + (\frac{b}{a}) X_2^{(1)}(k)) e^{-a(k-1)} + (\frac{b}{a}) X_2^{(1)}(k) +$$
$$+ (\frac{c}{a}) X_3^{(1)}(k) + (\frac{d}{a}) X_4^{(1)}(k) + (\frac{e}{a}) X_5^{(1)}(k)$$

The use of the gray model in red tide prediction

Red tide prediction includes the discrimination of red tide/non-red tides, the prediction of red tide occurrences and frequencies. The gray model makes an internal study from external and superficial information, to reveal the continuous long-term process. So the GM(n,h) model can be divided, theoretically, into the GM(1,h) model for determining a state model and the GM(n,1) model for a predicting model. Therefore, GM(1,h) and GM(n,1) could be employed, respectively, to discriminate red tides/non-red tides and to predict red tide occurrences and frequency.

The discriminant for red tides/non-red tides

As a state model, GM(1,h) means that it can produce one out of h inputs. That is, it needs h–1 of independent variables and obtains one dependent variable.

Kato et al. (1985), selected four important factors of salinity, dissolved oxygen, pH and PO_4–P, and deduced a function (Z) discriminating red tides/non-red tides as follows: Z = Sal–3.959 DO – 26.974 pH – 5.421 PO_4–P, and also a discriminating point for red tides/non-red tides as Z = –236.915.

This paper also chooses the four independent variables of salinity, dissolved oxygen, pH, PO_4–P, and Z as a dependent variable, to establish a state model— GM(1, 5).

Predicting red tide occurrences

Table 1 shows that the value of Z is negative but increasing. This paper selected Z as a variable and let Z′ = –Z; the non-negative and increasing requirement of the gray predicting model will be satisfied in this way. In this paper, we established a simpler predicting model GM(1,1) and the discrete response expression from this model may be used as the model predicting red tides.

The prediction of red tide frequencies

The frequency of red tides annual occurrences, in any one area, is always an irregular and positive integer. Taking a fit frequency (F) as the threshold, therefore, the sequence which is greater than the threshold could be satisfied to non-negative and increasing requirement of the gray model. This paper will set up a simpler GM(1,1) model in this way to predict the red tides frequencies.

Table 1
Verification of discriminant function against chlorophyll a
(Z < −236: red tide, Z > −236: non red tide)*

Red tide data

pH	DO (mL·1⁻¹)	PO4–P (µg·at·1⁻¹)	Salinity (‰)	Z**
9.05	7.90	0.46	13.1	−264.794
8.77	6.00	0.29	15.6	−246.296
7.50	6.10	0.27	4.94	−222.986
8.85	9.31	0.96	18.2	−262.593
8.64	6.79	0.62	22.8	−240.506
8.73	7.92	0.33	13.7	−254.936
8.64	8.28	0.10	22.4	−243.947
8.70	8.71	0.64	25.1	−247.536
8.95	8.71	0.15	18.6	−258.123
8.91	7.95	0.38	7.39	−266.492

Non red tide data

pH	DO (mL·1⁻¹)	PO4–P (µg·at·1⁻¹)	Salinity (‰)	Z**
8.20	4.52	0.53	30.8	−213.788
8.30	5.39	0.26	25.1	−221.539
8.56	6.07	0.06	28.7	−226.531
8.28	4.56	1.12	19.8	−227.585
7.78	4.81	1.15	7.90	−227.221
8.38	5.53	0.32	28.6	−221.077
8.43	5.70	0.11	28.7	−221.861
8.38	6.20	0.05	28.9	−221.966
8.26	5.06	0.21	29.8	−214.183
8.12	5.63	0.44	11.4	−232.310

* from Kato et al. (1985).
**Z values were calculated using the formula:
Z = Sal − 3.959 DO − 26.974 pH − 5.421 PO$_4$–P

RESULTS

The discrimination of red tides/non-red tides

From Table 1, five sets of data for red tides and non-red tides were obtained to construct a new sequence. Taking the four parameters of salinity, dissolved oxygen, pH, PO$_4$–P as independent variables and Z as the dependent, we built up a GM(1,5) gray state model. We put the calculated result of the formula: â = [(A ⋮ B)^T (A ⋮ B)]$^{-1}$ (A ⋮ B)^T Y$_N$ into equation (1), deriving the GM(1,5) model as follows:

$$\frac{dX_1^{(1)}(t)}{dt} + 1.522\ X_1^{(1)}(t) = -0.672\ X_2^{(1)}(t) + 0.861\ X_3^{(1)}(t) -$$
$$- 0.140\ X_4^{(1)}(t) - 43.514\ X_5^{(1)}(t) \quad (3)$$

In which, $X_j^{(1)}(i)$ are the accumulated values of the variables of Z, PO$_4$–P, DO, salinity, pH, respectively.

Let $X_1^{(1)}(1) = X_1^{(1)}(0) = -221.996$, solve equation (4), we have a formula response time:

$$\hat{X}_1^{(1)}(t) = (X_1^{(0)}(0) + 0.422\ X_2^{(1)}(t))\ e^{-1.522t} -$$
$$- 0.422\ X_2^{(1)}(t) + 0.566\ X_3^{(1)}(t) -$$
$$- 0.0920\ X_4^{(1)}(t) - 28.59\ X_5^{(1)}(t) \tag{4}$$

a discrete formula:

$$X_1^{(1)}(k) = (X_1^{(0)}(0) + 0.422\ X_2^{(1)}(k))\ e^{-1.522(k-1)} -$$
$$- 0.422\ X_2^{(1)}(k) + 0.566\ X_3^{(1)}(k) -$$
$$- 0.0920\ X_4^{(1)}(k) - 28.59\ X_5^{(1)}(k) \tag{5}$$

The values calculated with equations (4) and (5) are all accumulated values which can be reduced by following $\hat{X}_1^{(0)}(i) = \hat{X}_1^{(1)}(i) - \hat{X}_1^{(1)}(i-1)$. The reduced values of equation (5) are listed in Table 2.

Comparing the calculated values of the discrete formula (reduced value) with the initial values, we found that the precision is quite good, although two values differ rather largely (70% and 20%) (see Table 2). In order to get a higher precision, we could adopt the GM(1,1) model to predict for their differences, then add the obtained difference predicting value (s) to the preliminary predicting values. Table 3 shows that the precision has been improved.

The modified values and the initial data are compared in Figure 1 which shows that the result is quite coincident and the discriminating line of red tides/non-red tides intersects at point Z = −236. The swinging of the calculated values results from the irregularity of the four parameters, but a sharp change from non-red tides to red tides shows that the model can distinguish them. The curves (1) and (3) in Figure 1 are the ordinal sequences of the non red tide data and red tide data in Table 1, respectively. These two curves are obviously on both sides of the discriminating model curve of this paper, and give the same result as the Kato et al. (1985) values (Z). Equation (6) of this paper may, therefore, be used as the discriminating model for red tides/non-red tides in Ise Bay, Japan.

The model for predicting red tides

Take five data (Z) points out, respectively, from the two parts of red tides and non-red tides in Table 1, let Z = −Z, and build a non-negative and increasing new sequence. With the same treatment of the GM(1,5) model, we took the calculated result of formula $\hat{a} = [(A\!:\!B)^T (A\!:\!B)]^{-1} (A\!:\!B)^T\ Y_N$ into equation (1), and deduced a differential equation:

$$\frac{dX^{(1)}(t)}{dt} - 0.01564\ X_1^{(1)}(t) = 218.676 \tag{6}$$

If $X_1^{(1)}(1) = X_1^{(0)}(0) = -221.966$, we also get the corresponding response time formula and the discrete response formula, and can then reduce them.

Here, in order to get directly to the reduced predicting value, we take a simpler mathematical treatment to the discrete formula and obtain the predicting model as follows:

$$\hat{X}_1^{(0)}(k) = (\hat{X}_1^{(0)}(0) + 13982)\ e^{0.01564(k-1)}\ (1 - e^{0.01564}) \tag{7}$$

Table 2
The results for GM(1,5) modelling

$$dX_1/dt + aX_1 = bX_2 + cX_3 + dX_4 + eX_5$$

$$\hat{X}_1^{(1)}(k) = (X_1(0) - b/aX_2(k)) \cdot \exp(-a(k-1)) + b/aX_2(k) + c/aX_3(k) \cdot d/aX_4(k) + e/aX_5(k)$$

$$\hat{X}_1^{(0)}(k) = \hat{X}_1^{(1)}(k) - \hat{X}_1^{(1)}(k-1).$$

Initial value			Predicted value	Deviation
(1)	(2)	(3)	(1)–(2)	(1)–(3)
221.966	−238.710	−221.966	16.744	0
226.531	−70.427	−216.014	−156.104	−10.517
227.221	−183.037	−223.435	−44.184	−3.786
227.585	−228.188	−239.398	0.603	11.813
232.310	−228.392	−231.503	−3.918	−0.807
240.506	−245.131	−245.994	4.625	5.488
243.947	−244.328	−244.567	0.381	−0.620
246.296	−248.861	−248.928	2.565	2.632
247.536	−246.367	−246.386	−1.169	−1.150
254.936	−246.492	−246.497	−8.444	−8.439
		Non-red tides		
213.788	−228.529	−213.788	14.741	0.000
214.183	−68.546	−214.183	−145.637	0.000
221.077	−188.721	−213.533	−32.356	−7.544
221.539	−222.245	−223.431	0.706	1.892
221.861	−227.533	−228.730	5.672	6.869
221.966	−227.442	−228.647	5.476	6.681
226.531	−233.024	−234.237	6.493	7.706
227.221	−210.315	−211.536	−16.906	−15.685
227.585	−227.111	−228.340	−0.474	0.755
232.310	−218.281	−219.521	−14.029	−12.789
		Red Tides		
222.968	−218.519	−222.986	−4.467	0.000
240.506	−59.454	−240.506	−181.052	0.000
243.947	−220.112	−238.990	−23.835	−4.957
246.296	−248.317	−250.012	2.021	3.716
247.536	−249.776	−251.481	2.240	3.945
254.936	−253.058	−254.783	−1.878	−0.153
258.123	−259.173	−260.915	1.050	2.792
262.593	−256.204	−257.952	−6.389	−4.641
264.794	−262.384	−264.152	−2.410	−0.642
266.492	−259.490	−261.271	−7.002	−5.221

*(1) is from Kato et al. (1985).
** (2) is the predicted value; (3) = (2) + s (s is deviation value predicted using the GM(1,1) model).

Table 3
The results for modelling GM(1,1)
$$dX1/dt - aX1 = \mu$$
$$\hat{X}_1^{(0)}(k) = (X1(0) - \mu/a) * \exp(-a*(k-1)) * (1-\exp(a)).$$

Initial	Predicted	Initial − Predicted	%
221.966	220.419	1.547	0.7 (%)
226.531	223.893	2.638	1.2 (%)
227.221	227.422	−0.201	0.1 (%)
227.585	231.007	−3.422	1.5 (%)
232.310	234.648	−2.338	1.0 (%)
240.506	238.347	2.159	0.9 (%)
243.947	242.104	1.843	0.8 (%)
246.296	245.92	0.376	0.2 (%)
254.936	253.733	1.203	0.5 (%)

Non-red tides

Initial	Predicted	Initial − Predicted	%
213.788	215.280	−1.492	0.7 (%)
214.183	216.965	−2.782	1.3 (%)
221.077	218.662	2.415	1.1 (%)
221.539	220.374	1.165	0.5 (%)
221.861	222.098	−0.237	0.1 (%)
221.966	223.836	−1.870	0.8 (%)
226.531	225.587	0.944	0.4 (%)
227.221	227.353	−0.132	0.1 (%)
227.585	229.132	−1.547	0.7 (%)
232.310	230.925	1.385	0.6 (%)

Red Tides

Initial	Predicted	Initial − Predicted	%
222.986	236.805	−13.819	6.2 (%)
240.506	240.098	0.408	0.2 (%)
243.947	243.436	0.511	0.2 (%)
246.296	246.820	−0.524	0.2 (%)
247.536	250.252	−2.716	1.1 (%)
254.936	253.731	1.205	0.5 (%)
258.123	257.258	0.865	0.3 (%)
262.593	260.835	1.758	0.7 (%)
264.794	264.461	0.333	0.1 (%)
266.492	268.138	−1.646	0.6 (%)

* $a1 = -0.01564$; $\mu1 = 218.676$.
** $a2 = -0.00779$; $\mu2 = 214.454$.
*** $a3 = -0.01380$; $\mu3 = 235.364$.

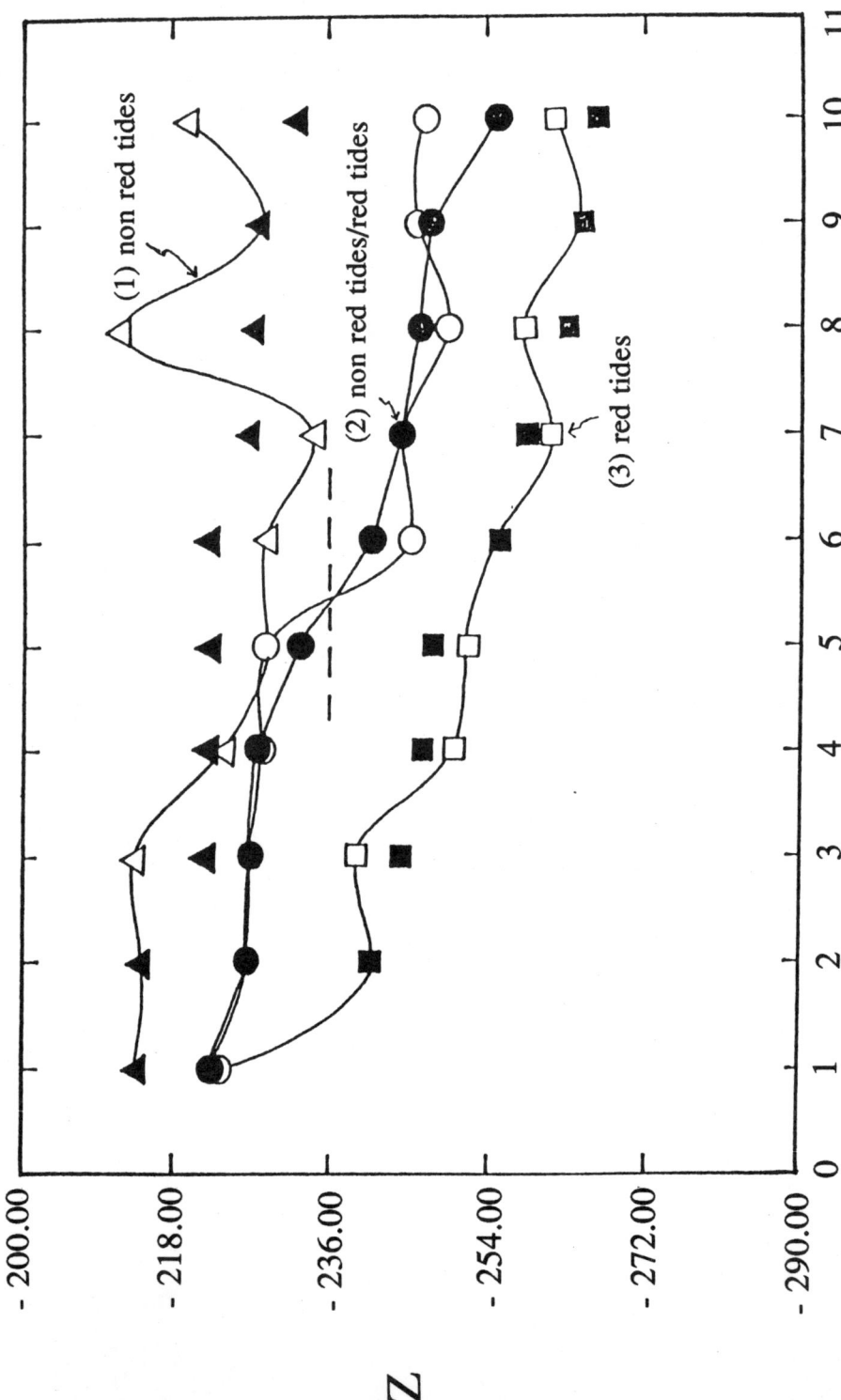

Fig. 1. Comparing the prediction values of GM (1, 5) with initial values.
▲, ●, ■ — initial values, △, ○, □ — prediction values.

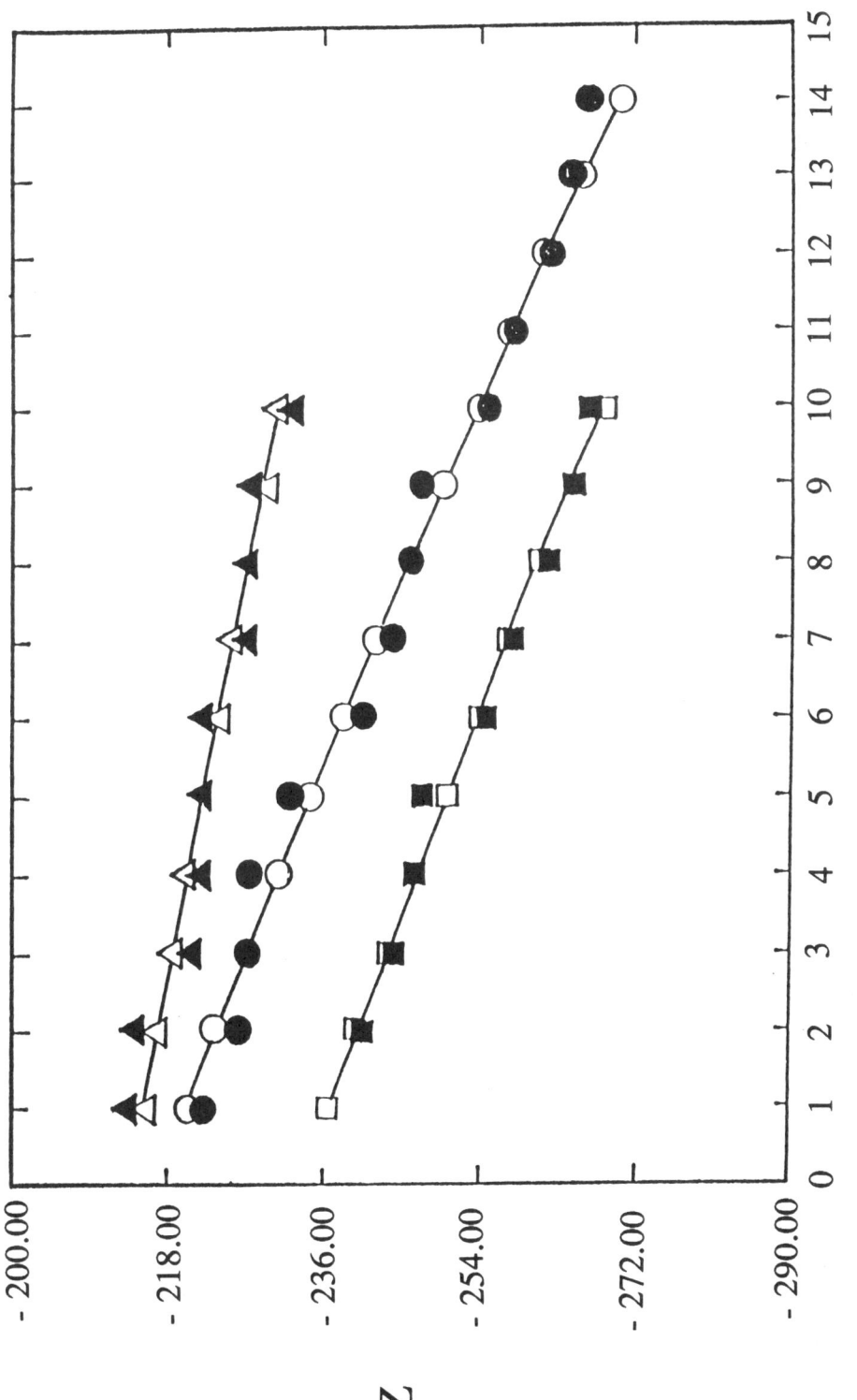

Fig. 2. Comparing the prediction values of GM (1, 1) with initial values. ▲, ●, ■ — initial values, △, ○, □ — prediction values.

in which, $\hat{X}_1^{(0)}(k)$ is the calculated Z values while k = 1, 2, ..., 10. Predicting the forecasting values of the model (the value of $X_1^{(0)}(k)$, k = N + 1, ..., N + 4) calculated from this equation are shown in Table 3 and Figure 2. The predicting precision of GM(1,1) is clearly higher than that of GM(1,5). Therefore, given the value of the discriminating function (Z), one may use the equation (7) as the predicting model of red tides in Ise Bay.

The prediction of red tide frequencies

The gray system prediction is based on the prediction of the GM(1,1) model. The prediction also covers the catastrophe prediction in addition to the sequence prediction, e.g., the model previous for predicting red tides. In this paper, the annual frequency of red tide occurrences in Tolo Harbour, can be illustrated as follows.

According to the Environmental Protection Department, Hong Kong (1988), the annual frequencies of red tides occurring in Tolo Harbour waters since 1977 has increased (Fig. 3). From Figure 3, the sequence of the initial data does not satisfy the requirement of the non-negative and increasing gray model. Accordingly, the approach taken in this paper, and taking the frequency (9 times) of red tides which occurred in 1983 as the threshold, we can gain a new sequence. Adopting the previous approach of setting up GM(1,1), we may get a prediction for annual red tide frequencies occurring in Tolo Harbour between 1983 to 1987 (Table 4, Fig. 3). The predicted results are satisfactory; but the forecast values for 1988 to 1991 should be tested.

Table 4
The results for modelling GM(1,1)

$$dx1/dt - a\, x1 = u$$
$$\hat{x}1(k) = (x1(0) - u/a) * \exp(-a*(k-1)) * (1 - \exp(a)).$$

Initial	Predicted	Initial − Predicted	%
221.966	220.419	1.547	.7 (%)
226.531	223.893	2.638	1.2 (%)
227.221	227.422	−.201	.1 (%)
227.585	231.007	−3.422	1.5 (%)
232.31	234.648	−2.338	1 (%)
240.506	238.347	2.159	.9 (%)
243.947	242.104	1.843	.8 (%)
246.296	245.92	.376	.2 (%)
247.536	249.796	−2.26	.9 (%)
254.936	253.733	1.203	.5 (%)

Forecast Value			
Initial	Predicted	Initial − Predicted	%
258.123	257.733	.39	.2 (%)
262.593	261.795	.798	.3 (%)
264.794	265.922	−1.128	.4 (%)
266.492	270.113	−3.621 1	.4 (%)

* initial data from Kato *et al.* (1985).
** a = −0.01564; u = 218.676.

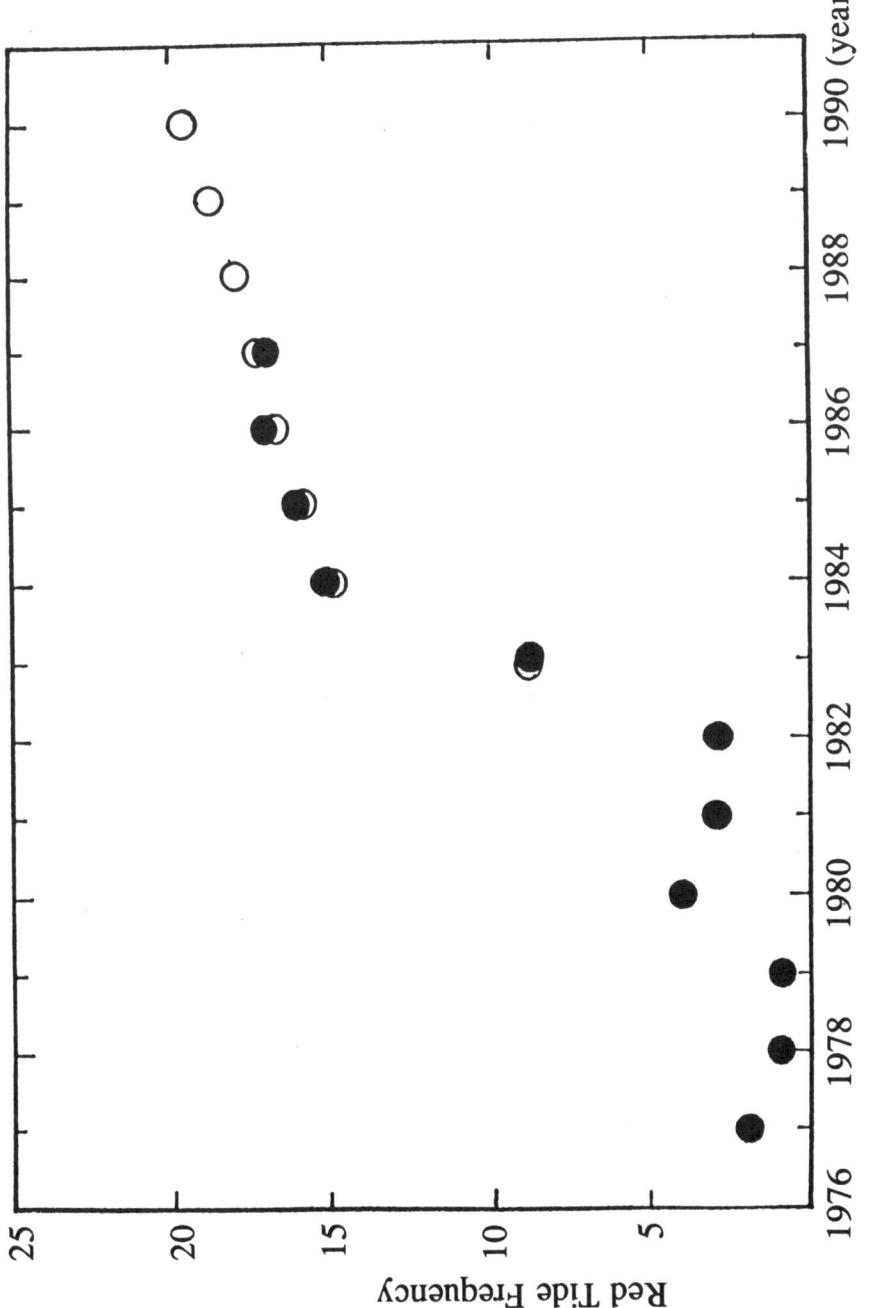

Fig. 3. Comparing the predicted red tide frequencies for Tolo Harbour with observed values. ● — observed values, ○ — predicted values.

DISCUSSION

Identification of the discriminating function (Z)

Based on Kato et al. (1985), we did a random sampling calculation of the discriminating function (Z) using data from Tolo Harbour and Shenzhen Bay in Guangdong province, China, where red tides occur (Fig. 4). The results showed that the obtained prediction values of (Z) are all greater than –236.915. It appears that this results from distinctions between environmental parameters in Tolo Harbour, Shenzhen Bay and Ise Bay during the period of red tides occurrences. We, therefore, need to examine further whether the discriminating function (Z) and the discriminating point (Z) = –236.915, which was deduced from data for dinoflagellate and diatom red tides occurring in Ise Bay are suitable for other types of red tides and other sea areas. However, if one tries to use the gray model for red tide occurrence, we suggest that one carries out a discriminating analysis of the research area first, and selects the important factors to set up the discriminating function (Z) fitting the area, then do the gray model calculation. We believe that the previous problem would not influence the useability of the model itself, although the GM(1,5) state model used in this paper also adopted the results of Kato et al. (1985).

Table 5
Prediction of the frequency of red tides occurring in Tolo Harbour, between 1980–87.

Year	Initial*	Predicted	Initial – Predicted	%
1982	4	4	0	0 (%)
1983	9	9.7	–0.7	7.7 (%)
1984	15	14.0	1.0	6.7 (%)
1985	16	15.5	0.5	3.1 (%)
1986	17	17.1	–0.1	0.6 (%)
1987	17	19.0	–2.0	11.8 (%)
		Forecast value		
1988	?	21.1	?	? (%)
1989	?	23.4	?	? (%)
1990	?	26.1	?	? (%)

* initial data from Environmental Protection Department, Hong Kong 1988.

The predicting precision of the model

To confirm the predicting value of the model, we can divide into two parts. That is, for: $t\epsilon\{ 0, 1, 2, ..., N \}$, where N is the present, one may compare the predicting sequence (accumulated value or reduced value sequence) with the initial sequence. The smaller the deviation, the higher the reliability. As shown in Tables 2 and 3, there is a lower precision of GM(1,5) than GM(1,1), but after amending the difference, its precision is improved.

However, for: $t\epsilon\{ N+1, N+2, ... , N+n, ... \}$, in which N+i means the forecasted

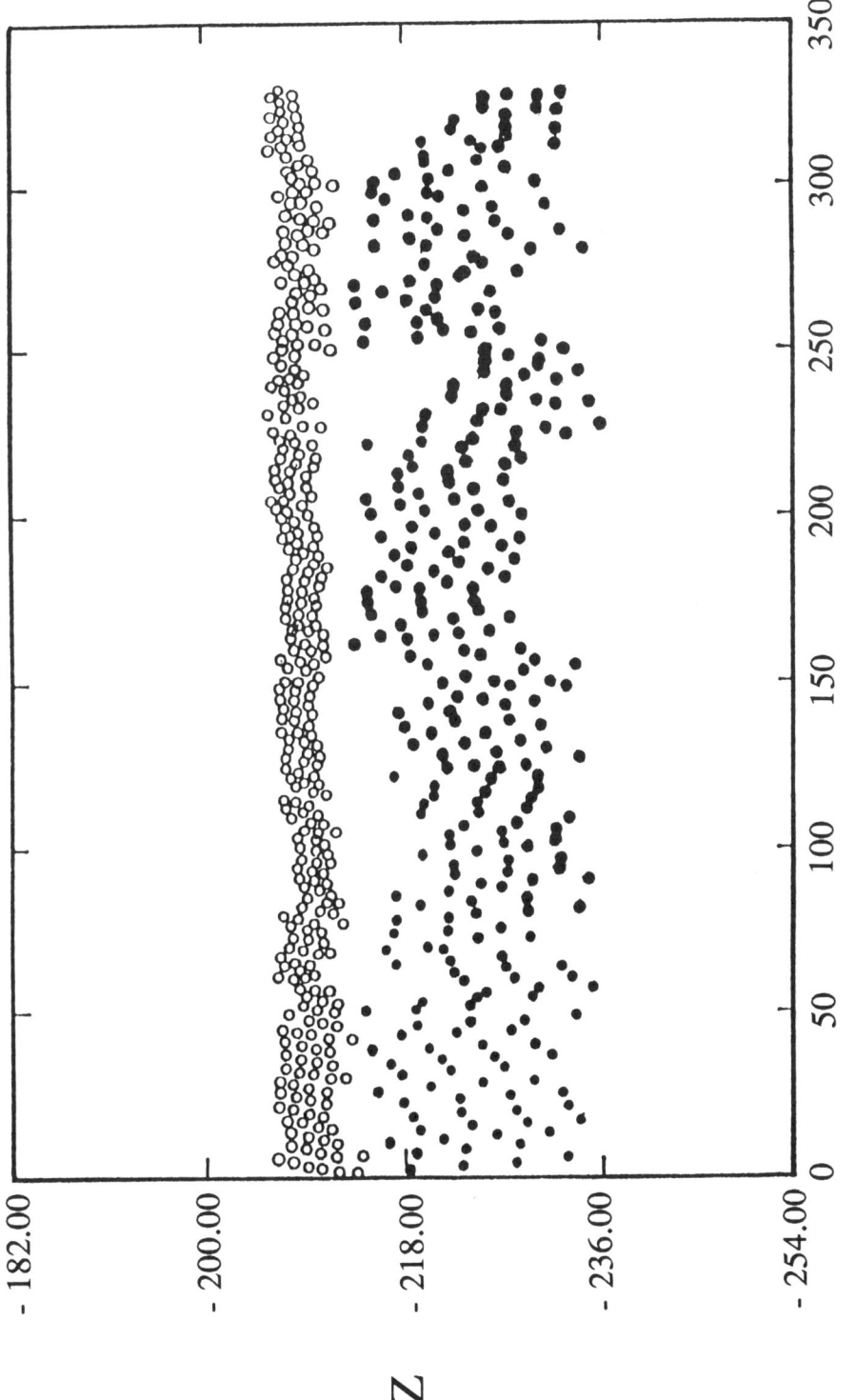

Fig. 4. The random sampling calculation of the discriminating function (z), using data from Tolo Harbour, Hong Kong and Shenzhen Bay, China.
○ — Shenzhen Bay, • — Tolo Harbour

values after N, one may compare the average line of the gray plane, i.e., the border plane of the possible range in future development, to the predicting value. The smaller the difference, the higher the credibility.

If the precision is not satisfactory, one can modify it by the previous deviation analysis. But, as the GM(1,1) model has only one exponent, its changing process with time is monotone (Fig. 2) so that it can not reflect fluctuating conditions. If there is a need to reflect fluctuating conditions, one may use the GM(2,1) model. As GM(2,1) is a second order model and has two characteristic roots, the dynamic process may reflect a different condition (monotone, non-monotone or fluctuating (oscillation)). Details can be obtained by reference to Deng (1986).

CONCLUSIONS

Based on the gray control system theory, this paper proposes a new method for predicting red tide events. This method regards red tide organisms and their living environment as a gray system, selects appropriate parameters, uses a short time data set and sets up a gray model describing dynamics. Such a discrete model can be used to discriminate red tides/non-red tides, predict the possible occurrence of red tides and their frequency.

According to the parameters of pH, dissolved oxygen, salinity, PO_4–P, and the discriminating function (Z), selected by Kato et al. (1985) to discriminate and analyse red tides in Ise Bay, this paper sets up a discrete expression of the GM(1,5) model. It discriminates between and predicts whether red tides will occur from the initial Z value and the value of pH, dissolved oxygen, salinity, PO_4 –P at any one time. Based on the Z value, the discrete expression of the GM(1,1) model set up in this paper is of good predicting accuracy. These two equations may, therefore, be suitable for the discrimination and prediction of red tides in Ise Bay.

From the prediction of red tides frequencies in Tolo Harbour one may find that it is necessary to choose a suitable threshold to create a new sequence which satisfies the non-negative and increasing condition.

According to the previous discussion, we suggest that when a gray model predicting red tides is set up in any sea area, it needs to first build for a discriminating function (Z) equation and identify the discriminating point (Z) of red tides/non-red tides. We will undertake a further examination of the gray predicting model proposed in this paper for red tides which occur in the Pearl River estuarine and adjacent waters.

ACKNOWLEDGEMENTS

This work was supported in part by the Science Foundation of the Chinese Academy of Sciences. We wish to express our thanks to colleagues in our research group for their kind support.

REFERENCES

Deng, J.L. 1986. *Gray Control System*. China: The Publisher of Central China College of Technology.
Environmental Protection Department. 1988. *Environment Hong Kong 1988*. Hong Kong: The Government Printer.
Ikeda, S. 1987. *Science on Red Tides*. Tsune Hoshi Medical Press.
Kato, S., Hirobe, H. and Maegawa, T. 1985. On the essential sea water parameters to discriminate between red tide and non red tide by discriminant anaylsis. *Bulletin of the Japanese Society of Scientific Fisheries* 51:7–12.
Ouchi, A. and Takayama, H. 1981. A red tide map study by the principal component analysis. *Bulletin of the Japanese Society Scientific Fisheries* 47:1275–9.
Ouchi, A. 1982. Prediction of red tide occurrence by means of multiple linear regression model. *Bulletin of the Japanese Society of Scientific Fisheries* 48:1245–50.
Ouchi, A. 1984. Prediction of red tide occurrence by means of discriminant analysis. *Bulletin of the Japanese Society of Scientific Fisheries* 50:1647–51.
Ouchi, A. and Takayama, H. 1984. Prediction of *Gymnodinium* 65 red tide by means of red tide map. *Bulletin of the Japanese Society of Scientific Fisheries* 50:1201–5.
Zou, J.Z., Dong, L.P. and Qin, B.P. 1985. Preliminary studies on eutrophication and red tide problems in Bohai Bay. *Hydrobiologia* 127:27–30.

AMMONIUM UPTAKE BY *ULVA LACTUCA* (CHLOROPHYTA: ULVALES)

Y.B. Ho

Department of Botany, The University of Hong Kong, Hong Kong

ABSTRACT

The ability of *Ulva lactuca* L. to grow well in waters with high ammonium (NH_4^+) concentrations resulting from domestic sewage contamination implies that the alga can utilize NH_4^+ as a nitrogen source. This assumption was tested by measuring the rate of NH_4^+ uptake and the results show that the alga has a high capacity to acquire NH_4^+. A fresh frond of *U. lactuca* weighing 1.2 g (0.24 g dry wt) removed 21 µmol of NH_4^+ in 50 minutes (at a temperature of 15°C and an irradiance of 40 µmol·m^{-2}·s^{-1}). The algal uptake rate was linearly proportional to NH_4^+ concentration in the medium and reached 3.7 µmol N·g dry wt^{-1}·min^{-1} at 24.3 µM, the highest concentration tested. Further, the alga took up NH_4^+ some four to five times faster when illuminated at an irradiance of 19 µmol·m^{-2}·s^{-1}, than in the dark. On transfer from a dark to a light regime, the rate of uptake increased, within 15 minutes, to the same level as when illuminated. The enhanced uptake rate in the light indicates that active uptake may occur with photosynthesis producing the ATP and/or carbon skeleton necessary for the uptake process. Overall results show clearly that *U. lactuca* takes up NH_4^+ readily from the medium and this may partly explain its high growth performance in ammonium-rich waters.

INTRODUCTION

Nitrogen is an essential element often in short supply in the marine environment and its limitation commonly restricts the growth of phytoplankton (Ryther and Dunstan 1971) and macroalgae (Hanisak 1983) in coastal waters. Strong evidence for nitrogen limitation in the coastal environment is that *in situ* addition of nitrogen enhanced the growth of macroalgae. Replenishment of nitrogen may be from sporadic, natural sources such as storms, upwelling, freshwater input, animal excreta, detritus decomposition, and fluxes from sediment. The first three sources usually provide high levels of nitrate while the other three release ammonia and organic nitrogen in the form of urea and amines. If the supply of nitrogen is sporadic, some macroalgae are able to take it up rapidly for storage in times of availability, thus sustaining algal growth even during periods of low nitrogen supply (Rosenberg et al. 1984). Indeed the ability of macroalgae for such 'surge' uptake confers competitive advantage to them since they will be able to make use of nitrogen sources whenever they are available, as was demonstrated for *Gracilaria* by Lapointe (1985).

Nitrogen replenishment in the coastal environment may be of a more permanent nature and its release from wastewater outfalls as a result of human activities is common. This generally results in substantial increases in the growth of certain macroalgae near the outfalls.

Members of the genera *Enteromorpha* and *Ulva,* in the Ulvaceae, are able to grow rapidly in nitrogen-enriched environments, e.g., Kautsky (1982), and DeBusk et al. (1986). This may be due partly to the fact that they can take up nutrients rapidly both under transient (Fujita 1985; O'Brien and Wheeler 1987; Thomas and Harrison 1987) and prolonged (Rosenberg and Ramus 1981; Kautsky 1982) nutrient supply conditions. Thus, both *Enteromorpha* and *Ulva* are often important contributors to primary productivity and play a significant role in nutrient recycling in intertidal and nearshore waters. Indeed these macroalgae have long been known to grow prolifically in areas with high nutrient input, such as those contaminated by domestic sewage, e.g., Letts and Richards (1911), Sawyer (1965).

In Hong Kong, previous survey work (Ho 1986a, b) indicated widespread occurrence and, at times, abundant growth of the alga *Ulva lactuca* L. in sewage-contaminated intertidal waters, e.g., Victoria Harbour. This indicates that the alga has the ability to utilize NH_4^+ which is a major source of nitrogen in domestic sewage. The present paper reports on experiments designed to test the capacity of *Ulva lactuca* to take up NH_4^+ from the medium with reference to its concentration, the light intensity, and the presence or absence of light. Preliminary results show that *Ulva* has a high capacity to take up NH_4^+ from the medium and this capacity is enhanced in the light. The results partly explain the ability of the alga to grow well in ammonium-rich waters.

MATERIALS AND METHODS

Collection and selection of materials

Fresh, vegetative, *Ulva* individuals were collected during low tide from the lower littoral zone. They were sealed in plastic bags and transported to the laboratory within one and a half hours. The plants were acclimated to laboratory conditions by keeping them overnight in a large tank of aerated, filtered (0.45 µm Millipore) seawater containing 2 µM PO_4^{3-}, 20 µM NO_3^-, and less than 0.5 µM NH_4^+.

The following criterion for the selection of *Ulva* thalli was adopted so as to obtain uniform algal materials for the NH_4^+ uptake experiments. The part of the thallus near the holdfast was not used since it has both a slower rate of growth and general metabolism, e.g., photosynthesis, than the other parts of the thallus (Ho, unpublished data). Similarly, marginal cells of the thallus, which readily turned reproductive and thus behaved physiologically different from the vegetative cells, were discarded. Only the central part of the thallus was used for the experiments. Previous culture work (Ho 1986c) showed that excised portions from the thallus continued to grow and behave apparently normally. Immediately before use, the algal thallus was wiped gently with a ball of cotton wool to rid it of as many adhering organisms as possible.

Experimental procedure

Preliminary uptake experiment. Ammonium uptake rates were measured by the perturbation method in which the alga was incubated in a container and the medium therein sampled repeatedly so that ammonium levels could be determined. Three-litre capacity Erlenmeyer flasks were used as incubation containers and the treatment was done in duplicate. At the start of the experiment, a sufficient volume of ammonium sulphate solution was added to each flask containing filtered seawater so as to make 1 dm^3 of medium with an ammonium concentration of about 25 µM. The medium was mixed thoroughly and then three 10 cm^3 samples were taken to determine the initial ammonium concentration. A piece of *Ulva* thallus (1–2 g fresh weight) was put into the flask at zero time and the medium was sampled at intervals (three 10 cm^3 samples each time) over 150 minutes to monitor the rate of ammonium removal by the alga. The concentration of NH_4^+ was determined by the phenol-hypochlorite method (Strickland and Parsons 1972). The irradiance level was 40 µmol·m^{-2}·s^{-1} (from cool-white fluorescent light), the temperature was 15°C, and aeration and mixing were effected by placing the flasks in a rotatory shaker set at 100 rpm. Two control flasks without any alga were also set up and it was found by monitoring their ammonium concentrations that the level did not vary by more than 1.5% throughout the experiment, thus indicating that no significant adsorption onto the surface of the container occurred. At the end of the experiment the algal thallus in each flask was retrieved, rinsed momentarily in distilled water, and dried at 80°C overnight to obtain the dry weight. Ammonium uptake rates were calculated as µmol N·g^{-1} dry wt·min^{-1}.

Ammonium uptake, dark versus light. To determine the effects of light and dark on the ammonium uptake rate of *Ulva*, four flasks were set up, two were covered with aluminium foil so that no light could penetrate, the other two left illuminated at an irradiance of 19 µmol·m^{-2}·s^{-1}. The ammonium uptake rates of the algal thallus kept in these flasks were determined as in the previous experiment, the other experimental conditions being identical.

Dark-light transition effect on uptake rate. In this experiment one flask was set up as the light control and received an irridance of 40 µmol·m^{-2}·s^{-1}. Three other flasks were covered with aluminium foil at the start of the experiment and the ammonium uptake by *Ulva* in all four flasks was monitored. After 46.5 minutes the foil covering two of the flasks was removed and their uptake rates and that of the light control were monitored for a further 115 minutes whereas the dark control was monitored for another 203.5 minutes following the initial 46.5 minutes. The other conditions were as for the first experiment.

RESULTS

For the preliminary uptake experiment temporal changes in the amount of NH_4^+ removed from the medium and the rate of ammonium uptake by *Ulva* are presented in Figure 1. The rapid uptake rate of the alga resulted in the removal of most of the NH_4^+ from the medium within 50 minutes. As the amount of NH_4^+ in the medium decreased, there was a corresponding drop in the uptake rate (Fig. 1) and this is also reflected in Figure 2 which showed an almost linear relationship between the ammonium uptake rate of *Ulva* and the ammonium concentration in the medium.

Figure 3 shows the changes in the concentration of NH_4^+ in the medium with time for both the dark and light treatments. The corresponding plots between the ammonium uptake rate of the alga and ammonium concentration in the medium are presented in Figure 4. After an initial lag phase lasting about 10 minutes (Fig. 3) the fall in ammonium concentration in the illuminated flasks was consistently faster than the covered ones. At high ammonium concentration, e.g., 20 µM, the illuminated alga took up NH_4^+ some 4.8 times faster than that under dark conditions (Fig. 4). *Ulva* was exposed to different irridiance levels in the first two experiments and Figure 5 shows clearly that ammonium uptake rate of the alga was faster at the higher irradiance level.

Figure 6 shows the decrease in the amount of NH_4^+ in the medium in the dark and light controls and in the dark-light transition treatment. The rate of decrease of NH_4^+ in the treatment medium was at first very similar to the dark control. But soon after exposure to light the amount of NH_4^+ in the treatment decreased rapidly, reaching a rate similar to that of the light control. Such a change is clearly illustrated in Figure 7 which gives the relationship between the uptake rate and ammonium concentration for the two controls and the treatment.

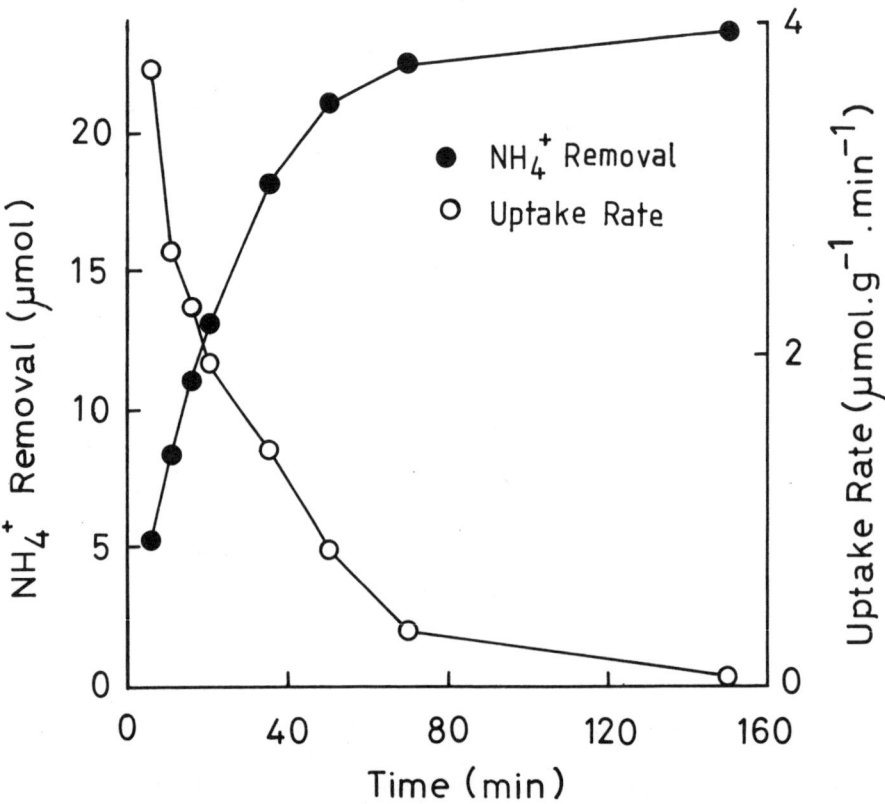

Fig. 1. Temporal changes in NH_4^+ removal from the medium and the rate of NH_4^+ uptake by *Ulva* in the preliminary experiment.

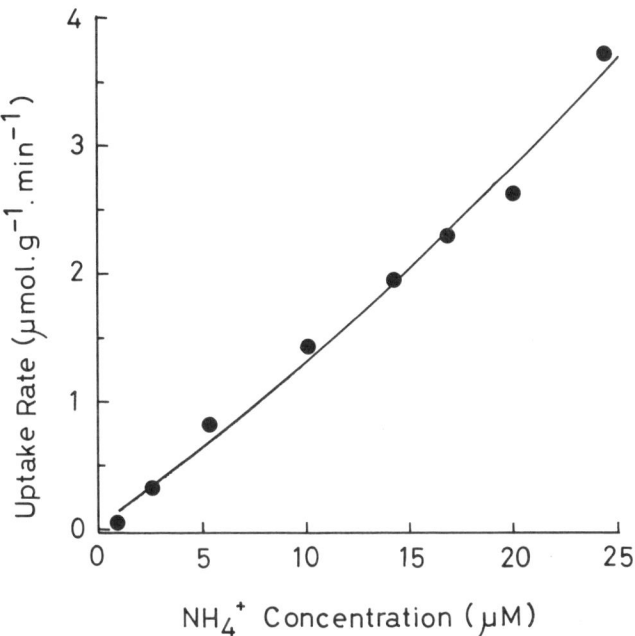

Fig. 2. Relationship between the rate of uptake of NH_4^+ by *Ulva* and NH_4^+ concentration in the medium.

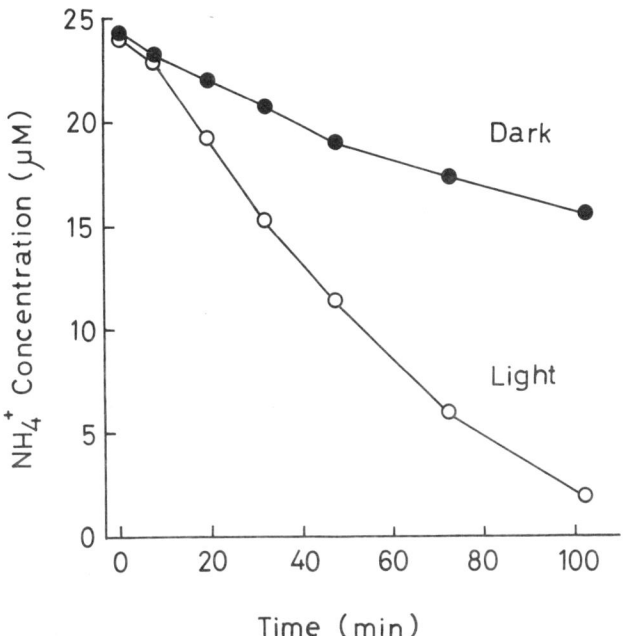

Fig. 3. Temporal changes in the ammonium concentration of the medium in the dark and light treatments.

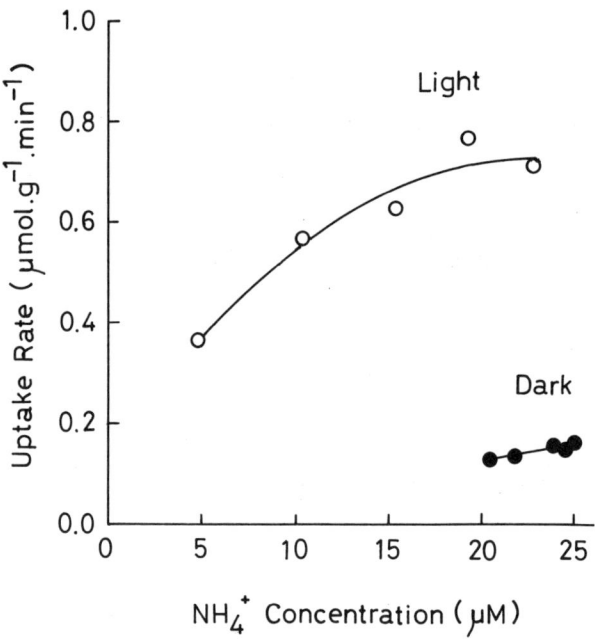

Fig. 4. Relationship between ammonium uptake rate of *Ulva* and ammonium concentration of the medium in the dark and light treatments.

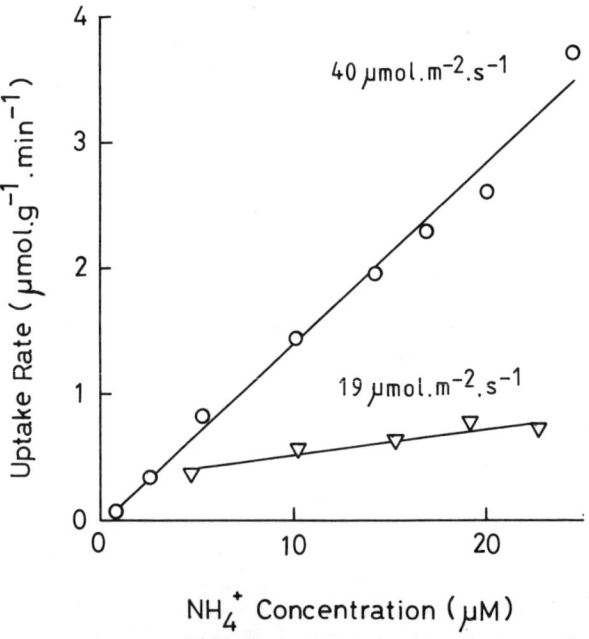

Fig. 5. Uptake rate versus ammonium concentration at two irradiance levels.

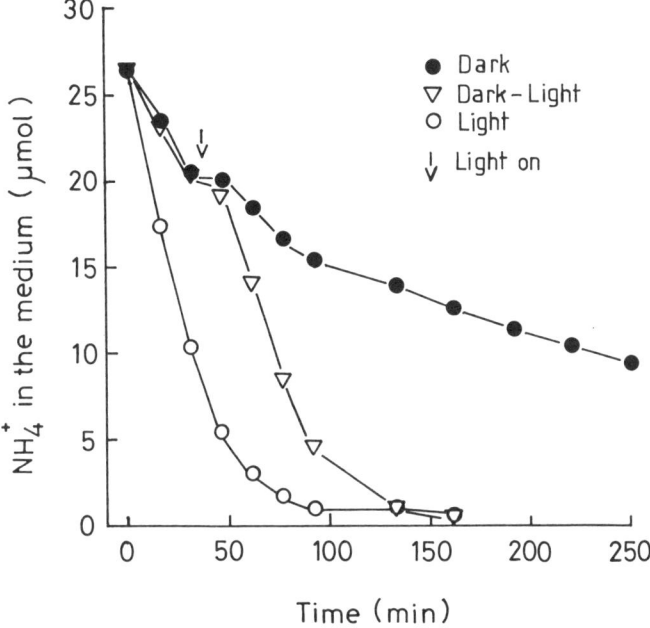

Fig. 6. Temporal changes in the amounts of NH_4^+ remaining in the medium in the dark and light controls and in the dark-light transition treatment.

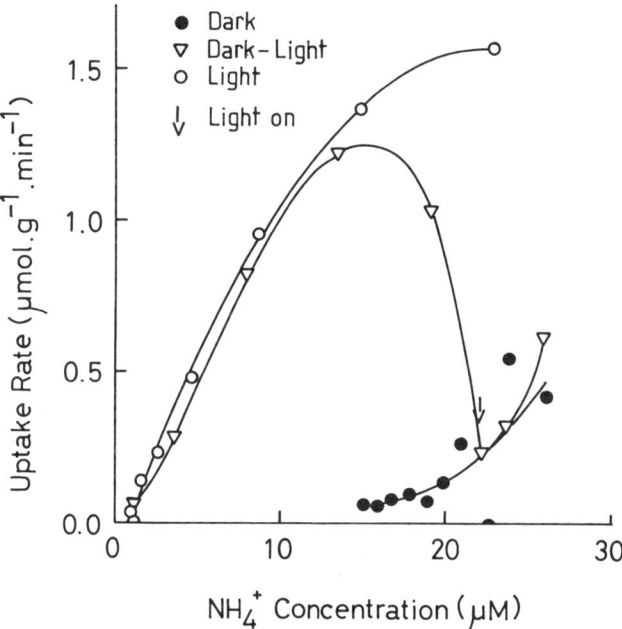

Fig. 7. Relationship between uptake rate and ammonium concentration for the dark and light controls and the dark-light transition treatment.

DISCUSSION

Some species of macroalgae grow better on NH_4^+ than on nitrate and, on the whole, they have higher maximum uptake rates for NH_4^+ than for nitrate (refer to the review paper by Hanisak 1983). Evidently *U. lactuca* is one such alga having shown an uptake rate of 3.71 µmol·g^{-1}·min^{-1} (some 220 µmol·g^{-1}·h^{-1}) at an ammonium concentration of about 25 µM (Fig. 2). Similar high NH_4^+ uptake rates have been found for other members of the Ulvaceae, namely, 188 µmol·g^{-1}·h^{-1} for *Enteromorpha prolifera* (Müller) J. Agardh (O'Brien and Wheeler 1987), 6 µmol·g^{-1}·min^{-1} for *U. lactuca* (Fujita 1985) and about 240 µmol·g^{-1}·h^{-1} for *U. curvata* (Hützing) DeToni (estimated from Fig. 2 of Rosenberg and Ramus 1984).

A positive linear relationship was found between algal uptake rate and concentration of NH_4^+ in the medium up to 24.3 µM, the highest concentration employed (Fig. 2). Thus, no saturation of uptake took place even at the highest concentration tested, indicating that over such a concentration range uptake was by diffusion and that Michaelis-Menten kinetics were not obeyed. Hence, the maximum uptake rate at saturating substrate concentration (V_{max}) and the half-saturation constant for the substrate (K_s) could not be found. Fujita (1985) also observed that freshly collected *U. lactuca* took up NH_4^+ rapidly and that uptake was a linear function of ammonium concentration up to at least 60 µM. Unlike *U. lactuca*, *Enteromorpha* spp. (Link) showed a distinctly biphasic pattern of uptake as a function of ammonium concentration (Fujita 1985). Here the uptake rate in the second phase, which started to operate when the ammonium concentration exceeded 30 µM, was much faster than the first one. The non-saturable rapid uptake of NH_4^+ by *U. lactuca* indicated its ability to utilize a wide concentration range of NH_4^+ as a source of nitrogen. This probably partly explains the cosmopolitan nature of the alga and its prolific growth in areas contaminated by domestic sewage.

Relatively few studies have been made on the effect of light on nitrogen assimilation in macroalgae. This study shows clearly that the uptake of NH_4^+ by *Ulva* is greater in the light (Figs. 3 and 4) and that an higher irradiance level increased the rate of uptake (Fig. 5). However the effect of light on nutrient uptake may vary according to the species, other environmental conditions, and the metabolic state of the alga concerned. The rate of ammonium uptake for *Macrocystis pyrifera* (L.) C.A. Agardh. was similar in the dark as well as in the light (Wheeler 1982). However, for *Codium fragile* (van Goor) Silva, the uptake of NH_4^+, as in the case of *Ulva*, was reduced in the dark (Hanisak and Harlin 1978).

Light may affect ammonium uptake primarily through photosynthesis in a number of ways. Through the process of photophosphorylation, light provides energy in the form of ATP for active transport. The photosynthetically fixed carbon may act as skeletons for the incorporation of NH_4^+ into larger molecules such as amino acids. The rapid increase in the NH_4^+ uptake rate of *Ulva* on transition from dark to light (Figs. 6 and 7) may be due to these effects. Further photosynthesis provides energy for the production of anions which establishes Donnan potentials for the uptake of cations like NH_4^+. Finally, light-induced increases in growth rate may in turn speed up nutrient uptake by the alga.

There are morphological, anatomical and physiological reasons which may account for the rapid uptake of NH_4^+ by *Ulva*. First, the thin, sheet-like thallus of the *Ulva* confers a high surface area to volume (SA:V) ratio for efficient nutrient uptake. Rosenberg and Ramus (1984) working on surge uptake of NH_4^+ and nitrate by four intertidal macroalgae, showed that uptake rates were positively correlated with the SA:V ratio. Amongst the four algae examined, *U. curvata* had both the highest SA:V ratio (165:1) and the highest uptake rates of both NH_4^+ and nitrate at all the nutrient concentrations tested. The authors suggested the possible use of the SA:V ratio as a comparative index of nutrient uptake capability in co-existing macroalgae.

Second, the distromatic structure of the thallus means that every cell is in direct contact with its surroundings and hence efficient exchange (including nutrient uptake) between the cell and the environment is possible. Further, all the cells in the thallus are photosynthetic, metabolically active and capable of rapid vegetative growth. All these features of the thallus indicate that *U. lactuca* is a species adapted to an opportunistic strategy. According to Littler and Littler (1980) opportunistic forms should possess relatively simple and undifferentiated thalli with a high SA:V ratio. They should also have high net productivity and fast rates of nutrient uptake thus providing a potential for rapid growth and enabling them to colonize newly available substrates along the shore.

Apart from surge uptake of nutrients, *Ulva* is also capable of prolonged uptake of NH_4^+ at relatively rapid rates. Fujita (1985) showed that *U. lactuca* took up NH_4^+ at a rate of 2.3 $\mu mol \cdot g^{-1} \cdot min^{-1}$ after prior exposure to a high flux of nitrogen. This indicates that the alga can take up NH_4^+ and then assimilate, incorporate and store it in the nitrogen pool within the cell efficiently. Storage of nitrogen after rapid uptake enables the alga to maintain a period of high growth rate even when the external supply of nitrogen drops to a low level. Indeed Fujita (1985) found that, after pulse feeding *U. lactuca* for 10 hours with NH_4^+ at a concentration of 20 μM, the alga continued to grow for 6 to 9 days under laboratory conditions without any further external supply of nitrogen. Presumably the alga made use of the stored nitrogen to maintain growth. Similarly DeBusk *et al.* (1986) pulse fed *U. lactuca* in outdoor cultures with a high level of nitrogen, either as nitrate or NH_4^+, for 24 hours every week for an eight-month period and found that the alga maintained a very high average growth rate of 18.8 g dry wt· $m^{-2} \cdot day^{-1}$. Using $^{15}N-NH_4^+$ as a tracer Fujita *et al.* (1988) also showed that assimilation of the nutrient at maximum rate for three hours would fulfil the daily nitrogen requirement of *U. rigida* C. Agardh for maximal growth. Further it was shown that NH_4^+ constituted less than 1% of the storage pool of nitrogen in the alga, thus indicating its rapid assimilation into other forms of soluble nitrogen. This allowed maximum uptake of NH_4^+.

The incorporation of NH_4^+ into *Ulva* elevated the nitrogen content of its tissue considerably. For example, when exposed to a high flux of NH_4^+ for 24 hours, the tissue nitrogen content of *U. lactuca* increased from 1.3% to 4.7% (DeBusk *et al.* 1986). In eutrophic waters the tissue nitrogen level of the alga often may exceed the critical nitrogen concentration, which is the tissue nitrogen content that just limits its maximum growth. If this happens, luxury consumption of the nutrient occurs. This probably applied to the *Ulva* harvested from Victoria Harbour where the tissue nitrogen content was mostly within the range of 4.3 to 5.3% (Ho 1987). This is not surprising, since due to sewage contamination, the ammonium (16 μM) and dissolved inorganic nitrogen (21 μM) concentrations of the Harbour waters were elevated. As a reference the critical nitrogen concentration for *U. rigida* was 3.0% (Fujita *et al.* 1989). Since *U. lactuca* is a common macroalga growing in Victoria Harbour, it is likely that in such an eutrophic condition, the high nutrient uptake ability, high growth rate and considerable nitrogen storage capacity of this opportunistic macroalga enable it to outgrow many other competing species.

REFERENCES

DeBusk, T.A., Blakeslee, M. and Ryther, J.H. 1986. Studies on the outdoor cultivation of *Ulva lactuca* L. *Botanica Marina* 29:381–6.

Fujita, R.M. 1985. The role of nitrogen status in regulating transient ammonium uptake and nitrogen storage by macroalgae. *Journal of Experimental Marine Biology and Ecology* 92:283–301.

Fujita, R.M., Wheeler, P.A. and Edwards, R.L. 1988. Metabolic regulation of ammonium uptake by *Ulva rigida* (Chlorophyta): a compartmental analysis of the rate-limiting step for uptake. *Journal of Phycology* 24:560–6.

Fujita, R.M., Wheeler, P.A. and Edwards, R.L. 1989. Assessment of macroalgal nitrogen limitation in a seasonal upwelling region. *Marine Ecology Progress Series* 53:293–303.

Hanisak, M.D. 1983. The nitrogen relationships of marine macroalgae. In *Nitrogen in the Marine Environment* (ed. E.J. Carpenter and D.G. Capone),699–730. New York: Academic Press.

Hanisak, M.D. and Harlin, M.M. 1978. Uptake of inorganic nitrogen by *Codium fragile* subsp. *tomentosoides* (Chlorophyta). *Journal of Phycology* 14:450–4.

Ho, Y.B. 1986a. Changes in the intertidal algal species in Victoria Harbour, Hong Kong, over the past 50 years. *Memoirs of the Hong Kong Natural History Society* 17:99–102.

Ho, Y.B. 1986b. Common intertidal algae of the southern part of Hong Kong Island. *Memoirs of the Hong Kong Natural History Society* 17:103–6.

Ho, Y.B. 1986c. *Ulva lactuca* (Chlorophyta: Ulvales) as an indicator species for eutrophication in coastal waters. In *Proceedings of the International Conference on Development and Management of Tropical Living Aquatic Resources, Serdang, 1983* (ed. H.H. Chan, K.J. Ang, A.T. Law, Mohd. Ibrahim b. Hj. Mohamed and Ishak b. Hj. Omar), 249–54. Serdang: Penerbit Universiti Pertanian Malaysia.

Ho, Y.B. 1987. *Ulva lactuca* (Chlorophyta: Ulvales) in Hong Kong intertidal waters - its nitrogen and phosphorus contents and its use as a bioindicator of eutrophication. *Asian Marine Biology* 4:97–102.

Kautsky, L. 1982. Primary production and uptake kinetics of ammonium and phosphate by *Enteromorpha compressa* in an ammonium sulfate industry outlet area. *Aquatic Botany* 12:23–40.

Lapointe, B.E. 1985. Strategies for pulsed nutrient supply to *Gracilaria* cultures in the Florida Keys: interactions between concentration and frequency of nutrient pulses. *Journal of Experimental Marine Biology and Ecology* 93:211–22.

Letts, E.A. and Richards, E.H. 1911. Report on green seaweeds (and specially *Ulva latissima*) in relation to pollution of the waters in which they occur. *Royal Commission on Sewage Disposal, 7th Report, II (Appendix III)*. London: H.M.S.O.

Littler, M.M. and Littler, D.S. 1980. The evolution of thallus form and survival strategies in benthic marine macroalgae: field and laboratory tests of a functional-form model. *American Naturalist* 116:25–44.

O'Brien, M.C. and Wheeler, P.A. 1987. Short term uptake of nutrients by *Enteromorpha prolifera* (Chlorophyceae). *Journal of Phycology* 23:547–56.

Rosenberg, G. and Ramus, J. 1981. Ecological growth strategies in the seaweeds *Gracilaria foliifera* (Rhodophyceae) and *Ulva* sp. (Chlorophyceae): the rate and timing of growth. *Botanica Marina* 24:583–9.

Rosenberg, G. and Ramus, J. 1984. Uptake of inorganic nitrogen and seaweed surface area:volume ratios. *Aquatic Botany* 19:65–72.

Rosenberg, G., Probyn, T.A. and Mann, K.H. 1984. Nutrient uptake and growth kinetics in brown seaweeds: response to continuous and single additions of ammonium. *Journal of Experimental Marine Biology and Ecology* 80:125–46.

Ryther, J.H. and Dunstan, W.M. 1971. Nitrogen, phosphorus, and eutrophication in the coastal marine environment. *Science, Washington, D.C.* 171:1008–13.

Strickland, J.D.H. and Parsons, T.R. 1972. *A Practical Handbook of Seawater Analysis*. Ottawa: Fisheries Research Board of Canada.

Sawyer, C.N. 1965. The sea lettuce problem in Boston Harbour. *Journal of the Water Pollution Control Federation* 37:1122–33.

Thomas, T.E. and Harrison, P.J. 1987. Rapid ammonium uptake and nitrogen interactions in five intertidal seaweeds grown under field conditions. *Journal of Experimental Marine Biology and Ecology* 107:1–8.

Wheeler, W.N. 1982. Nitrogen nutrition of *Macrocystis*. In *Synthetic and Degradative Processes in Marine Macrophytes* (ed. L.M. Srivastava), 121–37. Berlin: Walter de Gruyter.

THE OCCURRENCE OF SIX SPECIES OF RED TIDE ORGANISMS AND THEIR RELATIONSHIP WITH ENVIRONMENTAL FACTORS IN THE PEARL RIVER ESTUARY

Y.S. Lin and Z.D. Wang

South China Sea Institute of Oceanology, Academia Sinica, 164 West Xingang Road, Guangzhou, China

ABSTRACT

Annual variations in the numbers of six red tide species in the Pearl River estuary from February 1987 to February 1988 were studied. The species were the diatoms *Skeletonema costatum* and *Eucampia zoodiacus* and the dinoflagellates *Ceratium fusus, C. breve* var. *breve, C. furca* and *Noctiluca scintillans*. Correlation of their occurrence with environmental factors by multivariable regression showed that temperature was the most important factor; pH and dissolved oxygen influenced their occurrence in the bottom waters; the nutrients Si, N and P influenced them in decreasing order of magnitude (the effect in surface waters being more closely correlated with Si and N, while P correlated better in bottom waters); the trace metal Iron mainly influenced their occurrence in the surface waters, except in the case of *S. costatum*.

INTRODUCTION

There have been a large number of reports in recent years concerning the mechanism of red tide occurrence and methods for red tide prediction (Ikeda 1987). Most authors proposed a linear model that can reflect red tide occurrence through statistical analysis of observed data using multiple variable regressions (Ouchi 1982; Yang *et al.* 1983; Audert *et al.* 1984; Zou *et al.* 1985). This research has resulted in a deeper understanding concerning the mechanism of red tide occurrence and red tide prediction.

Studies of the phytoplankton and the marine environment of the Pearl River estuarine waters have been previously reported upon (Lin 1989; Wang 1989). This paper describes the relationship between six species of red tide organisms and marine environmental factors, through multiple variable regression based on data observed from February 1987 to February 1988 in Pearl River estuarine waters. It may supply the basis for an understanding of red tides in the estuary.

MATERIALS AND METHODS

The nine sampling stations were located between Zhuhai and Guishan Island in the Pearl River estuary (Fig. 1). Water samples, divided into surface and bottom, were collected monthly during the period of February 1987 to February 1988. Parameters analysed included phytoplankton biomass (sampled from bottom to surface), water temperature, salinity, pH, dissolved oxygen, ammonia, nitrite, nitrate, phosphate, silicate, iron, manganese and chemical oxygen demand. This paper uses six species of red tide organisms, i.e., *Skeletonema costatum*, *Eucampia zoodiacus*, *Ceratium fusus*, *C. breve* var. *breve*, *C. furca* and *Noctiluca scintillans*, as the target of discussion based on both the literature and the situation in the Pearl River estuary.

In order to obtain the best regression equation, the previous biomass of red tide organisms was used as the dependent variable and the previous values of environmental factors as the independent variables. First, factors were selected that have an important influence on red tide organisms and a multiple variable regression analysis made annually; second, a multiple variable regression was carried out for six species of red tide organisms at each station and for each month, respectively; a stepwise regression was then carried out to obtain the best regression equation; finally determined values for the independent variables were substituted into the best equation, and corresponding values of red tide biomass predicted. Comparing the predicted values with the determined values could test and verify the regression results.

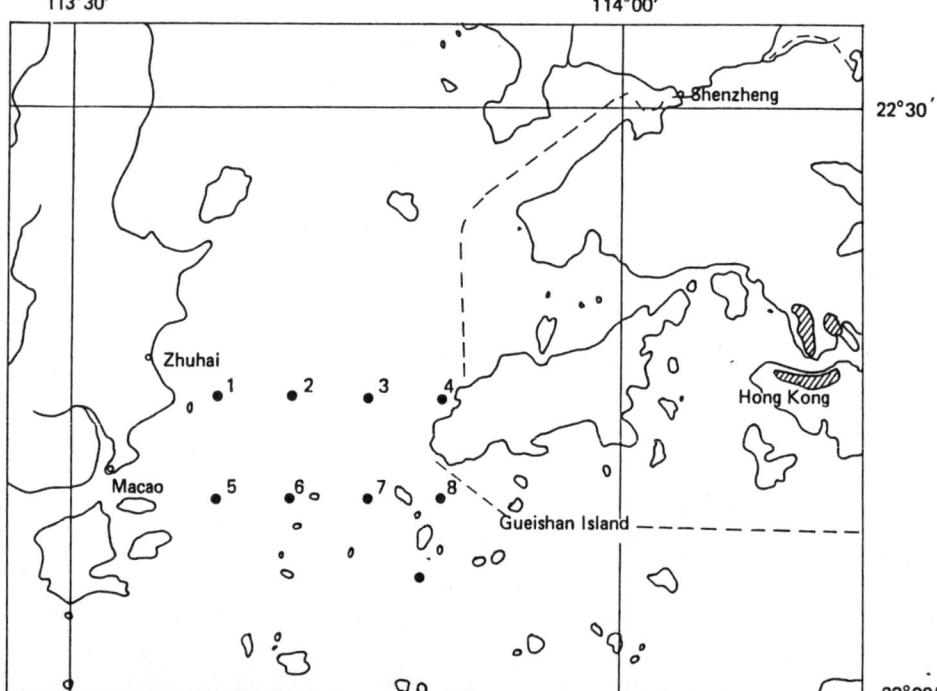

Fig. 1. Map showing the study area and sampling stations.

RESULTS

The distribution of red tide organisms

Annual variation in the mean biomass values for six species of red tide organisms in the Pearl River estuary survey area are shown in Figures 2 and 3.

Skeletonema costatum was the major red tide organism in the Pearl River estuary, its highest biomass occurring during July to December (the maximum was in October), while the lowest biomass was recorded from January to June. *Eucampia zoodiacus* showed the reverse pattern, its maximum biomass appeared during December to June

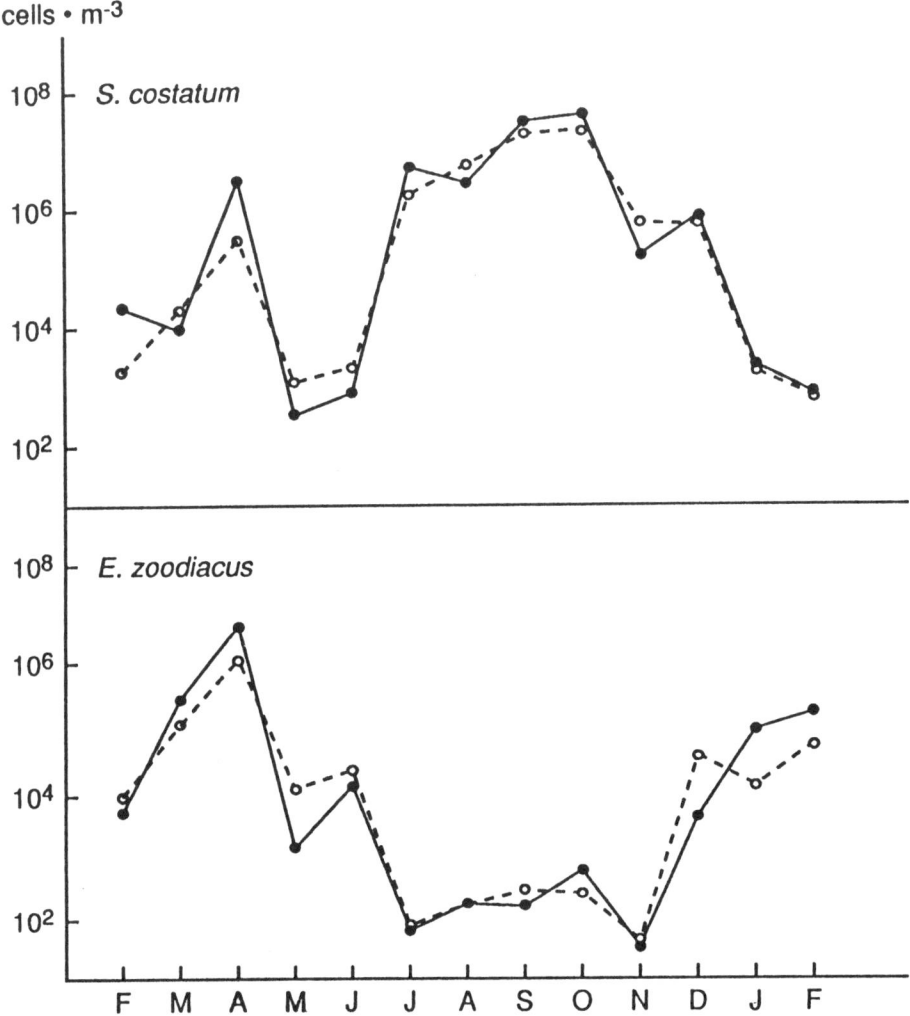

Fig. 2. Annual distribution of mean biomass for *Skeletonema costatum* and *Eucampia zoodiacus* compared with the values estimated by stepwise multiple regression.

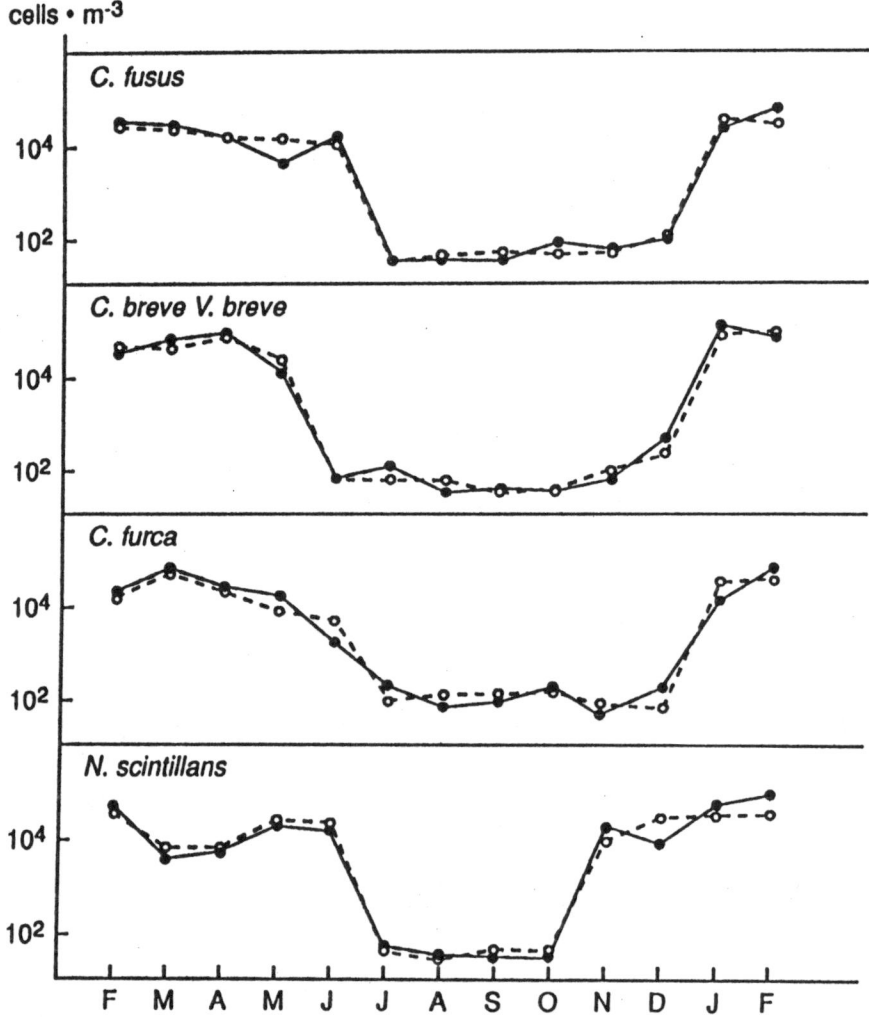

Fig. 3. Annual distribution of mean biomass for four dinoflagellates compared with the values estimated by stepwise multiple regression.

(with the highest biomass in April), and its lowest biomass occurred from July to November. A similar pattern was also shown by the other four species. The biomass of the three *Ceratium* species was, thus, higher from January to June than July to December. In the case of *Noctiluca scintillans*, however, the high biomass period was rather long, lasting for almost eight months (November to June); biomass was lower only from July to October.

Variations in the biomass of the six species of red tide organisms at the nine stations observed are shown in Figures 4 and 5.

The annual mean biomass values for *Skeletonema costatum* was relatively lower at Stations 4 and 5, but the values for the other stations were almost the same. During December to June, the biomass of *Eucampia zoodiacus* was lowest at Station 2, with

Stations 1 and 3 having relatively higher values and the other stations being more or less the same. During July to November, the biomass was highest at Station 1, and lowest at Stations 2 to 6. Among the four dinoflagellates, *Ceratium furca* showed the greatest variation during both periods at all stations, whereas in the case of the other three species there was often little variation.

The relationship between the distribution of red tide organisms and marine environmental factors

Based on stepwise regression analysis using annually recorded data, the major factors related to the distribution of red tide organisms were water temperature, salinity, pH, dissolved oxygen, ammonia, nitrite, nitrate, phosphate, silicate, and iron. On this basis,

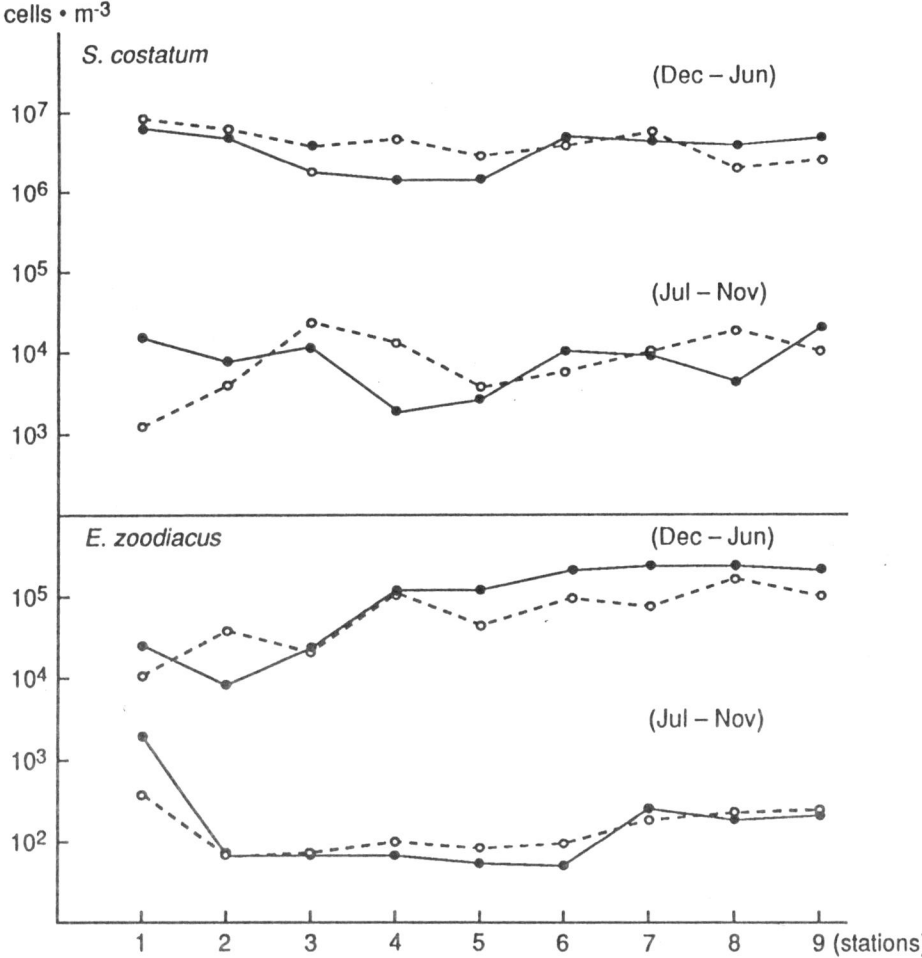

Fig. 4. The annual mean biomass for *Skeletonema costatum* and *Eucampia zoodiacus* at various stations compared with the values estimated by stepwise multiple regression.

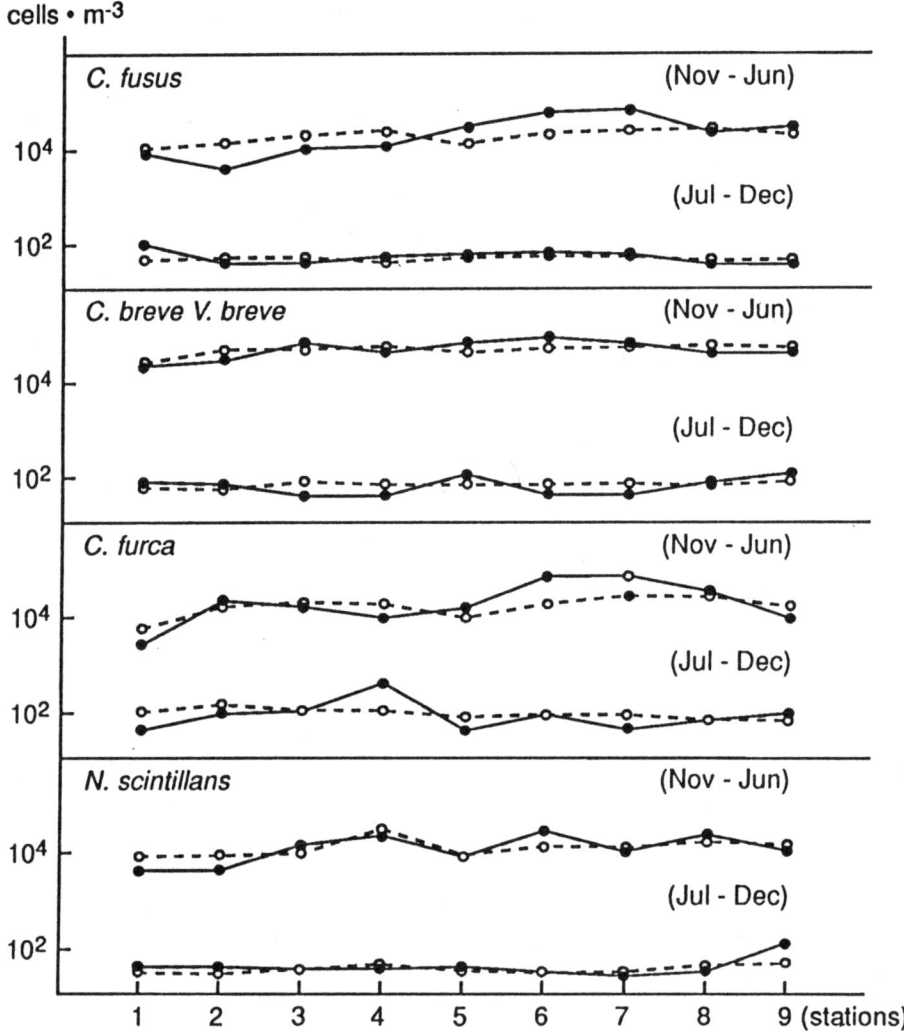

Fig. 5. The annual mean biomass of four dinoflagellates at various stations compared with the values estimated by stepwise multiple regression.

a multiple variable regression was carried out for the six species of red tide organisms against eight environmental factors. The results showed that the coefficient for the complex correlation of regression equation ranged between 0.416 and 0.749 (Table 1), the coefficients for *Skeletonema costatum* and *Eucampia zoodiacus* being the better ones. The F values for *S. costatum* (from July to December and from January to June), *E. zoodiacus* (from November to June), *Ceratium breve* var. *breve* (from January to May), *Ceratium furca* (from January to June), and *Noctiluca scintillans* (from November to June) were all significant at the 0.01 level, while values for *E. zoodiacus* (from July to November) and *C. furca* (from July to September) only showed significance at the 0.05 level, and the other showed no significance.

Table 1

The results of multiple linear regression for six red tide organisms during two periods of the year using eight variables.

Species	Month	t(°C)	s(‰)	pH	DO	DIN	PO$_4$	SiO$_3$	Iron	Constant	n	R	F	Sig.
Skeletonema costatum	Jan-Jun	-.246 (-.064)	-.090 (.028)	7.936 (.505)	.266 (.317)	0.053 (.063)	-.357 (-.185)	-.028 (-.223)	-.015 (-.140)	-54.779	62	.658	5.059	**
	Jul-Dec	.107 (.507)	-0.089 (-.452)	-.971 (.238)	.422 (.072)	-.034 (-.112)	-.168 (-.096)	-.006 (.113)	-1.241 (-.232)	13.125	54	.749	7.186	**
Eucampia zoodicus	Dec-Jun	-.121 (-.036)	.003 (.162)	5.717 (.515)	.212 (.278)	.039 (-.081)	-.562 (-.289)	-.024 (-.308)	-.793 (-.333)	-40.204	71	.649	5.628	**
	Jul-Nov	.193 (.302)	-.008 (.075)	-1.159 (.096)	.468 (.135)	.021 (-.304)	.533 (.045)	-.035 (-.400)	1.042 (.122)	5.063	45	.632	2.988	*
Ceratium fusus	Jan-Jun	-.072 (-.266)	-.003 (.301)	-1.036 (-.038)	-.122 (.118)	.003 (-.290)	-.288 (-.128)	-.013 (-.254)	-.419 (-.171)	15.540	62	.440	1.589	—
	Jul-Dec	.009 (-.206)	-.007 (.134)	-.488 (.045)	.178 (.252)	.006 (-.150)	.034 (.232)	-.010 (-.213)	-.107 (.057)	4.788	54	.416	1.175	—
C. breve v. breve	Jan-May	-.098 (-.339)	-.005 (.287)	.950 (.230)	-.058 (.174)	.014 (-.153)	.106 (-.076)	-.007 (-.154)	-.463 (-.399)	-0.554	53	.615	3.344	**
	Jun-Dec	-.052 (-.374)	.028 (.334)	.095 (-.106)	-.111 (.043)	.004 (-.079)	-.005 (.047)	.002 (-.158)	-.289 (.103)	2.082	63	.444	1.656	—
C. furca	Jan-Jun	.014 (-.264)	.097 (.380)	-1.106 (.057)	.290 (.376)	.028 (-.277)	-.231 (-.102)	-.007 (-.300)	-.435 (-.211)	8.648	62	.615	3.344	**
	Jul-Dec	-.123 (.018)	-.086 (-.223)	1.263 (.071)	-.444 (-.004)	-.036 (.015)	-.010 (.120)	.008 (.154)	-1.461 (-.179)	-0.243	54	.525	2.522	*
Noctiluca scintillans	Nov-Jun	-.018 (-.248)	.040 (.394)	.343 (-.028)	-.246 (-.081)	-.034 (-.409)	-.290 (-.071)	.013 (-.101)	.140 (.037)	2.466	80	.543	3.714	**
	Jul-Oct	-.143 (-.397)	.006 (.218)	.391 (-.067)	-.096 (-.213)	.001 (-.082)	-.210 (-.253)	.001 (-.172)	-.439 (-.147)	2.890	36	.471	0.964	—

Table 2

The results of multiple linear regression for six red tide organisms during two periods of the year using eight variables.

Species	Month	Variables								Constant	n	R	F	Sig.
		t(°C)	s(‰)	pH	DO	DIN	PO4	SiO$_3$	Iron					
Skeletonema costatum	Jan-Jun	.108		7.382	.646	-.036				-60.158	62	.578	14.807	**
	Jul-Dec		-.078		.271					5.102	54	.728	13.744	**
Eucampia zoodiacus	Dec-Jun			6.476	.537				-.804	-50.972	71	.608	13.077	**
	Jul-Nov	.165			.262			-.022		-2.412	45	.572	6.666	**
Ceratium fusus	Jan-Jun		.048							3.002	62	.301	5.981	**
	Jul-Dec				.122					1.004	54	.252	3.523	*
C. breve v. breve	Jan-May	-.072		1.101						-2.702	53	.579	8.264	**
	Jun-Dec	-.071			-.153				-.400	4.340	63	.418	6.363	**
C. furca	Jan-Jun		.052		.355					1.054	62	.501	6.478	**
	Jul-Dec		-.031						-.458	2.691	54	.223	2.728	*
Noctiluca scintillans	Nov-Jun				-.210	-.050		-.012		5.918	80	.513	9.056	**
	Jul-Oct	-.197								7.159	36	.397	6.374	*

The stepwise multiple linear regression results between six species of red tide organisms and eight environmental factors are shown in Table 2. The coefficients of complex correlation for the regression equation ranged between 0.223–0.728, all showing significance at the 0.05 level by F testing; some reached significance at the 0.01 level, the exceptions being *Ceratium fusus* (from July to December), *C. furca* (from July to December) and *Noctiluca scintillans* (from July to October).

DISCUSSION

As seen in Figures 2–5, the annual distribution of six species of red tide organisms can be divided generally into two parts: high value and low value periods. Based on this, multiple linear regression and the stepwise selected method were applied to six species of red tide organisms at each station during two periods of the year.

Skeletonema costatum lives in waters experiencing a wide range of water temperature and salinity and grows during the whole year in the Pearl River estuary, usually at high concentrations. Its optimum water temperature lies between 20–26°C, and its optimum salinity between 25–30‰. Maximum rainfall occurs from April to August and the increased runoff brings abundant nutrients into the Pearl River estuary. These cause *S. costatum* to increase quickly in July, reaching a maximum in October. The stepwise selected method results showed that there is a close relationship between biomass and factors such as water temperature, salinity, DO and DIN during this high biomass period (from July to December); whereas there is only a relationship between biomass and pH and DO during the low biomass period (from January to June), and water temperature and salinity became secondary factors.

The optimum breeding period of *Eucampia zoodiacus* occurred during months of lower water temperature; the biomass thus reached a maximum in April since a great deal of SiO_3 was consumed during this rapid increase, *E. zoodiacus* growth is closely related with water temperature, pH, DO and SiO_3. This is in accordance with the results obtained using the stepwise selected method.

The four species of red tide dinoflagellates are best adapted to low water temperature and high salinity, which is in agreement with the results from the regression analysis, i.e., water temperature and salinity are the major influencing factors.

Based on the stepwise selected method results shown in Table 2, the biomass of the six species of red tide organisms was closely related with environmental factors such as water temperature, salinity, pH and DO (especially DO in the case of *Skeletonema costatum* and *Eucampia zoodiacus* throughout the year) but was not closely correlated with nutrients, especially PO_4-P. Iron exerted some effect on *E. zoodiacus*, *Ceratium breve* v. *breve* and *C. furca* during the high biomass period, and there was a significant correlation between Iron and the biomass of the organisms.

Substituting the mean values for the two parts of the year and then the mean values for each station into the optimization equation using the stepwise selected method, and comparing the estimated values with the observed values, gave the results show in Figures 2–5. The fits for both annual and station values were satisfactory, especially in the case of the four species of dinoflagellates. This paper has, thus, shown that regression equations can reflect the relationship between these six species of red tide organisms and environmental factors in the Pearl River estuary during the study period.

ACKNOWLEDGEMENTS

This work was supported by a grant from the Chinese Academy of Sciences and by funds from the Environmental Protection Agency of Zhuhai, China. The authors express their thanks to members of the research group, especially Mr Peng Yunhui, for their support, and are very grateful to all cooperators in the EPA for their kind cooperation and support.

REFERENCES

Audert, M., Augier, H. and Aubert, J. 1984. Prediction of red tides. *Revue International d' Oceanographie Medicale* 75/76: 5–25.
Ikeda, S. 1987. *Science on red tides*. Tsune Hoshi Medical Press.
Lin, Y.S., 1989. The dominant red tide organisms in the Pearl River estuary, China. In *Red Tides* (ed. T. Okaichi, D.M. Anderson and T. Nemoto), 105–8. New York: Elsevier.
Ouchi, A. 1982. Prediction of red tide occurrence by means of multiple linear regression model. *Bulletin of the Japanese Society of Scientific Fisheries* 48:1245–50.
Wang, Z.D., 1989. Evaluation of water quality in the Pearl River estuary, China. In *Red Tides* (ed. T. Okaichi, D.M. Anderson and T. Nemoto), 109–12. New York: Elsevier.
Yang, D.B., Kim, E.S. and Lee, K.W. 1983. Sea water quality and red tides in Jinhae Bay in 1979–1982. *Bulletin of the Korea Ocean Research and Development Institution* 5:15–20.
Zou, J.Z., Dong, L.P. and Qin, B.P. 1985. Preliminary studies on eutrophication and red tide problems in Bohai Bay. *Hydrobiologia* 127:27–30.

ACCUMULATION OF AN ANTIFOULING TOXIN, TRIBUTYLTIN, IN *ARGOPECTEN IRRADIANS* (BIVALVIA: PECTINIDAE)

Liu Jianjun*

Institute of Oceanology, Academia Sinica, 7 Nanhai Road,
Qingdao 266071, China

ABSTRACT

The accumulation and tissue distribution of TBT and total tin as well as the effect of $SnCl_4$ on the accumulation of TBT in the scallop, *Argopecten irradians* Lamarck, were studied under laboratory conditions. For the external TBT concentrations of 4 µgTBT·L^{-1}, 20 µgTBT·L^{-1} and 150 µgTBT·L^{-1}, the maximum accumulated concentrations in the scallop were 14 µg·g^{-1}, 21 µg·g^{-1} and 22 µg·g^{-1}; and the bioconcentration factors of TBT were 10,000, 3000 and 400, respectively. The present study has shown that the accumulated concentration of TBT is determined by the following two processes: (1) the simple accumulation process and (2) the metabolic breakdown process of TBT in the scallop. The $SnCl_4$ taken up by the scallop has an inhibitive effect on the above two processes. The experiment has also shown that TBT can be accumulated significantly in the gill/mantle, viscera and kidney but not in the adductor muscle during seven days' experiment under an external TBT concentration of 20 µgTBT·L^{-1}.

INTRODUCTION

Organotin compounds are used as thermal stabilizers for polyvinyl chloride, as catalysts in the production of polyurethane foams and as biocides (Piver 1973; Zuckerman *et al*. 1978). In addition, during the last ten years, tributyltin compounds (TBT) have been used more and more as active biocides, especially in the antifouling paints of boats and ships. TBT as an antifouling toxin is very effective. However, following the wide use of TBT, concern over the deleterious effects of TBT on non-target aquatic organisms arose initially over problems encountered with the commercial cultivation of the Pacific oyster in France (Alzieu *et al*. 1980).

* Present Address: Department of Zoology, Duke University, Durham, NC 27706. USA

Oysters grown in areas of heavy boating and active shipping exhibited shell malformation, poor growth, reduced reproductive capacity and an elevated body burden of tin (Waldock and Thain 1983; Alzieu et al. 1986).

Several studies have demonstrated the accumulation of TBT in the oyster and scallop under natural conditions (Waldock and Miller 1983; Alzieu et al. 1986; Davies et al. 1986). In the present study, the accumulation and tissue distribution of TBT in the scallop have been demonstrated under laboratory conditions.

MATERIALS AND METHODS

Two groups of the scallop *Argopecten irradians* Lamarck with average shell lengths of 44.0 mm and 48.0 mm, collected from the Taipin Promontory at Qingdao in September and November 1988, were used in the experiments. They were acclimated under laboratory conditions for 48 hours before use in experiments, and then exposed to sea water contaminated with TBT concentrations of 4 µgTBT·L^{-1}, 20 µgTBT·L^{-1} and 150 µgTBT·L^{-1}, respectively. TBT was dissolved in acetone before being added to the experimental sea water which was changed twice a day. Five (for body burden analysis) or eight (for tissue distribution analysis) scallops were sampled in the triplicate experiment for chemical analysis at intervals of either 10, 24, 48, 72, 96, 120, 144, 168 and 192 or 4, 9, 24, 28, 33, 38, 48, 58 and 72.

The concentrations of TBT and total tin in tissues were determined by McKie's method (McKie 1987). The accumulated concentrations of TBT and total tin were expressed as tin·unit dry weight^{-1}.

RESULTS

The accumulation of TBT and total tin in the scallop

This experiment showed the accumulated concentrations of TBT and total tin in the soft tissue of the scallop under the different external TBT concentrations of 4 µgTBT·L^{-1}, 20 µgTBT·l^{-1} and 150 µgTBT·L^{-1}. As shown in Figures 1 and 2, TBT is accumulated more and more rapidly following the increase of the external TBT concentration in the three test groups. The maximum accumulated concentrations (AC) of TBT in the three test groups were 14 µg·g^{-1}, 21 µg·g^{-1} and 22 µg·g^{-1}. The maximum AC of TBT in the 4 µgTBT·L^{-1} group was obviously less than that in the 20 µgTBT·L^{-1} group and 150 µgTBT·L^{-1} group; and there was no obvious difference between the two maximum ACs of TBT in the latter two groups. When the external TBT concentration is below 20 µgTBT·L^{-1}, the body burden of TBT in the scallop increased with the increase of the external TBT concentration; but after the external TBT concentration exceeded 20 µgTBT·L^{-1}, the body burden of TBT in the scallop did not increase again with the further increase of the external TBT concentration. This indicated that the body burden of TBT in the scallop could not increase limitlessly following the increase of the external TBT concentration. It was estimated that the maximum body burden of TBT in the scallop was about 20 µg·g^{-1}.

If we calculate the TBT bioconcentration factor (BF) on the basis of the maximum AC of TBT, the BFs of TBT in the three test groups were 10,000, 3000 and 400, re-

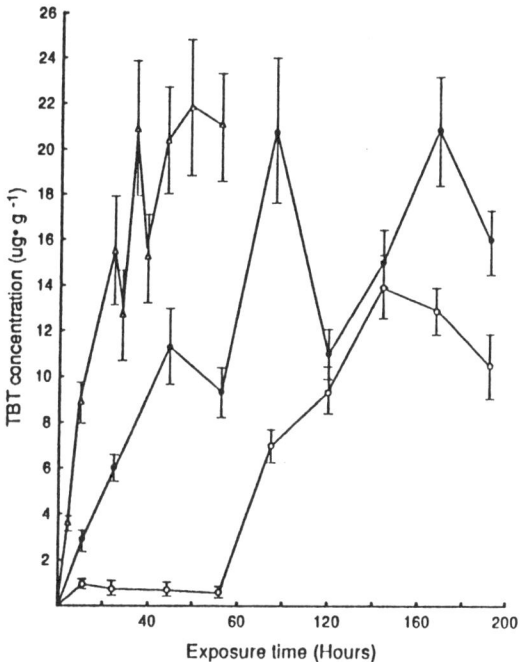

Fig. 1. The relationship of accumulated concentration of TBT with exposure time under the different external TBT concentrations in the scallop (S.D.).
○ 4 μgTBT·L^{-1} • 20 μgTBT·L^{-1} △ 150 μg TBT·L^{-1}

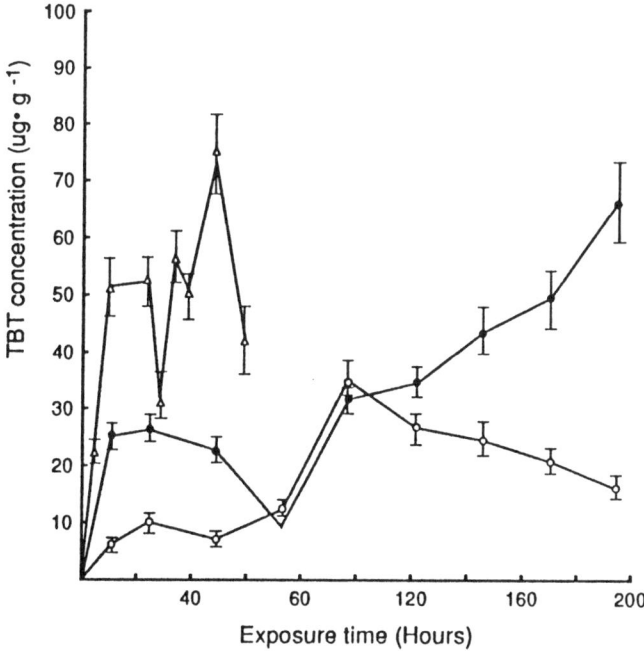

Fig. 2. The relationship of accumulated concentration of total tin with exposure time under the different external TBT concentrations in the scallop (S.D.).
○ 4 μgTBT·L^{-1} • 20 μgTBT·L^{-1} △ 150 μg TBT·L^{-1}

spectively. Thus the TBT BF decreased with the increase of the external TBT concentration. This indicated that the ability of the scallop to accumulate TBT would be reduced following the increase of the external TBT concentration.

Surveying the accumulation curves of TBT in the three test groups (Fig. 1), we can find that, in the initial period of the accumulation (up to 80 hours), there is a poor accumulation of TBT but a significant accumulation of total tin in the 4 μgTBT·L^{-1} group; however, in 20 μgTBT·L^{-1} and 150 μgTBT·L^{-1} groups, there are obvious accumulations of both TBT and total tin. In the later period of the accumulation (after 80 hours), there are obvious accumulations of TBT and total tin in the scallop in all the three test groups. The AC of total tin in the scallop is composed of the AC of organotin and the AC of inorganic tin. If the AC of total tin increases but the AC of organotin does not, it is clear that the AC of inorganic tin in the scallop must increase. Therefore, it can be concluded that, in the initial period of the accumulation in the 4 μgTBT·L^{-1} group, there is accumulation of inorganic tin in the body of the scallop.

The effect of $SnCl_4$ on the accumulation of TBT in the scallop

The effect of $SnCl_4$ on the accumulation of TBT in the scallop was shown in Figures 3 and 4. According to the significant test on the difference of the ACs of TBT between the 4 μgTBT·L^{-1} group and the 4 μgTBT·L^{-1} + 16 μgSnCl$_4$·L^{-1} group as well as between the 20 μgTBT·L^{-1} group and the 20 μgTBT·L^{-1} + 20 μgSnCl$_4$·L^{-1} group (Table 1), the effect of $SnCl_4$ on the accumulation of TBT in the scallop is significant. For the 4 μgTBT·L^{-1} group, the effect of $SnCl_4$ was dual: initially, the AC of TBT in the scallop was enhanced because of the presence of $SnCl_4$ in the experimental sea water; but later the AC of TBT was reduced. For the 20 μgTBT·L^{-1} group, the AC of TBT in the scallop was reduced in the whole period of the accumulation because of the presence of $SnCl_4$.

The tissue distribution of TBT in the scallop

The accumulation of TBT in the kidney, gill/mantle, viscera and adductor muscle tissue of the scallop at the external TBT concentration of 20 μgTBT·L^{-1} is shown in Figure 5. The accumulation in the gill/mantle was most rapid and the AC of TBT in the gill/mantle was much higher than that in the other three tissues. There was an obvious accumulation of TBT in the kidney and viscera, but not in the adductor muscle tissue during the whole period of the seven days' experiment. The maximum ACs of TBT in the gill/mantle, kidney and viscera of the scallop were 33 μg·g^{-1}, 6.24 μg·g^{-1} and 9.33 μg·g^{-1}, respectively.

DISCUSSION

TBT as an antifouling toxin is very toxic to many marine organisms. The accumulation of TBT in the body of an organism can induce poisoning and disorder of the regular metabolism of the organism. In addition, this effect will become more and more strong following the increase of the external TBT concentration. Therefore, because of the disorder of the regular metabolic process of the organism, it is possible that the ability

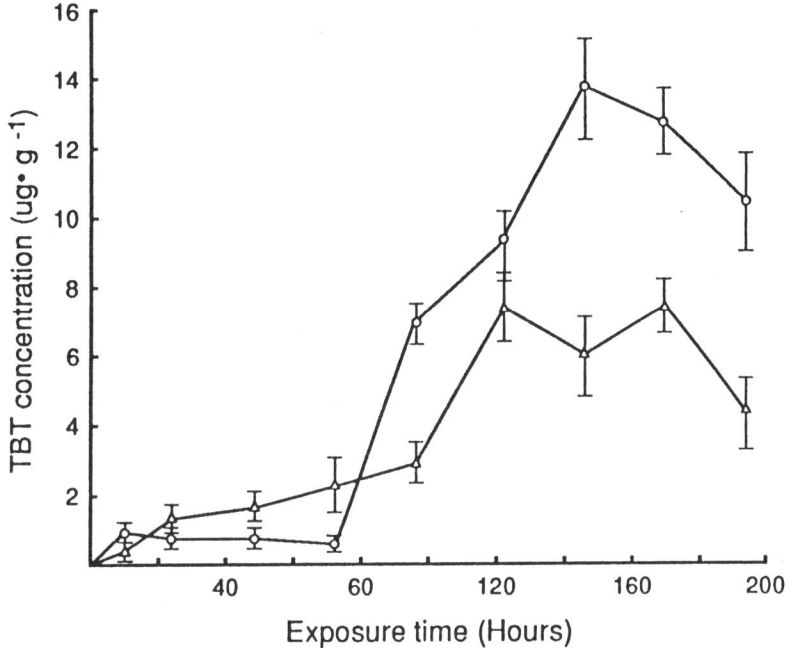

Fig. 3. The effect of $SnCl_4$ of 16 $\mu gSnCl_4 \cdot L^{-1}$ on the accumulation of TBT in the scallop under the external TBT concentration of 4 $\mu gTBT \cdot L^{-1}$. (S.D.).
○ 4 $\mu gTBT \cdot L^{-1}$ △ 4 $\mu g\ TBT \cdot L^{-1}$ + 16 $\mu gSnCl_4 \cdot L^{-1}$

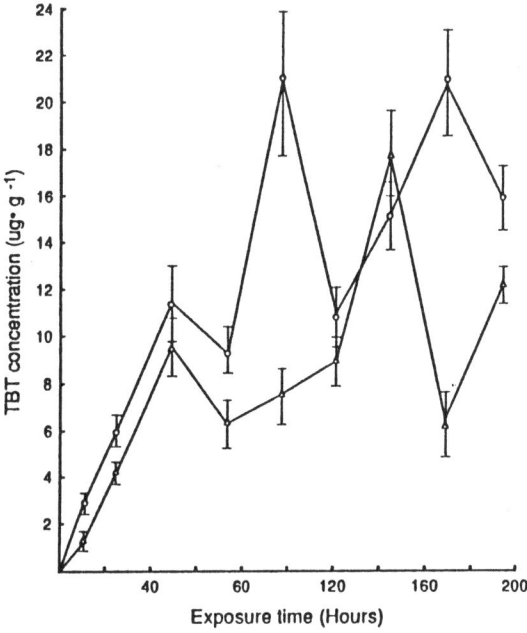

Fig. 4. The effect of $SnCl_4$ of 20 $\mu gSnCl_4 \cdot 1^{-1}$ on the accumulation of TBT in the scallop under the external TBT concentration of 20 $\mu gTBT \cdot L^{-1}$. (S.D.).
○ 20 $\mu gTBT \cdot L^{-1}$ △ 20 $\mu g\ TBT \cdot L^{-1}$ + 20 $\mu gSnCl_4 \cdot L^{-1}$.

Table 1
Results of the significance test on the effect of $SnCl_4$ on the accumulation of TBT.

Group	Accumulated concentrations of TBT (S.D.) $\mu g \cdot g^{-1}$								
	10h	24h	48h	72h	96h	120h	144h	168h	192h
4 $\mu g TBT \cdot L^{-1}$	0.98 (0.21)	0.89 (0.28)	0.89 (0.37)	0.70 (0.19)	7.00 (0.68)	9.33 (1.02)	13.92 (1.35)	12.85 (0.97)	10.53 (1.33)
4 $\mu g TBT \cdot L^{-1}$ + 16 $\mu g SnCl_4 \cdot L^{-1}$	0.50 (0.26)	1.51 (0.42)	1.75 (0.44)	2.35 (0.77)	2.95 (0.61)	7.52 (0.98)	6.02 (1.18)	7.52 (0.80)	4.28 (1.07)
P=	0.1	0.1	0.05	0.05	0.002	0.1	0.01	0.01	0.01
20 $\mu g TBT \cdot L^{-1}$	2.90 (0.41)	6.07 (0.49)	11.36 (1.64)	9.30 (1.11)	20.81 (3.21)	10.81 (1.03)	15.08 (1.24)	20.89 (2.41)	15.79 (1.42)
20 $\mu g TBT \cdot L^{-1}$ + 20 $\mu g SnCl_4 \cdot L^{-1}$	1.23 (0.41)	4.18 (0.49)	9.51 (1.13)	9.30 (1.02)	20.81 (1.21)	10.81 (0.89)	15.08 (1.95)	20.89 (1.43)	15.79 (0.79)
P=	0.01	0.05	0.1	0.05	0.02	0.1	0.1	0.01	0.05

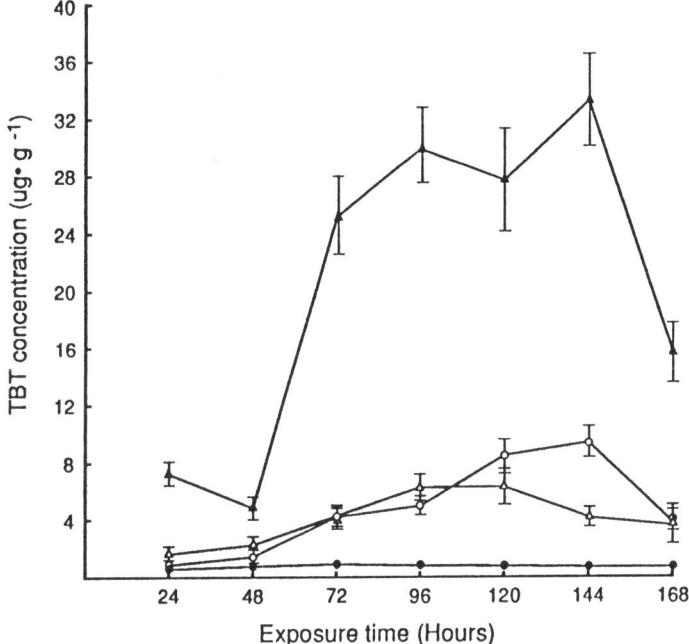

Fig. 5. The relationship between the accumulated concentration of TBT in the different tissues of the scallop with exposure time under the external TBT concentration of 20 μgTBT·L^{-1} (S.D.).
△ Kidney   ▲ Gill/Mantle   ○ Viscera   ● Adductor muscle

of the organism to accumulate TBT will decrease following the increase of the external TBT concentration, and consequently the BF of TBT in the organism will decrease. A similar result has been obtained in previous studies (Waldock and Thain 1983; Uensal 1984).

During the experiment on the accumulation of TBT in the scallop, no inorganic tin was added to the experimental sea water. The accumulation of inorganic tin in the scallop in the initial period of the accumulation of the 4 μgTBT·L^{-1} group could not, therefore, be caused by the uptake of inorganic tin from the experimental sea water by the scallop, but can only be caused by the uptake of TBT. There must be, therefore, a pathway through which TBT taken up by the scallop can be changed into inorganic tin in the body of the scallop. Previous studies (Blunden *et al.* 1984; Lee 1986) have shown that, in some marine organisms, there is some metabolic process through which the organic groups of organotin can be broken down, and this effect of such metabolic process could cause a poor accumulation of TBT in some seaweeds (Maguire *et al.* 1984). In addition, the study of Clark *et al.* (1988) has also indicated that the effect of any such metabolic mechanism process will be reduced and even disappear following poisoning of the organism because of the increase of the body burden of TBT. It is possible that there is also such a metabolic breakdown process in the body of the scallop which breaks down the organic groups of TBT and changes it into inorganic tin and, therefore, causes a poor accumulation of TBT but a significant accumulation of inorganic tin as well as total tin in the initial period of the accumulation of the four $\mu gTBT \cdot L^{-1}$ group. Nevertheless, in the later period of the accumulation, as more and more TBT is taken up into the scallop, regular metabolism is disrupted and the effect of the above metabolic breakdown of TBT is also reduced and even disappears. Consequently TBT begins to be accumulated in the body of the scallop.

The AC of TBT in the scallop is determined by two processes: (1) the simple accumulation process of TBT and (2) the metabolic breakdown process of TBT. The first process makes the AC of TBT in the scallop high but the second process makes the AC of TBT low; the effect of the second process will be reduced and even disappear following an increase in the body burden of TBT.

In the initial period of accumulation of the 4 $\mu gTBT \cdot L^{-1}$ test group, because the poor accumulation of TBT in the scallop is produced by the strong effect of the metabolic breakdown of TBT, the enhanced accumulation of TBT caused by the presence of $SnCl_4$ in the experimental sea water must be produced by the inhibitive effect of $SnCl_4$ on the metabolic breakdown of TBT. In the later period, because the effect of the metabolic breakdown of TBT disappears and the simple accumulation process of TBT plays an important role in the significant accumulation of TBT, the reduced accumulation of TBT must be induced by the inhibitive effect of $SnCl_4$ on the simple accumulation process of TBT. We conclude that $SnCl_4$ taken up has an inhibitive effect on the simple accumulation process of TBT as well as the metabolic breakdown process of TBT in the scallop. Many past studies (Blunden and Chapman 1986) have shown that triorganotin compounds can bind to certain proteins in the body of the organism, although the exact nature of the binding site is still unknown. From the present study, I speculate that the binding sites of tin cation and TBT in the scallop are same. The uptake of tin cation in the scallop might, therefore, induce binding site competition between tin cation and TBT, and therefore reduce the accumulation of TBT. However, we do not understand why $SnCl_4$ has an inhibitive effect on the metabolic breakdown of TBT.

Davies *et al.* (1986) found that the AC of TBT in the adductor muscle was much higher than that in the gonad, digestive gland and gill/mantle after 30 weeks of accumulation under natural conditions. The difference between the present experimental results and the results of Davies *et al.* (1986) may be caused by the different experimental durations: the former seven days, the latter 30 weeks. TBT, therefore, only can reach the adductor muscle after a long period of accumulation. Therefore, the biotransfer route of TBT in the scallop may be that TBT is first accumulated in the gill/mantle which is in direct contact with the external environment, then in the kidney and the viscera, and finally in the adductor muscle, although I do not understand the details of how.

ACKNOWLEDGEMENTS

I wish to acknowledge Associate Professor Xiuming Huang and other colleagues of Marine Fouling Research Group in the Institute of Oceanology, Academia Sinica for their help in this study. Gratitude is also expressed to an anonymous reviewer and Prof. Brian Morton for helpful comments on the manuscript.

REFERENCES

Alzieu, C.L., Thibaud, Y., Heral, M. and Boutier, B. 1980. Evaluation des risques dus l'emploi des peintures antisalissures dans les zones conchylicoles. *Revue des Travaux de L'institut des Peches Maritimes* 44:301–49.

Alzieu, C.L., Sanjuan, J., Deltreil, J.P. and Borel, M. 1986. Tin contamination in Arcachon Bay: effects on oyster shell anomalies. *Marine Pollution Bulletin* 17:494–8.

Blunden, S.J. and Chapman, A. 1986. Organotin compounds in the environment. In *Organometallic compounds in the environment* (ed. P.J. Craig). Harlow, U.K.: Longman Group Limited.

Blunden, S.J., Hobbs, L.A. and Smith, P.J. 1984. The environmental chemistry of organotin compound. In *Environmental Chemistry* (ed. H.J.M. Bowen), vol. 3, 49–77. London: The Royal Society of Chemistry.

Clark, E. A., Sterritt, R.M. and Lester, J.N. 1988. The fate of TBT in the aquatic environment. *Environmental Science and Technology* 22:600–4.

Davies, I.M., McKie, J.C. and Paul, J.D. 1986. Accumulation of tin and TBT from antifouling paint by cultivated scallops, *Pecten maximus*, and pacific oysters, *Crassostrea gigas*. *Aquaculture* 55:103–14.

Lee, R.L. 1986. Metabolism of bis(tributyltin) oxide by estuarine animals. In *Oceans'86. Proceedings of the Organotin Symposium of the Oceans '86 Conference; Marine Technology Society: Washington, D.C.,* 1182–8. New York, NY: IEEE Publishing Services.

Maguire, R. J., Wong, P. T. S. and Rhamey, J.S. 1984. Accumulation and metabolism of TBT cation by a green alga, *Ankistrodesmus falcatus*. *Canadian Journal of Fisheries and Aquatic Science* 41:537–40.

McKie, J.C. 1987. Determination of total tin and TBT in marine biological materials by electrothermal atomic absorption spectrometry. *Analytica Chemica Acta* 197:303–8.

Piver, K.W.T. 1973. Organotin compounds: industrial applications and biological investigation. *Environmental Health Perspectives* 4:61–79.

Uensal, M. 1984. Accumulation and loss of tin by the mussel. *Oceanologica Acta* 7:493–8.

Waldock, M.J. and Miller, D. 1983. The determination of total tin and tributyltin in seawater and oysters in areas of high pleasure craft activity. ICES, C. M. 1983/E: 12, 17pp.

Waldock, M.J. and Thain, J, E.1983. Shell thickening in *Crassostrea gigas*: Organotin antifouling or sediment induced? *Marine Pollution Bulletin* 14:411–5.

Zuckerman, J.J., Reisdorf, R.P., Ellis, H.V. and Wilkinson, R.R. 1978. Organotins in biology and the environment. In *Organometals and organometalloids, occurrence and fate in the environment* (ed. F.E. Brinckman and J.M. Bellama), No. 82, 388–422. American Chemical Society Symposium.

The Marine Biology of the South China Sea
(ed. B. Morton). Proceedings of the First
International Conference on the Marine
Biology of Hong Kong and the South China Sea,
Hong Kong, 28 October – 3 November 1990.
Hong Kong: Hong Kong University Press, 1993.

THE EFFECTS OF URBAN SEWAGE ON BENTHIC COMMUNITY STRUCTURE IN XIAMEN BAY, CHINA

J.X. Jiang, J.S. Song and Z.G. Huang

Third Institute of Oceanography, State Oceanic Administration, Xiamen, China

ABSTRACT

The effects of urban sewage discharge on benthic community structure in Xiamen Bay based on a quantitative benthic monitoring survey undertaken from March 1988 to February 1989, was investigated. Variations in benthic community structure were described by means of analysis of the following parameters: species diversity (H'), richness (D), evenness (J) and the log-normal distribution specis comprising each community.

The benthic communities of Xiamen Bay can be divided into three types: (1) an *Aglaophamus dibranchis* Grube, *Poecilochaetus paratropicus* Gallardo and, *Haploscoloplos* sp. community; (2) a *Nucula* cf. *kawamurai* Kuroda, *Trigonothracia jinxingae* Xu, *Aglaophamus dibranchis*, and *Neoxenophthalmus obscurus* (Henderson) community and (3) a *Neoxenophthalmus obscurus, Amphioplus laevis* (Lyman), and *Amphioplus impressus* (Ljungman) community. The distribution of these communities was closely related to urban sewage discharge, sediment types and hydrography.

INTRODUCTION

Many research studies on sublittoral and estuarine benthic community structure have been reported upon (Sanders 1960; Boesch and Wass 1976; Wu and Richards 1981; Dugan and Livingson 1982; Mahoney and Livingson 1982).

In China, some studies on the benthic ecology of Jinzhou Bay, Bohai Bay, Jiaozhou Bay, Changjian River estuary, Hangzhou Bay and Xiamen Bay have been reported upon (Jia *et al.* 1982; Cui and Sun 1983; Wu *et al.* 1985; He *et al.* 1988; Li and Jiang 1989a). In the present study, variations in benthic species numbers and community structure in relation to seasonal changes in environmental factors were studied in Xiamen Bay to provide ecological information useful for local economic development and marine environmental protection.

MATERIALS AND METHODS

Benthic surveys were undertaken in Xiamen Bay from March 1988 to February 1989. The quantitative information was based on monthly sampling at 10 stations during a study period of one year. The study area was from 24°04'0" to 24°33'30" N and 118°02'0" to 118°05'0"E. Quantitative sampling was with a grab (Model 50 Ocean) with a sampling area of 0.05 m². Five replicate samples were taken at each station. The benthic organisms collected in the samples were separated from the sediment by washing through a 1 mm mesh sieve.

Species diversity at each station was calculated using the Shannon-Weaver equation:

$$H' = -\sum_{i=1}^{s} \frac{n_i}{N} \log_2 \frac{n_i}{N};$$

Species richness was calculated using the Margalef equation:

$$d = \frac{s-1}{\log_2 N};$$

Species evenness was calculated using Pielou's equation:

$$J = \frac{H'}{\log_2 S};$$

The coefficient of similarity was calculated using the Sanders equation:

$$PSC = 100 - 50 \sum |a' - b'|$$

Where S is the number of species in the sample; ni is the individual numbers of the first dominant species and n is the total number of individuals in the sample; a' and b' are the percentage densities of the same species at two different stations.

RESULTS

Based on the distributions of dominant species and the relationships between sediment, water temperature, salinity and current flow and, by using community parameters, i.e., community similarity coefficient, species diversity, richness and evenness, the benthic organism communities in Xiamen Bay have been divided into three types (Figs. 1 and 2). The distributional features of these communities can be described as follows:

The *Aglaophamus dibranchis*, *Poecilochaetus paratropicus* and *Haploscoloplos* sp. community

This community, designated as community I, was distributed in the northern area of the Western Harbour, Xiamen, and included Stations 1, 2, 3 and 4. Of a total of 84 species in this community, polychaetes were the dominant group with 36 species comprising

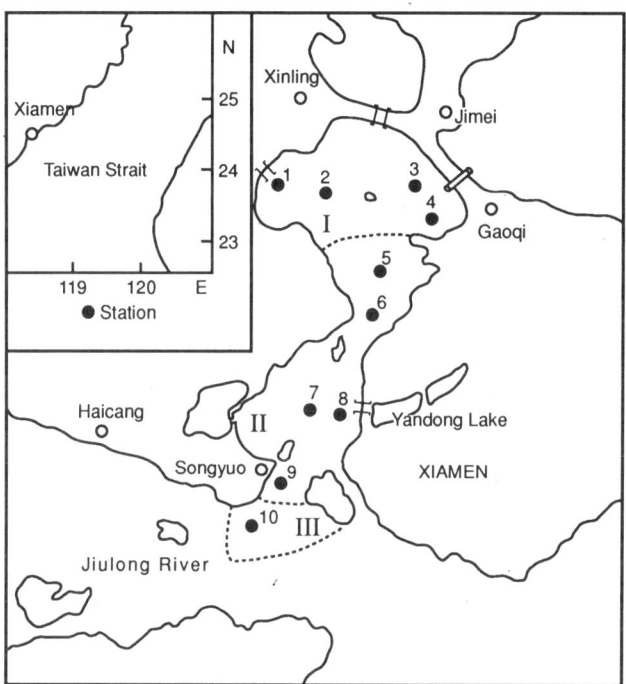

Fig. 1. Distribution of benthic communities in Xiamen Bay. I, *Aglaophamus dibranchis* Grube, *Poecilochaetus paratropicus* Gallardo and *Haplosocoloplos* sp. community. II. *Nucula* cf. *kawamurai* Kuroda, *Trigonothracia jinxingae* Xu, *Aglaophamus dibranchis* and *Neoxenophthalmus obscurus* (Henderson) community. III, *Neoxenophthalmus obscurus*, *Amphioplus laevis* (Lyman) and *Amphioplus impressus* (Ljungman) community.

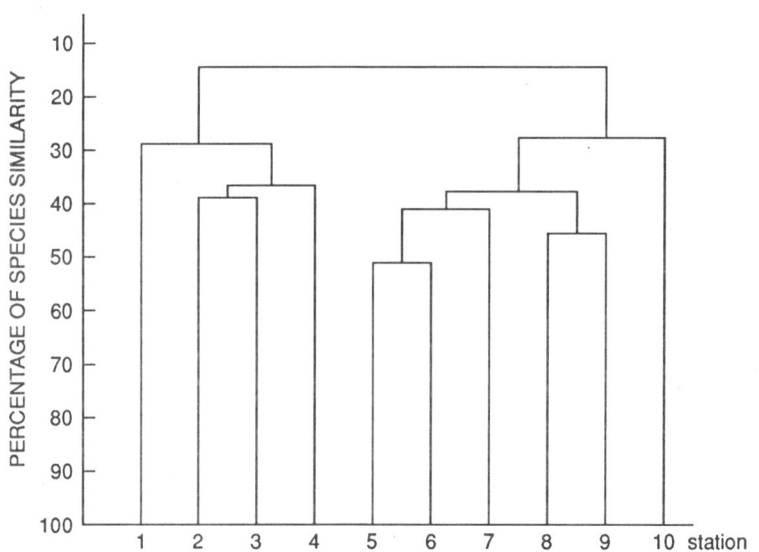

Fig. 2. Community assemblages in Xiamen Bay based on species percentages.

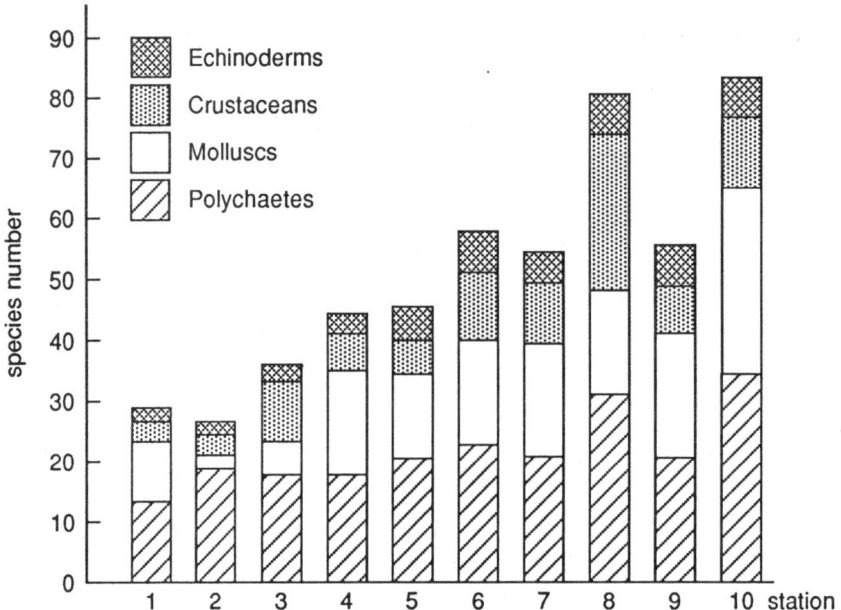

Fig. 3. Comparison of benthic species numbers at sampling stations in Xiamen Bay.

43% of the total species numbers. There were 28 species of molluscs and 15 species of crustaceans as well as 5 species of echinoderms (Fig. 3). Dominant species included *Poecilochaetus paratropicus*, *Aglaophamus dibranchis*, *Haploscoloplos* sp., *Lumbrineris* sp., *Theora lata* (Hinds), *Neoxenophthalmus obscurus* (Henderson), *Nassarius hepaticus* (Pulteney), *Zeuxis* sp., *Graptacme buccinula* (Gould) and *Euniphysa aculeata* (Wesenberg-Lund). This benthic community had a lower species diversity and richness in comparison with other assemblages in the study area (Table 1).

The species numbers of this community also varied seasonally. From Figure 4, it is clear that the greatest number of species occurred in April (25 species) and the least in September (5 species). The number of species in March, May, June and October were higher and in the range of 20 to 23 species. This variation in species numbers was mainly due to the number of polychaete species collected.

The total biomass and numbers of individuals comprising community I was relatively low, i.e., 6.7 g·m^{-2} and 47 individuals·m^{-2}, respectively. In respect of biomass, molluscs were dominant (32%) followed by polychaetes (29%). However, in terms of individual density, the dominance was by polychaetes (60%) followed by Mollusca (25%). The proportions of Crustacea and echinoderms were relatively low in terms of both biomass and density.

Both total biomass and the individuals of this community shared a marked seasonal variation (Fig. 5). A maximum occurred in May with the biomass of 20.67 g·m^{-2} and a density of 112 individuals·m^{-2}. The lowest occurred in September and February with a biomass of 1.87 and 1.75 g·m^{-2}, respectively, and a density of 16 individuals·m^{-2}. Such seasonal variations were mainly related to changes in polychaete biomass and individuals (Fig. 6).

Table 1
Species diversity (H'), species richness (D) and species evenness (J) at sampling stations in Xiamen Bay

Station	1	2	3	4	5	6	7	8	9	10
H'	2.56	2.73	2.52	2.86	2.03	3.03	3.77	3.81	3.50	3.00
D	1.05	1.19	1.04	1.25	1.01	1.95	1.91	2.23	1.73	2.06
J	0.91	0.91	0.98	0.95	0.64	0.74	0.99	0.91	0.95	0.71

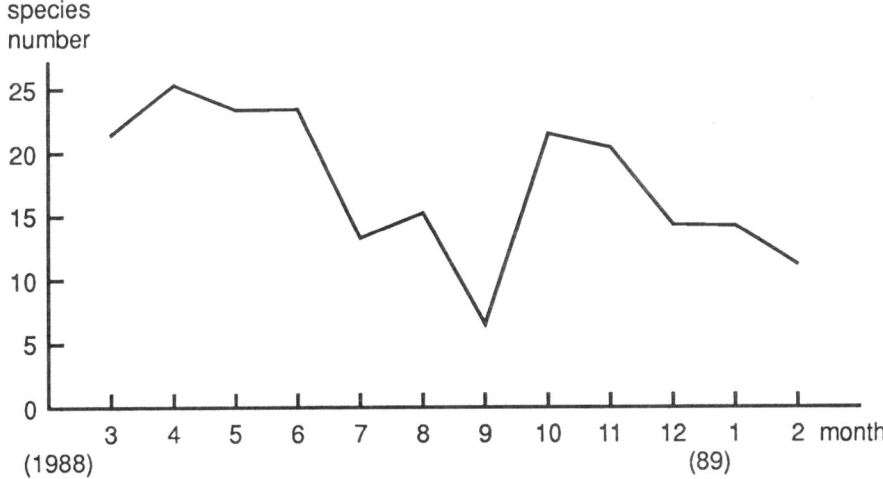

Fig. 4. Seasonal variations in species numbers of Community I in Xiamen Bay.

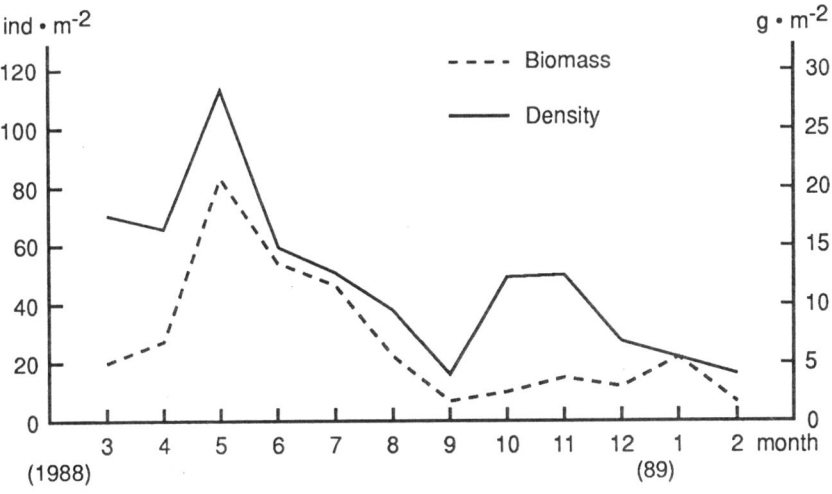

Fig. 5. Seasonal variations in total biomass and total density of Community I in Xiamen Bay.

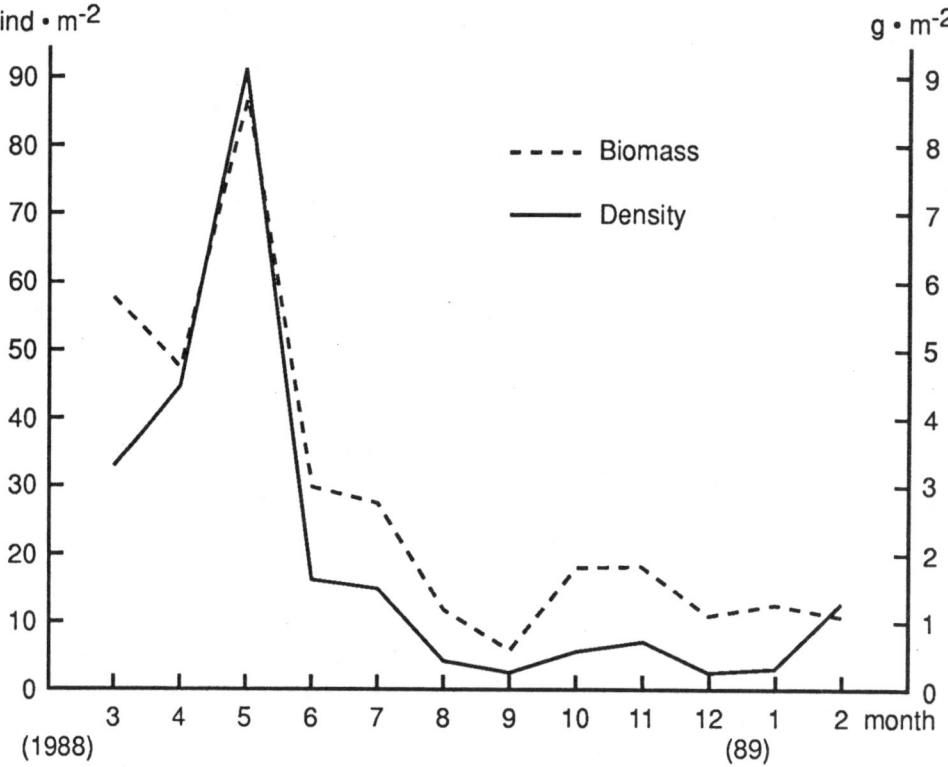

Fig. 6. Seasonal variations in the polychaetes of Community I in Xiamen Bay.

The *Nucula* cf. *kawamurai*, *Trigonothracia jinxingae* *Aglaophamus dibranchis* and *Neoxenophthalmus obscurus* community

This community, designated as community II, was distributed in the centre and southern areas of Xiamen Bay, including Stations 5, 6, 7, 8 and 9. The community structure was complex with a record of 143 species. The dominant species group was the Polychaeta (56 species) followed by molluscs (40 species), Crustacea (30 species) and echinoderms (14 species). Dominant species included *Nucula* cf. *kawamurai*, *Neoxenophthalmus obscurus*, *Trigonothracia jinxingae*, *Aglaophamus dibranchis*, *Hexapus granuliferus*, *Lumbrineris* sp., *Euniphysa aculeata*, *Diopatra neapolitana* Della Chiaje, *Protankyra bidentata* (Woodward and Barrett) and *Typhlocarcinus* sp. This community had a high diversity (3.03–3.81 except Station 5), high species richness (1.73–2.23) and high evenness.

Species numbers in this community showed little seasonal change (Fig. 7), with most species being recorded in June (44 species) and the least in January (27 species). The biomass of this community was also high with a total of 39.87 g·m^{-2} and a total annual average density of 127.8 individuals·m^{-2}. Echinoderms were dominant (70%) with respect to biomass and the Mollusca second (18%). In terms of density, polychaetes were dominant (51 individuals·m^{-2}; 40%), Mollusca second (30%) and echinoderms least, i.e., 15 individuals·m^{-2}. The community was characterized by seasonal variations (Fig. 8), with three peaks in biomass occurring in April, October and June, i.e., 76.84, 70.02

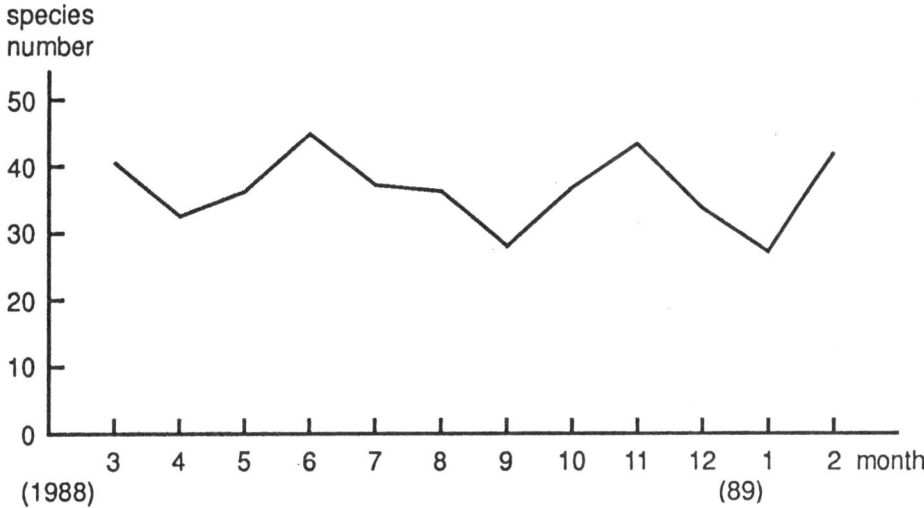

Fig. 7. Seasonal variations in species numbers of Community II in Xiamen Bay.

and 62.48 g·m^{-2}, respectively. Two low values occurred in December and July. Peak values in density occurred in June (196 individuals·m^{-2}) and October (183 individuals·m^{-2}). The lowest density was recorded in February (69 individuals·m^{-2}). These variations in biomass and density were related closely to seasonal changes in some species with a large body size, e.g., *Protankyra bidentata*, or in numbers, e.g., *Nucula* cf. *kawamurai*, *Trigonothracia jinxingae*, *Hexapus granuliferus* and *Neoxenophthalmus obscurus*. Seasonal variations in the benthic community were mainly related to the Mollusca, Echinodermata and Crustacea (Figs. 8 and 9).

The *Neoxenophthalmus obscurus*, *Amphioplus laevis* and *Amphioplus impressus* community

This community, designated as Community III, was distributed in the mouth of Xiamen Bay and the Jiulong River and is thus characterized by subtropical estuarine species. From data obtained at Station 10, there was 83 species, the most for all sampling stations in this area. There were 34 species of polychaetes (41%), 31 species of molluscs, 12 species of crustaceans and six species of echinoderms. Dominant species included *Neoxenophthalmus obscurus*, *Amphioplus laevis*, *Amphioplus impressus*, *Hexapus granuliferus*, *Reticunassa* sp., *Typhlocarcinops canaliculata* and *Cycladicama* sp. In this community, both species diversity and richness were high with an even distribution of individuals among species.

Figure 10 shows a marked seasonal variation in species numbers for this community. Peak values occurred in June and August and the lowest in December (Fig. 10).

The total biomass and numbers of individuals comprising this community were large with an annual average of 34.17 g·m^{-2} and 201 individuals·m^{-2}, respectively. With regard to the composition of both biomass and individual density, echinoderms were dominant (biomass 20.3 g·m^{-2}, 60%; density 89 individuals·m^{-2}, 44%). The second domi-

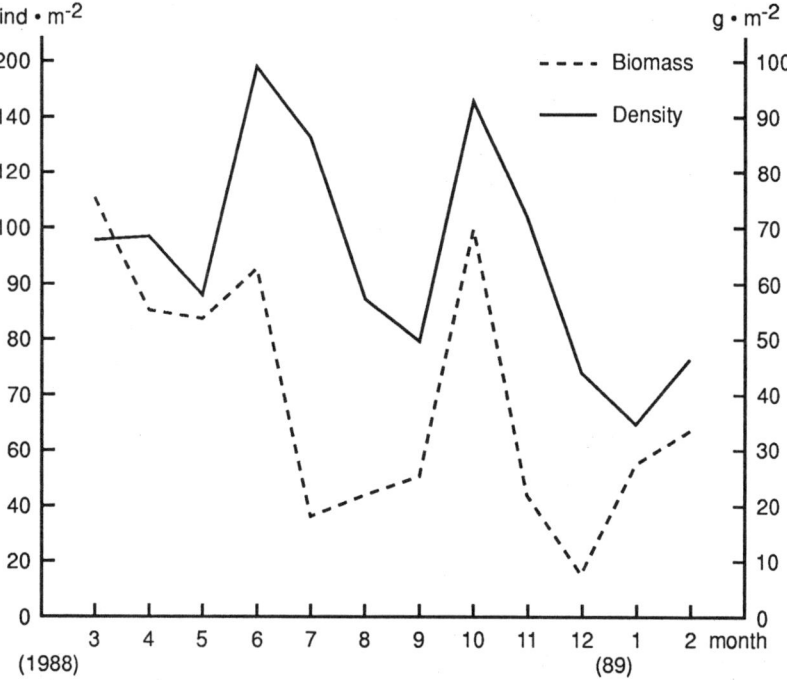

Fig. 8. Seasonal variations in total biomass and total density of Community II in Xiamen Bay.

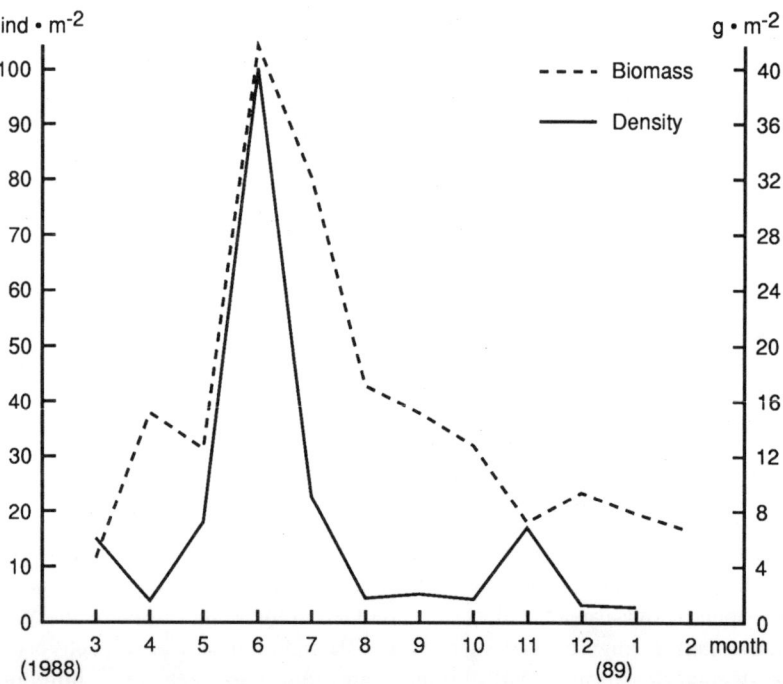

Fig. 9. Seasonal variations in mollusc numbers of Community II in Xiamen Bay.

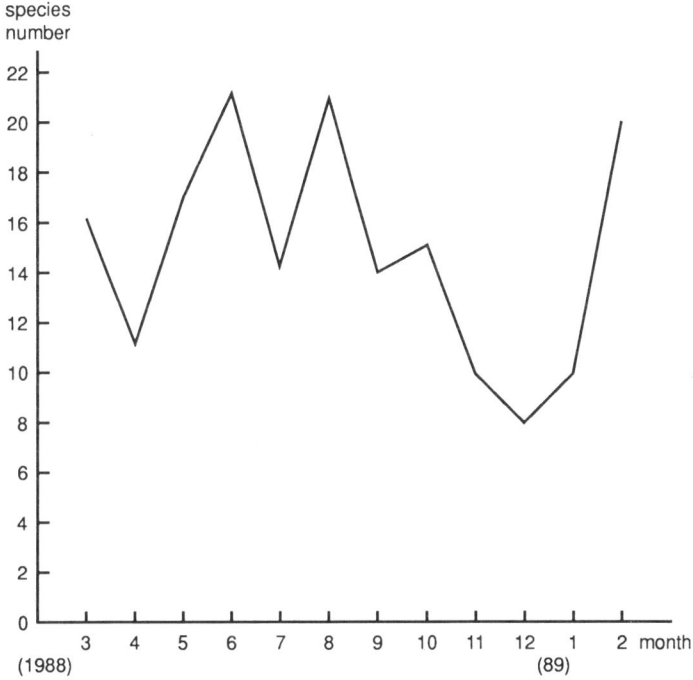

Fig. 10. Seasonal variations in species numbers of Community III in Xiamen Bay.

nant group was crustaceans with a biomass of 6.06 g·m^{-2} and a density of 48 individuals·m^{-2}. Both the biomass and density of molluscs were rather low, being 3.85 g·m^{-2} and 27 individuals·m^{-2}, respectively.

Biomass and density of this community also showed marked seasonal changes (Fig. 11). The maximum biomass value was recorded in December, resulting from a single large-sized individual of *Asterina* sp. in the sample with a wet weight of 200.44 g. With omission of this individual, the highest biomass was recorded in August (40.08 g·m^{-2}). For individual densities, greatest numbers occurred in June and August, being 456 individuals·m^{-2} and 412 individuals·m^{-2}, respectively. Such seasonal variations were mainly due to the occurrence of *Amphioplus laevis*, *Amphioplus impressus* and *Neoxenophthlmus obscurus*. The seasonal variations in the main groups of this community were similar, except for echinoderms (Fig. 12).

Community distributions in relation to hydrodynamics

Residual flow in terms of river runoff and tidal residual flow exists in most areas of Xiamen Bay. The surface residual flow is mainly towards the mouth of the bay, whereas the bottom current flows into the bay. Because of such residual flow, floating pollutants can be carried easily out of the bay but not submerged substances (Chen *et al.* 1985).

Community I is distributed in northern Xiamen Bay where both the surface and bottom residual flows move around Baozhu Island in an anticlockwise direction due to obstruction by the Jimei-Gaogi sea wall. A large amount of waste water from industrial

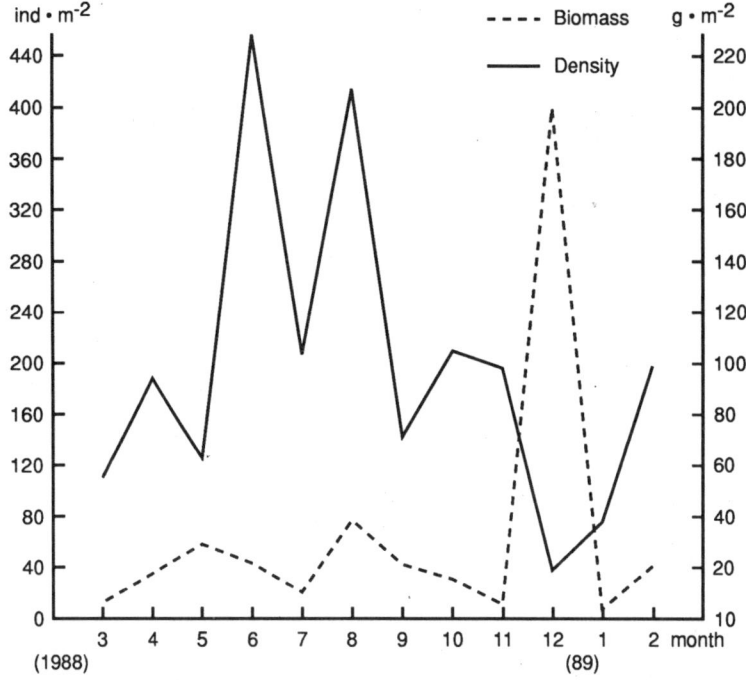

Fig. 11. Seasonal variations in total biomass and density of Community III in Xiamen Bay.

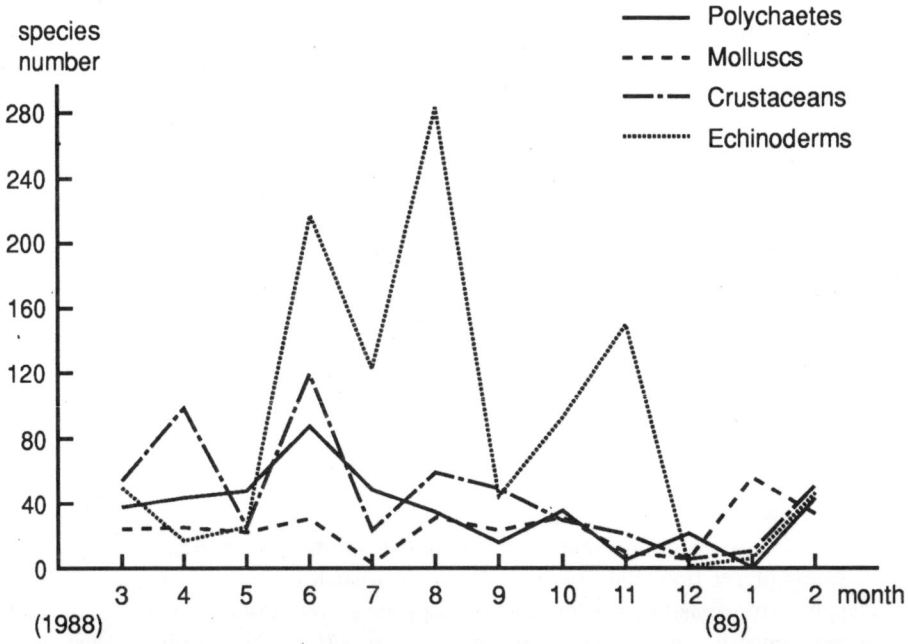

Fig. 12. Seasonal variations in main species group densities of Community III in Xiamen Bay.

areas in Xinglin is discharged from Maluan Bay into this area. In addition, treated waste water from Yandang Lake is carried by tidal currents into Xiamen Bay. As a result, pollutants are trapped in this area and are deposited on the bottom. Such deposition changes the characteristics of the water column and sediment and influences the original habitat, disturbing community structure. Therefore, rather low species numbers (84) and relatively low biomass and individual densities (6.79 $g \cdot m^{-2}$ biomass, 47 individuals $\cdot m^{-2}$ density) characterise this community. Species diversity and richness are also low.

Community II is located in the central and southern areas of Xiamen Bay, where there is a strong tidal current and residual flow. With the incoming tide, waste water from Yandang Lake can be dispersed towards the bay along Stations 5 and 6. During low tide, however, part of the waste water returns through Stations 5 and 6 and converges at the waste water discharge outlet near Stations 7 and 8. Such flows move the Xiagu Strait and Songgu Water towards the open sea. The effects of waste water on this area is thus not as evident as in the northern part of the bay. Only Stations 7 and 8 are affected by such waste water discharges. The structure of this community is rather complex and rich in species (143 species) with a high biomass and individual density (39.89 $g \cdot m^{-2}$ biomass and 128 individuals $\cdot m^{-2}$). A rather even distribution of individuals among species is also typical of this community.

Community III is located in the estuarine area of the Jiulong River, where there exists a greater water exchange due to strong tidal action and better water quality. In addition, this area has a rather stable sediment regime with a low organic content (0.89%). The benthic community of this area is diverse and has a high individual density (201 individuals $\cdot m^{-2}$).

Community distribution in relation to sediment

The effects of sediment on benthic community structure are complex, involving not only the types of sediment but also the deposition rate of suspended matter, nutrient composition and pollutant content. Sediment types at sampling stations in Xiamen Bay are similar, i.e., either silty clay or clay-silt, except Station 10 with sand-silt-clay.

The organic matter in the sediment of community I was high (1.6–2.2%) with the highest record located at the western side of the community (more than 2.0% at Station 10 over the study period). This community had a low species diversity (2.56), few species (28 species) and low biomass. The annual average for biomass and density was 0.30 $g \cdot m^{-2}$ and 13.5 individuals $\cdot m^{-2}$, respectively. It is apparent that sampling Station 1 is seriously organically polluted.

The organic matter content of the sediment of Community II was 1.3–1.9%. Station 8 is located at the discharge outlet of Yandang Lake, where the organic matter content was 1.3–2.0%. Although this station is near the outlet, pollutants can be carried quickly by strong tidal currents and residual flow. As a result, organic matter at this station was rarely high. Species diversity at this station was high, with many species (80) and high biomass and individual density values.

The organic matter content in the sediment of Community III was low (0.89%) due to greater water exchange. Pollutants can, therefore, be carried quickly by the outflow from the Jiulong River into the sea.

Long-normal distribution

Figure 13 indicates, that the four stations of Community I are polluted to different extents. Since Stations 1 and 2 are influenced directly by waste water from Maluan Bay and the industrial areas of Xinglin, the slope of the correlation line is small, indicating that community structure has been seriously disturbed by polluted discharges. The correlation lines for Stations 3 and 4 bend, indicating that community structure has been disturbed and is now at a transitional stage.

Two different situations are shown in Figure 14 for Community II, the correlation lines of Stations 5 and 6 with large slopes and short spans indicate that community structure is not disturbed. However, the correlation lines for Stations 7 and 8 bend and have a long span indicating that disturbance to the benthic community has taken place.

For Community III, the correlation lines have a large slope and short span (Fig. 15). Both Stations 9 and 10 have a stable benthic community structure.

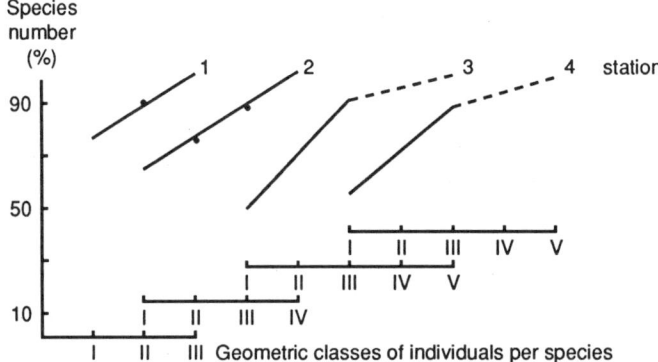

Fig. 13. Log-normal distribution of benthic individuals among species of Community I in Xiamen Bay.

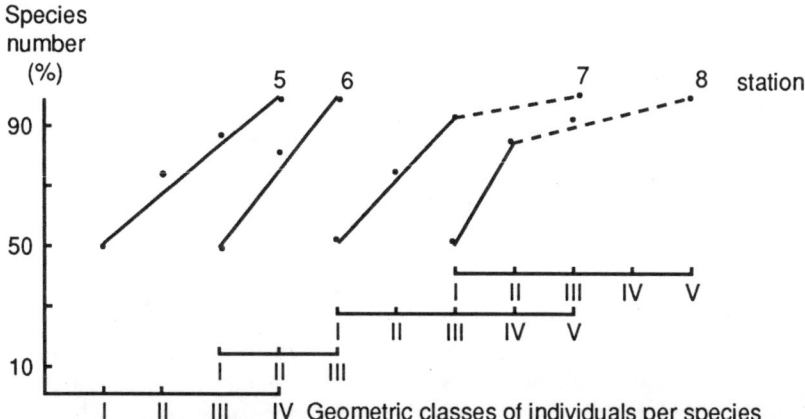

Fig. 14. Log-normal distribution of benthic individuals among species of Community II in Xiamen Bay.

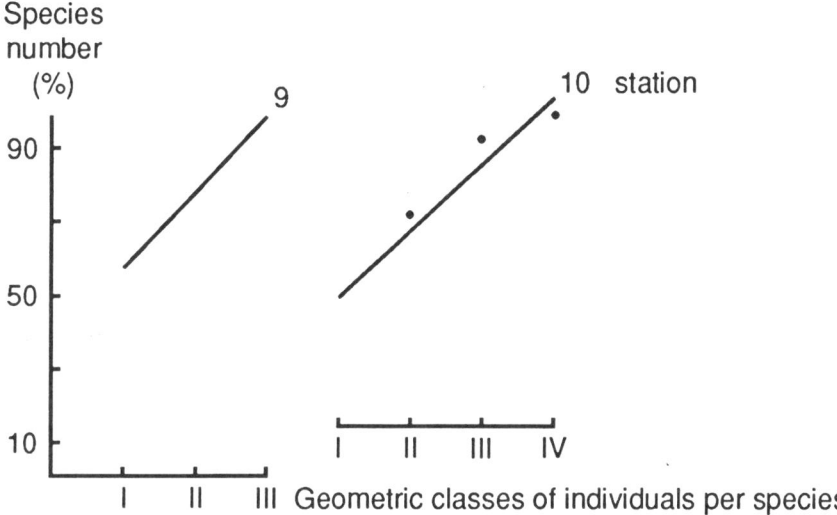

Fig. 15. Log-normal distribution of benthic individuals among species of Community III in Xiamen Bay.

DISCUSSION

Three benthic communities characterize Xiamen Harbour. The structure of Community I is simple with a few species (84), low biomass (6.7 g·m^{-2}) and low individual densities (47 individuals·m^{-2}). The dominant species in this community are polychaetes and some rare echinoderms. This community is characterized by low species diversity (H': 2.56–2.73) and richness (D: 1.05–1.19).

The main reason for such a few species and the low individual density of this community is poor hydrodynamic conditions, high organic matter content and sulphide in the sediment. This area is also affected by tidal currents, bottom water and local circulation, all of which slow down dilution and dispersion of pollutants. In particular, particulate pollutants tend to stay in the sediment and pollutants from Maluan Bay also accumulate here. As a result, the organic matter content (about 2%) is higher than that of other areas, but lower than an evelation standard (3.4%) for sediment pollution. It is thus shown that because of the effects of urban sewage on the sediment, this area is polluted. Analysis of benthic community structure has shown that the sewage discharge outlet in the northern part of Xiamen Bay (the area where Stations 1 and 2 are located) should be relocated.

The structure of Community II is complex, with high diversity (143 species), biomass (39.87 g·m^{-2}) and individual density (128 individuals·m^{-2}). The numbers of echinoderm species in this community was higher than that in Community I, contributing 70% to the total biomass. The numbers of polychaete, mollusc and crustacean species were similar. Both species diversity (H': 3.03–3.81, except Station 5) and richness (D: 1.73–2.23) were high and individuals among species were evenly distributed.

From the structure and composition of the community, it is apparent that the influence of urban sewage was slight. Although this area is located at the discharge outlet of Yandong Lake which receives a large amount of waste water from Xiamen City, strong tidal currents and good water exchange cause rapid dispersion of pollutants, including particulates.

Community III was characterized by a single station. Its species numbers were high, equalling the total species numbers of all four stations of Community I. The biomass (34.17 g·m^{-2}) and density (201 individuals·m^{-2}) were also high in comparison to Communiy I . A feature of this community was that echinoderms were dominant with regard to both biomass and density, i.e., 60% and 44%, respectively. Relatively high species diversity (H': 3.00), richness (D: 2.06) and moderate evenness (J: 0.71) values characterize this community. This community is located in the mouth of Xiamen Bay where there is mixing between the bay and the Jiulong River, with good water exchange, better water quality and low organic matter content (0.89%). Since this community is not influenced by urban sewage, the community composition is typical of a subtropical estuarine habitat.

ACKNOWLEDGEMENTS

We are grateful to Zheng Fengwu, Wu Qiguan, Lu Lin, Li Rongguan, Cai Erxi, Xu Huizhou and Li Shungdan for their help in identification of species.

REFERENCES

Boesch, D.F. and Wass, M. L. 1976. The dynamic of estuarine benthic communities. In *Estuarine Processes, Vol. 1: Uses, Stresses and Adaptation to the Estuary*, 177–96. New York: Academic Press.
Chen, J.Q., Fu, Z.L., He, F.X., Ke, X.H., Liu, M.S. and You, Q.M. 1985. Tidal and residual currents in the Xiamen Bay and their effects on the movement of silt and polluting substances. *Journal of Oceanography in Taiwan Strait* 4:16–20.
Cui, Y.H. and Sun, D.Y. 1983. A quantitative survey of the macrobenthos in the outfall area of the Bohai Bay. *Marine Sciences* 3:29–35.
Dugan, P.J. and Livingson, R.J. 1982. Long-term variation of macroinvertertebrate assemblages in Apalachee Bay, Florida. *Estuarine, Coastal and Shelf Science* 14:391–403.
He, M.H., Cai, E.X., Wu, Q.Q., Jiang, J.X., Lin, S.D., Xu, H.Z., Liu, Q.S., Zheng, F.W. and Li, R.G. 1988. Ecology of benthos in west harbour of Xiamen. *Journal of Oceangraphy in Taiwan Strait* 7:194–8.
Jia, S.L., Wang, S.H., Tian, L. and Zhuang, Y.H., 1982. Pollution effects of Wulihe River outfall on the benthic communities of the Jinzhou Bay. *Marine Environmental Science* 1:79–87.
Li, R.G. and Jiang, J.X. 1989a. Variation of macrobenthos community in the western waters, Xiamen. *Journal of Oceanography in Taiwan Strait* 8:144–9.
Li, R.G. and Jiang, J.X. 1989b. The relation of Mollusca species diversity to the sediments in Xiamen Bay. *Acta Ecologica Sinica* 9:271–3.
Mahoney, B.M.S. and Livingson, R.J. 1982. Seasonal fluctuations of benthic macrofauna in the Apalachicola estuary, Florida, USA: the role of predation. *Marine Biology* 69:207–13.
Sanders, H.L. 1960. Benthic studies in Buzzards Bay. III. The structure of the soft-bottom community. *Limnology and Oceanography* 5:138–53.
Wu, Q.Q., Cai, E.X., He, M.H., Jiang, J.X., Lin, S.D., Xu, H.Z. and Liu, Q.C. 1985. Ecological study on the benthic organisms in west area of Taiwan Strait. I. Analysis of benthic animal community. *Acta Oceanologica Sinica* 7:378–87.
Wu, R.S.S. and Richards, J. 1981. Variations in benthic community structure in a sub-tropical estuary. *Marine Biology* 64:191–8.